18.95

A photographic guide to

Insects of the New Forest
and surrounding area

Paul D. Brock

First published 2011.

British-Library-in-Publication Data
A catalogue record for this book is available from the British Library.

ISBN 978-1-874357-46-9

Designed and published by Pisces Publications

Pisces Publications is the imprint of NatureBureau, 36 Kingfisher Court, Hambridge Road, Newbury, Berkshire RG14 5SJ
www.naturebureau.co.uk

Printed and bound in China by 1010 Printing International Ltd

Cover photographs
Front cover: Silver-studded Blue attended by ants (Philip Corley); Golden-ringed Dragonfly (Paul Brock); New Forest Shieldbug (Paul Brock); Black-headed Cardinal Beetle (Paul Brock)
Back cover: Large Marsh Grasshopper (Paul Brock)

CONTENTS

ACKNOWLEDGEMENTS

I have been bug-hunting for 50 years, starting in my back garden whilst a toddler. Whilst for much of that time, I have specialised in the mainly tropical stick and leaf insects, I have always been fascinated by all insects. It is not, however, possible to be expert in every insect order and I have consulted many publications, as well as discussed these insects with professional and amateur entomologists.

To add to the pressure, I decided to use digital photographs taken mainly in the Forest since my move to the New Forest in 2008. It has needed a lot of time and patience to obtain suitable photographs of the species required and I am grateful to those who assisted.

Particular thanks are due to Gary Palmer [GP], for his help and enthusiasm in finding and photographing a huge range of insects in various habitats; Steven Falk [SF] for his input on the Diptera (flies) and Hymenoptera (bees, wasps and ants), including photographs which have enriched these sections and Richard Coomber [RC] for many images of moths. 20 or more photographs on the following subjects were also obtained from: David Green [DG] moths, including larvae; Graham Hoggarth [GH] mainly dragonfly and some insect behaviour and Clive Turner [CT] beetles and insect behaviour. My sister, Helen Brock has accompanied me on many bug-hunts often finding rarities.

I have not been able to photograph everything I wanted to and in addition to the six photographers mentioned above, I am very grateful to the following for allowing one to ten of their images to be reproduced: Rich Andrews/www.cvlbirding.co.uk [RA], Jim Asher [JA], Tristan Bantock [TB], Andrew Burns [AB], Philip Corley [PC, whose amazing photo of Silver-studded Blue and ants is reproduced on the front cover], Peter Creed [PCr], Steve Covey [SCo], Simon Currie [SC], Tara Dempsey [TD], Peter Eeles [PE], Keith Godfrey [KG], Martin Goodey [MG], Pauline Mellor Greenhalgh [PMG], Peter Greenwood [PG], Robin Harley [RH], Jerry Hawker [JH], Neil Hulme [NH], Roger Key [RK], Tim Melling [TM], Christian Owen [CO], Chris Packham [CP], Trevor and Dilys Pendleton/www.eakringbirds.com [TP], Mark Pike [MPi], Ian Pratt LRPS [IP], Maurice Pugh [MP], Stuart Read [SR], Richard Reeves [RR], Gary Richardson [GR], Peter Ridout [PR], Michael Skelton [MS], Vincent Smith [VS], Keith Tailby [KT], Brian Valentine [BV], John Walters [JW] and Russell Wynn [RW]. Lena Ward kindly gave permission to reproduce the late Jim Grant's [JG] cicada images. Robin Ford provided a photograph of his late grandfather and an image of Frohawk from June Chatfield; Richard Tratt for an image of one of his paintings in the Forest; Tony Johnson for a photograph of Gulliver, postcards of Brockenhurst and an entomological advertisement.

In many cases, the photographers named above assisted in other ways, along with the following, who helped with either allowing access to private land, discussions on the insect fauna, finding insects, confirming identification, providing papers, tracing old records and in some cases making constructive comments on drafts of various sections of the book: Phil Budd [Southampton Natural History Society] has been of particular help, with introductions to new localities and searches for rarer insects; Keith Alexander, Tony Allen, Colin and Lindsay Andrews, Grant Bailey, Andy & Linda Barker, Max Barclay, Tony Bates, George Beccaloni, David Biggs, Juliet Bloss, Peter Booth, Laura Bower, Isabella Brey, Gavin Broad, Sara Cadbury, Bob Chapman, Clive Chatters, Andy Collins, Dominique Collins, Jonathan & Jane Cook, Charlotte Corney, Richard Dickson, Tracy Dove, Mike Duffy, John Durnell, Pete Durnell, Roger Edmondson, Mike Edwards, George Else, Martin Evans, Reg Fry, Mike Gibbons, Conrad Gillett, Barry Goater, Jack Hasenpusch, Stuart Hine, David Hubble, Andrew Jarman, Steve Lankester, Malcolm Lee, Graham Long, Sue Lynes, Craig Macadam, Darren Mann, Erica McAlister, George McGavin, Judith Marshall, Jon Martin, Jolyon Medlock, Martin Noble, Tim Norriss, Matthew Oates, Lizzie Peat, Bryan Pinchen, Colin Plant, Chris Raper, Martin Rejzek, Paul Ritchie, Stuart Roberts, John Ruppersbery, Dr Michael Salmon, Graham & Janice Smith, Matt Smith, Warren Spencer, Alan Stubbs, Mark Swann, Dmitry Telnov, Alan Thornbury, Ian Wallace, Mick Webb, Simon Weymouth, Keith Wheeler, Ashley Whitlock, Bryan Wilson and Paul Winter. Robert Colin-Stokes, Jonathan Cook, Andy Page and other New Forest Keepers also assisted. The Christopher Tower New Forest Reference Library at Lyndhurst was a valuable resource, also the Hampshire County Council Museums Service, Chilcomb House, Winchester, where I examined the insect collections, with thanks to Chris Palmer and Christine Taylor.

Peter Creed (NatureBureau http://www.naturebureau.co.uk/) has been enthusiastic about the project from the outset and has done an excellent job on the design and layout of the pages, and seeing the book through to publication.

Any errors in identification remain firmly mine.

Paul D. Brock, April 2011

GLOSSARY

Although technical terms have been avoided or explained within the text wherever possible, the basic terms below may be useful.

ABDOMEN the third, rear part of an insect (see STRUCTURE OF AN INSECT)
ABDOMINAL SEGMENTS subdivisions of the insect abdomen
ADULT the final (mature) stage of an insect, during which reproduction occurs
ANTENNA (plural ANTENNAE) the paired sensory appendages of the head, also known as 'feelers' (see STRUCTURE OF AN INSECT)
BODY LENGTH length from top of head to end of abdomen, excluding cerci and female ovipositor (when present)
CERCUS (plural CERCI) the paired, segmented appendages at the end of the abdomen (see STRUCTURE OF AN INSECT)
COCOON a silk case made by some pupating larvae
COMPLETE METAMORPHOSIS egg, larva, pupa, adult e.g. Coleoptera, Hymenoptera, Lepidoptera
DORSAL upper surface
EGG first stage of an insect (hatches into a larva [or caterpillar] in Lepidoptera, a nymph in Hemiptera)
ELYTRA see forewings; often used for rigid wing covers of many beetles, which are not used in flight
ENTOMOLOGY the branch of zoology concerned with the study of insects [insects are studied by entomologists]
EXUVIA larval skin shed during moulting, often used to describe the larval case of Odonata
EYE a large eye (compound eye) made up of many separate units (see STRUCTURE OF AN INSECT)
FAMILY in zoological classification, a rank below the Order and above the Genus, ending in '–idae'
FEMALE the sex in which eggs are developed
FEMUR (plural FEMORA) the third segment and longest part of the insect leg attached to the base of the body by the trochanter and coxa (see STRUCTURE OF AN INSECT)
FOREWINGS paired outgrowths of the second thoracic segment, also known as elytra and tegmina (see STRUCTURE OF AN INSECT)
GALL Abnormal plant growth caused by bacterium, virus, fungus, mite or insect
GENUS an assemblage of species agreeing in one or more character(s) (the first scientific name of two for each species, e.g. *Aglais* in *Aglais io*)
HEAD first division of the insect body, bearing the mouth and antennae (see STRUCTURE OF AN INSECT)
HINDWINGS paired outgrowths of the third thoracic segment, also known as alae
IMMIGRANT Considered to have reached Britain by natural flight
INCOMPLETE METAMORPHOSIS egg, nymph, adult e.g. Hemiptera, Odonata, Orthoptera
KEEL ridge, for example of the pronotum in grasshoppers (see STRUCTURE OF AN INSECT)
KEY a tabulation of characters of species, genera etc., serving to identify them
LARVA (plural LARVAE) immature stage of insects with complete metamorphosis, i.e. hatching from egg, examples being Lepidoptera (also known as caterpillar(s))
LATERAL at or from the side
LENGTH see body length
LIFE CYCLE time between fertilisation of egg and death of adult; successive stages of reproduction, growth and development
METAMORPHOSIS includes change during successive stages of development
MESOTHORAX the second thoracic segment
METATHORAX the third thoracic segment
MOULT to shed or cast the skin or outer covering of the body (ecdysis)
NOCTURAL active at night
NYMPH the immature stage of insects with incomplete metamorphosis, i.e. between egg and adult, such as in Hemiptera
ORDER major groups based on structural differences in classification of insects
OOTHECA egg pod, in cockroaches

OVUM (plural OVA) egg
OVIPOSITOR the egg-laying apparatus of a female (see STRUCTURE OF AN INSECT)
PARASITE an organism that lives in or on another (the host), from which it obtains food, shelter, or other requirements
PARTHENOGENESIS egg development without fertilisation
PROBOSCIS extended mouth structure; term often used for Lepidoptera, which have a coiled tongue-like appendage adapted for nectar feeding
PRONOTUM dorsal (upper) surface of the first thoracic segment (see STRUCTURE OF AN INSECT)
PROTHORAX the first segment of the thorax (dorsal surface = pronotum)
PUPA (plural PUPAE) final immature stage of insects with complete metamorphosis, i.e. between larva and adult, such as in Lepidoptera (also known as chrysalis, plural chrysalides)
ROSTRUM tubular, sucking mouthparts of some insects e.g. Hemiptera; also used for prolonged part of head of scorpionflies and some weevils
SCUTELLUM dorsal cover of the hind part of mid or hind thorax e.g. in some Hemiptera
SPECIES form; kind; individuals alike in appearance and structure, mating freely (if bisexual) and bear fertile offspring resembling each other and their parents, including all varieties and races (the second scientific name of two for each species, e.g. *io* in *Aglais io*)
SPERMATOPHORE a 'sperm package' produced by a male in order to fertilise the female
STING modified ovipositor in certain Hymenoptera used for injecting venom
STUCTURE OF AN INSECT

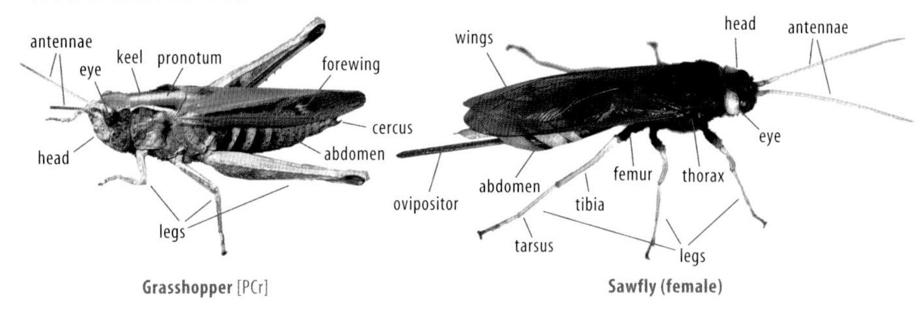

Grasshopper [PCr]　　**Sawfly (female)**

SUBFAMILY major subdivisions of a family, containing a related group of tribes or genera, whose name ends in '-inae'
SUBORDER division of an order higher than a Family, based on character(s) common to a large series of species
SUBSPECIES a subdivision of a species based on small difference in structure, colour or size and separated geographically from other such subdivisions. For example the third name in *Zygaena viciae ytenensis* [New Forest Burnet] denotes the English subspecies, whereas in Scotland subspecies *argyllensis* is found
SYNONYM each of two or more scientific names of the same rank to denote the same taxon
TARSUS (plural TARSI) the segmented foot of insects (see STRUCTURE OF AN INSECT)
TAXON (plural TAXA) a division or rank, in classification
TAXONOMY classification or its principles
TENERAL recently emerged adult, where the colour has not been completed, a term often used in Odonata
THORAX second major division of the insect body, bearing legs and, if present, wings (see STRUCTURE OF AN INSECT)
TIBIA (plural TIBIAE) the fourth segment and second long portion of the leg (see STRUCTURE OF AN INSECT)
VENTRAL underside
VESTIGIAL small, poorly developed or non-functional e.g. applied to wings
WINGSPAN twice the distance from the centre of the thorax to the tip of the forewing [some prefer wing length, measuring from the start of the wing to the tip of the forewing]

INTRODUCTION

About this book

Why a book on New Forest insects? The New Forest is a vast area of woodland and heath in south Hampshire and south Wiltshire, bordered by Ringwood and Fordingbridge on its western edge, Lymington to the south and east, teeming with insect life. Ever wondered about that bug in the garden or seen on a woodland walk? Until now, there has been very little information available for residents, naturalists and visitors to the area, to learn more about the fascinating world of insects, even though there are some of the rarest, most beautiful insects in Britain on our doorsteps. Whilst for some individuals, insects have a bad reputation, are disliked or dismissed as having no use, for others hours can be lost watching the antics of some of these insects, or trying to obtain photographs of fast-flying dragonflies! There has always been a huge interest in the fauna and flora of the New Forest. Botanists are fortunate to have their own book, *Flowers of the Forest* by Clive Chatters, published in 2009 and a book on insects is timely. Like it or not, insects are the most abundant and successful animals on Earth; they are everywhere and cannot be avoided! There are more than 24,000 British species, a tiny percentage of the well over a million insects described in the world, with many still undescribed.

It is hoped that readers will gain some understanding as to how the New Forest – the richest and most popular area for insects in the country in the Victorian era – went downhill for insects by the mid 1900s, but is now, once again, one of the most popular spots in Britain for butterfly watchers. The main aim of this field guide though, is to impart some understanding of the various rich (although vulnerable) habitats, as well as provide clear photographs of a wide range of insects. The images will assist in identification of the majority of insects likely to be encountered and the concise text gives information on behaviour as well as their present-day conservation status. Serious naturalists will welcome notes on areas to look for rarities, in order to watch or photograph them and pointers on where to look for additional information on particular insect groups. Many photographs show fascinating, sometimes seldom observed behaviour of certain insects. The area surrounding the Forest has not been neglected in the text and the book is equally useful to naturalists in Dorset, Hampshire, Sussex, Wiltshire and the Isle of Wight; indeed, with its wide species coverage, of interest to naturalists throughout Britain.

The New Forest and surrounding area

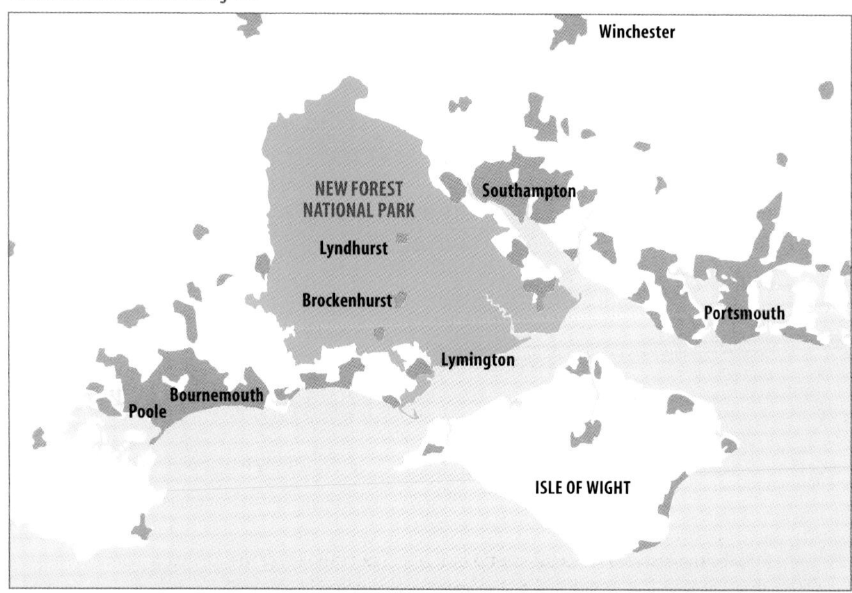

The nomenclature [= classification] used in this book follows the division of insects into major groups called orders, such as Coleoptera (beetles) = sheath wings. Each order is divided into families, whose name ends in –idae i.e. Lucanidae (stag beetles). Families are divided into a genus or genera (plural) containing one or more closely related species, with names obtained from the latest accepted checklist or publication(s). The most used English name (where given), is followed by the scientific name. As they are in usage worldwide, scientific names are often preferred by entomologists, as the English name would not mean much to a biologist in another country. Changes may be made by entomologists, i.e. some recent textbooks list the Six-spotted Longhorn Beetle *Anoplodera sexguttata* as *Leptura sexguttata*. In this example, the genus [an assemblage of species agreeing in character(s)] has changed following revision, whilst the species [individual kind of insect] remains the same. The English name is derived from the Latin *sexguttata*, i.e. six-spotted and names are often made up of features, habitat, or the collector. Very few insects have a stable classification, followed by all researchers studying the group and modern genetics work is leading to some changes in nomenclature, even to previously familiar names.

Although distribution is widely known for certain major groups of popular insects, data is incomplete for lesser studied groups; hence maps are not included in this guide.

Enjoy the insect fauna, who knows you might even become an entomologist, someone of any age, who takes an interest in insects, and studies them. No expensive equipment is needed, you can go outdoors and explore in your back garden. Or better still, take a trip to one of the Forest Inclosures or the coast and take time to watch and learn – it's a fascinating world!

Key to New Forest status categories

Examples given from the butterflies, to indicate the present status of species and allow comparison with previous publications, for example *The Butterflies of Hampshire* (2000).

Common – found in much of the suitable habitat for the species and likely to be present in reasonable numbers, with plenty of dots for records in 2-km squares. *Example*: Large Skipper

Widespread – found in part / much of the suitable habitat for the species but dots well spread; likely to be occasional or present in small numbers. *Example*: Silver-washed Fritillary

Local – infrequently encountered i.e. found in relatively few 2-km square records, although they may be common in those areas. *Example*: Marbled White

Rare – probably reliable sites, but only one or two and then not present in high numbers. *Example*: Small Pearl-bordered Fritillary

Very rare – fortunate to see one or two specimens in a season. *Example*: Purple Emperor

Extinct – believed to be extinct i.e. no recent records despite extensive searches. *Example*: Brown Hairstreak [last recorded early 1970s]

Vagrant – wandering in from outside the Forest. *Example*: Clouded Yellow.

HISTORY OF ENTOMOLOGY IN THE NEW FOREST

Collecting insects

The New Forest became a magnet for Victorian entomologists when the railway line was constructed. In 1847 the railway station was opened at Brockenhurst, as part of the Southampton to Dorchester line. By the 1860s, eminent entomologists visited for the weekend, on a route direct from London, with four stations providing direct access to the forest. The Holmsley branch line was added later and opened up the southwestern part of the Forest. There is a Brockenhurst record from 1864 stating that 'Fly catchers' had visited, usually three or four individuals; at that time there was only one vehicle for hire, from the Rose & Crown. In other works, they were called 'bughunters' and 'the brotherhood of the net'. To some though, the pursuit of butterflies must have been regarded as a sign of lunacy. Many famous entomologists have collected in the New Forest, which is frequently referred to in glowing terms in the Victorian County History (1900), where it is clear that collectors of all orders found insects, including rarities, often in abundance. The journey was, however, expensive, as recorded by W.C. Dale (1879) who found that difficulties stood in the way of a visit by young entomologists, namely 'time and expense.' He added 'Many a young clerk, tied to his desk in the bank or the merchant's office, can only get a day's holiday at the most…..A journey to Brockenhurst or Lyndhurst averages three hours, at an expense of twenty-two shillings.' Visits in Victorian times were therefore mainly from the gentry and newly wealthy middle class. The less well off subsidised their hobby by selling specimens and livestock, thus the hobby opened up to a great multitude. It is no surprise to see a pre-1871 photograph of Charles Darwin in Brockenhurst railway station, amongst the famous visitors from that era.

Brockenhurst Railway Station c.1910

Rose & Crown, Brockenhurst c.1905

For a flavour of collecting in the New Forest, I can do no better than quote from Salmon *et al.* (2005), who state: 'During the last decades of the nineteenth century and for the first few of the next, the New Forest in Hampshire was arguably the richest and most popular collecting area in the country. Each season huge numbers of entomologists were irresistibly drawn to it like proverbial moths to a flame; nowadays, there is very little evidence of 'entomologising' to be seen. A century ago, however, the scene was very different – the Forest then fairly hummed with activity. 'Most inns at Lyndhurst and Brockenhurst were virtually taken over during the summer months by collectors. Livestock and desirable specimens were traded on Saturday nights at certain hostelries by professional dealers and impecunious collectors seeking to make their hobby self-financing. Several of the New Forest keepers (crown foresters) ran lucrative sidelines in selling insects and acting as weekend guides.' (Oates, 1996).' Several hundred collectors each summer made a very welcome and important contribution to the local economy, with some locals providing accommodation and packed lunches, in addition to arranging dog-carts and general assistance with collecting.

However, there is evidence of unscrupulous practices by an increasing number of 'dealers' in the New Forest, who collected specimens in large numbers. Lawrance (1903) refers to one 'netting all the White Admirals he could possibly lay his hands on, and then retailing them to schoolboys, &c., at one halfpenny each. I should not wonder if he retired this season.' Some dealers sold not only butterflies, but all insect orders, with moths and beetles particularly sought after, also bird eggs.

It is not believed that collectors managed to cause extinction of species, except possibly in the case of the New Forest Burnet moth, which was lost in 1927.

Dealer's advertisement

Visitors to New Forest.
This Season's Collection of all Orders. A good Collection of TINEINA and TORTRICES—HYMENOPTERA, COLEOPTERA, DIPTERA.
Information about localities gratis to Visitors.
B. PIFFARD, Ivy Cottage, near New Church and Post Office, Brockenhurst, New Forest.

Charles Gulliver, Brockenhurst c.1890

Most moths are nocturnal and often only seen when attracted to moth lights. It is less common for today's moth hunters to 'sugar' trees [paint the bark of trees with molasses or black treacle and other ingredients, in order to attract moths] or use wine ropes, but sugaring was a frequent practise in Victorian times, particularly useful in attracting females for breeding, as well as males. By comparison, moth lights today mainly attract males. At Ladycross, near New Copse Inclosure, there is evidence of past sugaring of centuries old oaks, although the moths are also attracted to sap runs. Upon arriving in Brockenhurst, Sidney Bell (1905) was shocked to find that 'sugaring' in the New Forest was strictly prohibited to amateur collectors. This followed complaints, allegedly from dealers, about a particular visitor who had labelled a favourite ride as his own and defied anyone else to use it at their peril. If evidence of sugaring was found, the keeper plastered over the patches. In 1911 there was further comment on the prohibition in the entomological literature and warning notices erected, for example in Pondhead Inclosure.

Frederick W. Frowhawk (1861–1946) was an excellent entomological illustrator, well known for his books on British butterflies. A regular visitor to the New Forest, who became known as 'the old man of the forest', in 1888 he recorded in a journal about the first time he visited the Forest, at the age of twenty seven (Chatfield, 1987): 'Insects of all kinds literally swarmed. Butterflies were in profusion, the Silver-washed Fritillary were in hoards in every

Frohawk in the New Forest

ride and the beautiful var[iation] valezina was met with at every few yards as were both the Dark Green and High Brown Fritillaries, the elegant White Admiral were sailing about in quantity everywhere. On a bank under a sallow was a large female Purple Emperor with its wings expanded in the sun, evidently washed out of the sallow by rain. The Large Tortoiseshell was a frequent occurrence and the Brimstone abundant in every ride.' He so liked the Forest that he returned practically every year, including for his honeymoon in 1895, which doubled as a collecting trip. He noticed changes in the number of butterflies first hand, publishing a paper on the 'remarkable scarcity of butterflies in the New Forest' in 1925. The Argentinean-born author and naturalist W. H. Hudson (1841–1922), author of the popular *Hampshire Days* (1903), had a fond regard for the Forest, including its insect life. He stayed frequently at Boldre, strongly disapproved of killing things and described Lyndhurst as the place where 'London vomits out its annual crowd of collectors, who fill its numerous and ever-increasing brand-new red-brick lodging-houses, and who swarm through all the adjacent woods and heaths, men, women, and children (hateful little prigs!) with their vasculums, beer and treacle pots, green and blue butterfly nets, killing bottles, and all the detestable paraphernalia of what they would probably call "Nature Study."'

The Forest is also mentioned in the 1896 to 1909 summary of records for the Milford on Sea Record Society, which lists 49 species of butterflies in Milford and immediate surrounds, including Brown Hairstreak, Long-tailed Blue, Adonis Blue, Duke of Burgundy, Wood White, Camberwell Beauty, Queen of Spain Fritillary, High Brown Fritillary, Glanville Fritillary, Marsh Fritillary, Pearl-bordered Fritillary, Small Pearl-bordered Fritillary and Purple Emperor (the latter in Sway). The Large Tortoise-shell was said to be 'very abundant in some years' and there were hundreds of Clouded Yellow and Pale Clouded Yellow in the clover and lucerne fields in 1900. Alas, how times have changed.

The Forest is also renowned beetle country. LePard (2000) refers to a memory of 'an enthusiastic coleopterist [studies beetles] friend pursuing his hobby near Acres Down one hot Bank Holiday Monday many years ago. Having collected a heap of cowpats, in varying degrees of decomposition, he spent two happy hours pulling one to pieces and examining the fragments for signs of beetle observation, all the time completely oblivious to the fascinated horror with which he was regarded by passers-by'. Barry Goater recalls an amusing story by A.E. Gardner [known as Eric] (1913–1976) at an entomological meeting. Gardner periodically travelled from London to collect beetles in the Forest and informed Barry and others about one such trip, where he found what he thought was an old Hornet's nest. Having poked it with a stick, he was promptly stung on the head by a Hornet, but still managed to obtain the large Hornet Rove Beetles associated with such nests.

David Sharp (1840–1922) was a prolific coleopterist, who published many papers and edited the Zoological Record for 30 years. He made excursions to the Forest with collectors, including Crotch. Not all was rosy, Sharp often spoke of the primitive conditions in years gone by to be found in the New Forest and told amusing stories of their difficulties in procuring food and lodgings. Nevertheless, Sharp retired to Brockenhurst in 1904, where he died 18 years later; he lived on the edge of the Forest at a property he had built known as Lawnside, facing the heath of Black Knowl and took his almost daily walks into the Forest he loved so well.

Horace Donisthorpe (1870–1951) was a well known coleopterist, who published several books and discovered beetles and ants new to Britain, although most of his 'new' species are now synonyms of earlier species. In particular, he collected in Windsor Great Park, but also the New Forest, including Matley Bog.

There are a number of fascinating recollections of finding (and sometimes failing to catch!) scarce aberrations of butterflies, highly-prized by collectors. The last well known collector of these was Donald Russwurm (1904–2001), who illustrated many aberrations of British butterflies, a number collected in the New Forest, or reared in his Brockenhurst home. Many of Russwurm's illustrations are featured in Alec Harmer's *Variation in British Butterflies* published in 2000. Robert Watson (1916–1982) from Sandy Down was another well known collector of aberrations, whose collection of only perfect

Micro moth collectors L.T. Ford (centre), Dr Mansfield & Dr Young, New Forest 1913 [via RF]

FOREST POINT

Under personal management of owners:
Mr. & Mrs. A. J. DIACK
is the first place you see as you enter Lyndhurst on the main London to Bournemouth road via Winchester, Romsey and Cadnam.

Railway Stations—
Lyndhurst Road three miles.
Brockenhurst Station four miles.
Southampton Station nine miles.

Hotel car can meet trains by arrangement.
Telephone—Lyndhurst 2420.

Interests: Lyndhurst Golf Course adjoining: this is free to residents of the hotel. Bramshaw Golf Club 3 miles, Brockenhurst Manor 4 miles.
Hunting and Hacking from own stables with instruction if required.
Easy and delightful walking.
Your dog, horse or pony is welcome.
Entomology.
Swimming in the sea at Milford, 10 miles.
Yachting at Lymington, 7 miles.

Situation: In practically the centre of the New Forest, with its historic charm, wild ponies, etc. The views from Forest Point are magnificent.

Telephone: Lyndhurst 2420 LICENSED A.A. ** R.A.C.

FOREST POINT HOTEL
ROMSEY ROAD, LYNDHURST

FOREST POINT LICENSED — The Hotel with the Friendly Atmosphere where a warm welcome awaits you.

TERMS:—Daily or weekly quoted as required.

Forest Point is beautifully situated with lovely open forest views. Peaceful, yet within 3 mins. of the centre of Lyndhurst village.

We have a reputation for good food and service. There are two good lounges, one with Television, and an excellent restaurant. Gas fires, hot and cold running water in bedrooms, central heating. Lock-up Garages for your car, and spacious car park for 20 cars.

Electric razor points in every room.

Hotel advertisement

specimens, was bequeathed to the Natural History Museum, London, including a striking red form of the Cinnabar Moth, which he bred over 25 years.

Some insect collections from Victorian times are in natural history museums, others are lost. In many cases the data is rather limited; 'New Forest', 'Brockenhurst' or 'Lyndhurst' in an unspecific manner.

A decline in insect populations

By 1960, there were noticeable declines in most butterflies, generally attributed to a combination of conifer afforestation (since the Forestry Commission took over management of the crown lands in 1924), grazing by ponies in some Inclosures, mowing of rides and cutting of ride side scrub such as brambles (from the late 1940s, which resulted in less nectar sources for butterflies) and adverse weather for butterflies i.e. wet summers. This also affected populations of grasshoppers and Bush-crickets; Tubbs (2001) remarks 'the rides were alive with....grasshoppers in the 1950s and 1960s, but the three species persist only in low numbers.' There is a lack of information concerning how other insect orders have been affected. One response to butterfly scarcity was that the Forestry Commission introduced a charge for collecting permits. Positive steps were taken to address the main issues mentioned above and improve insect populations. There is evidence that some butterflies are increasing their range, whilst others are in decline throughout Britain. However, there is little doubt that the New Forest is, once again, becoming a very popular area for butterfly watchers.

More well known naturalists / entomologists residing in or associated with the Forest

Some well known naturalists resided in the New Forest; Lt. Col. Cyril W. Mackworth-Praed (1891–1974) lived at Burley, where he ran a moth trap nightly for over thirty years. He first reported the Chequered Skipper's presence in Scotland in 1942 and captained the gold medal winning Great Britain rifle shooting team at the Olympic Games in 1924. Well known film-makers and naturalists have featured insects of the Forest in their work, including Eric Ashby (1918–2003), a well known wildlife film-maker, who lived at Linwood, near Ringwood and Jack Hargreaves (1911–1994) lived in Beaulieu, then Minstead. John Wise (1831–1890) included notes on insects in his 1863 work *The New Forest; its History and Scenery*. Colin R. Tubbs (1937–1997) from Lyndhurst was an eminent scientist, naturalist and conservationist, author of the much read *The New Forest* published in The New Naturalist series, 1986 (a 2nd edition was published in 2001), which includes important sections on insects from someone with a vast knowledge about the New Forest and the Solent, and its wildlife. His defense of wildlife sites under threat was always based on the best available scientific evidence, often his own. In Clive Chatters' *Flowers of the Forest* (2009), his dedication is to 'Colin Tubbs, without whom the Forest would be in a sorry state.' Nowadays, apart from a wide range of visitors, and the resident naturalist and television presenter Chris Packham, there are some enthusiastic, mainly amateur entomologists and naturalists, who may regularly run moth traps, and report sightings of butterflies to the Hampshire & Isle of Wight Branch of Butterfly Conservation, send insect records to the Southampton Natural History Society or via the Hampshire Biodiversity Information Centre (HBIC), or even directly to national recorders. Amongst the better known is Michael Salmon from Woodgreen, near Fordingbridge, author of fascinating books on the history of butterfly collecting. Also from Fordingbridge is the artist Richard Tratt, whose 2005 book *Butterfly Landscapes* features some of his numerous paintings of butterflies in their natural habitat, in the Forest and surrounds.

Barry Goater lives in Hampshire, outside the Forest, but his extensive knowledge of the area is reflected in a 1974 book *The Butterflies & Moths of Hampshire and the Isle of Wight* and in 2001, *Moths of Hampshire and the Isle of Wight*, written jointly with Tim Norriss, amongst other publications. A companion volume to moths, *The Butterflies of Hampshire* was published in 2000 by Matthew Oates, John Taverner, David Green and others, with the dedication 'This book is dedicated to the memory of the New Forest, and also to its future.' Indeed, each author has a strong association with the Forest. Researchers have a valuable resource of specimens and literature in the biology collections, Hampshire County Council Museums Service, Chilcomb House in Winchester.

Many other entomologists have an association with the Forest; an Invertebrate Site Survey on the Forest (issued 1984) by the Nature Conservancy Council, included records and information on sites and species by well known specialists mainly from outside the Forest, including: Keith Alexander, David Appleton (both Coleoptera), Richard Dickson (Lepidoptera), George Else (Hymenoptera), Ken Halstead (ants), Arthur Massee (Coleoptera), Ivan Perry, Alan Stubbs (both Diptera) and Colin Welch (Coleoptera).

The move to conservation

Times change and rightly so. The Victorians collected drawers of butterflies and this is now both unnecessary and frowned upon by conservationists. For some years it has been necessary to obtain a collecting permit for the New Forest and collecting of butterflies, dragonflies and certain other protected insects is not permitted at all. Nowadays it is normal to just photograph insects and this is a popular pastime. However, some mainly smaller insects do need to be examined carefully to confirm their identity, perhaps with a hand-lens, or under a microscope, hence a butterfly net is useful, in order to catch them. Many of the insects photographed for this book have been found by careful searching of their habitat, whilst others have appeared at random; some insects would not have been seen at all without assistance from a beating tray (a canvas cloth held beneath branches or shrubs, which are struck sharply with a stick), or by using a sweeping net, which involves sweeping the net through grasses or flowers. These collecting tools cannot be used in the National Park without a permit.

Unfortunately there have been reported instances in 2009 of collectors netting rare butterflies in the Forest, possibly to transport to other counties, and it is hoped this practice ceases in order to help conserve these insects; in one case the butterfly is legally protected anywhere in Britain.

Hope for the future

Whilst, with much effort in some cases, it is still possible to find many rare insects in the Forest, it is difficult to visualise the vast numbers of insects present in Victorian times. Let's not dwell on that, by management of habitat, some species are just about holding on nowadays, but in many other parts of Britain a combination of loss or reduction of habitats such as wildflower meadows, ponds and woodlands, as well as changes in farming and pesticides have changed the countryside for future generations. This has happened in parts of the Forest along with other issues already discussed, but at least its protected status gives hope that some of our rarest insects will continue to flourish, so they can be enjoyed by future generations.

At the time of writing in early 2011, there is much discussion on the sale of England's forests by the government; heritage woods including the New Forest "jewels in the crown", are likely to continue to be publicly funded, with a new charity expected to be set up to manage them. Further news is awaited.

'Thistles corner', Churchplace Inclosure, painted by Tratt

UNDERSTANDING THE NEW FOREST HABITATS

There are estimates that the New Forest is rich in insect life. The very latest figures in this photographic guide confirm this, with 80% of Britain's butterfly species recorded, 58% of moths [although micro moths are under-recorded, so the true figure is probably c.66%], 71% of dragonflies and damselflies, and 87% of grasshoppers and crickets. Put in perspective, there are more than 24,000 insect species in Britain, at a conservative estimate over 15,000 i.e. 63% of them recorded in the New Forest, although a minority are probably now extinct. Why such a rich fauna, higher than many whole counties? The extensive woodland and heathland habitats help, along with transitional edge habitats. Mention the New Forest to an entomologist (someone who studies insects) and they will probably mention rarities such as the New Forest Cicada, Noble Chafer beetle, Mole Cricket, one of the crimson underwing moths or comment on dragonflies. Species may be rediscovered after long periods of time, for example the blister beetle *Sitaris muralis* was recorded in Brockenhurst in 2010, the first Forest record since 1947, which gives hope that other rarities in the Forest still exist. For many though, the Silver-studded Blue butterfly is the 'face' of the New Forest, a frequent sight on the heathlands in July and August.

The New Forest was formed in 1079, when King William I declared a vast area of land south of Winchester a royal hunting ground. Laws have changed over time, timber production has often been important, and 'commoners' owning or occupying certain land, still have rights to graze their livestock on the Forest. The boundaries have changed over time, including in 2004, when the forest was designated a National Park, with conservation of prime importance. Since Victorian times, certain management of the Forest has left us with a mixed legacy and habitats have suffered due to tree planting (often conifers), wetland drainage or neglect; however, specific management for some rarer species is paying off, with an increase in numbers of, for example, some of our butterflies. Today, the New Forest is recognised as a major tourist area (with up to 18 million visitors a year), a living, working place with stunning scenery. Visitors marvel at the sight of ponies, cattle and donkeys roaming over the landscape, if fortunate they may catch a glimpse of other plentiful wildlife, including deer, badgers and foxes. The mosaic of different habitats can broadly be divided into categories of woodlands, lawns (grasslands) and heaths, although these often interlink and there are numerous streams. There are also coastal areas to enjoy. Organisations involved in conservation strive to create living landscapes i.e. wildlife-rich reserves linked with well managed habitat beyond the boundaries, where insects can re-colonise the landscape. In the New Forest, this is largely already in place.

The total size of the National Park is 56,651 hectares (ha) (566 square kilometres), with close to 50% being land with open public access. 13,481 ha (almost 24%) is farmland and 32,103 ha (almost 56%) designated as a Site of Special Scientific Interest (SSSI). The Open Forest is that part of the New Forest where the commoners' livestock are free to roam. The extent of Open Forest changes over time, predominantly, but not exclusively, through the erection and removal of fences around Inclosures. This accounts for c.22,000 ha. The Crown lands are lands that are the property of the Crown and vested in the Secretary of State who turns to the Forestry Commission for their management. In addition to the Crown lands the Forestry Commission manage freeholds and leaseholds in the New Forest; the combined total of Forestry Commission land is in the region of 27,000 ha (48% of the total size of the National Park) of which c.20,000 ha falls within the Open Forest. Inclosures are areas where the Crown has a legal right to interfere with the commoners' rights, in order to grow timber. There are c.8,500 ha subject to these rights, but at any one time there may be far less actually fenced off from livestock and in recent years selected Inclosures have been cleared of plantations with the intention of them reverting to previous habitats such as Ancient and Ornamental woods, heaths, bogs and lawns. Inclosures that survive today date from 1700 to 1968.

The type of habitat associated within Open Forest and Statutory Inclosures is listed below.

Ancient and Ornamental woodlands (in Crown land c.4000 ha, 15%) – These are in Open Forest, where continual grazing by animals has resulted in leafy glades with little scrub. This lack of understorey is beneficial to some animals, but for butterflies, the Forest Inclosures are a much more suitable environment. However, the fauna of the trees themselves and wood is not widely affected by grazing and it is not surprising that surveys indicate there are numerous species of invertebrates, including many beetles, flies and moths found in these woodlands, many associated with the abundant dead and decaying wood, possibly c.10,000 species. The very rare New Forest Cicada was

Denny Wood [PCr]

Wootton Coppice Inclosure

Heathland towards Burley across Clayhill Bottom [GP]

first discovered in the Forest in 1812, thought to be extinct by 1941, but rediscovered in 1962 in the old woods between Brook and Fritham, where the late Jim Grant made extensive studies on it. Some of the oak and beech trees are hundreds of years old. There are also plenty of holly, yew, whitebeam, for example around Fritham, and woods with hazel and field maple in the extreme south of the Forest. The Open Forest is the largest area of ancient wood pasture in the lowlands of Western Europe. Denny Wood is well known to entomologists, particularly specialists in beetles and is one of the last known sites for the New Forest Cicada, in 1991. Mark Ash is also a popular site and many tourists visit the Knightwood Oak at Bolderwood, believed to be about 500 years old.

Woodland Inclosures (in Crown land c.8,500 ha, 32%) – Inclosures have been created since the 17th century, which comprise broadleaved (47%) and coniferous (53%) trees, some areas with clearings and wide woodland rides, which are particularly attractive to insects; in some Inclosures, there may be heathlands, meadows and streams present. Nowadays, public access may be restricted at certain times of the year, due to timber felling operations. The planting of conifers in the past has affected the wildlife; whilst conifer plantations support populations of Pine Hawkmoths and other pine specialists, less light reaches the woodland floor, which is covered in fallen needles. This reduces suitable habitat for many animals, plants and insects; many of the deciduous Inclosures appear to abound with insect life, compared with coniferous woodlands and ancient and ornamental woodlands, simple because they are much more visible. Butterflies can be observed, grasshoppers and bush-crickets are more frequent (but still patchy), flies, bees and wasps nectar along the rides, sometimes with hornets in pursuit. Dragonflies are more readily seen and Wood Crickets frequently heard in high summer. Southern Wood Ants are abundant, building enormous nest mounds. However, Inclosures lack some of the rich dead wood fauna of Ancient and Ornamental woodlands. Well managed sites, with a plentiful supply of nectar plants along the Forest rides, and no grazing animals, are more productive; in several cases these are the very sites frequently visited by Victorian entomologists, such as Wootton Coppice Inclosure, the only place in the area where all four species of woodland fritillaries (Pearl-bordered Fritillary, Small-Pearl Bordered Fritillary, Silver-washed Fritillary and Dark Green Fritillary) present in the Forest, can be seen.

Heathlands, mires and bogs (c.19,200 ha, 34% of the Forest; in Crown land c.11,000 ha, 41%) – Mainly present within the Open Forest, but also within Inclosures. These interlink with other habitats, to ponds, streams and rivers, which attract the often specialist wildlife associated with heathlands, such as the delightful Silver-studded Blue and Grayling butterflies. All butterflies except the Silver-studded Blue breed in fairly low numbers in heathland, the Green Hairstreak is occasionally spotted flitting near gorse. The day-flying Emperor and Fox moths, each with stunning larvae, are likely to be occasionally encountered during walks through heathland. Other moth larvae are specialists on heather. A rich variety of dragonflies and damselflies use the water as breeding sites and hunt for food on the heathlands; in particular, the valley mires are known to be prime breeding sites. Crockford is a good example, where overgrown marl (= chalk-rich clay) pits can be found at Crockford Bridge – the surrounding area is a nationally important site for dragonflies; the rare Southern Damselfly occurs in good numbers. The New Forest National Park has 75% of the valley mires in north-western Europe (90 out of 120), with permanently waterlogged soils. The Forest's bogs comprise deposits of saturated peat and provide some of the richest flora; this is ideal habitat for the UK's largest species of grasshopper, the rare Large Marsh Grasshopper, often seen on low vegetation by sphagnum moss; the Forest is the stronghold for it and the Bog Bush-cricket also prefers this habitat. Our other species of grasshopper are commoner in heathlands and bogs than in woodland in the Forest, including the rare Heath Grasshopper. Twenty-five or more of the UK's ant species are found on heaths and acid grasslands of the Forest, including the endangered Black Bog Ant, known from a few Forest mires. Various ants have close relationships with other insects, including blue butterflies. Heather Beetles are common, but many beetles found on heaths are predators, such as the Green Tiger Beetle, often seen on paths. Kugelann's Ground Beetle is extremely rare and restricted to a few sites, mainly in one New Forest heathland sandpit. The spider hunting wasp *Anoplius viaticus* is a colourful addition to the fauna, watch carefully and you may see it paralysing its spider prey, whereas the sand wasps *Ammophila sabulosa* and *Ammophila pubescens* hunt for caterpillars to place in their underground burrows. The New Forest Shieldbug is a rarity mainly restricted to the Forest heathlands and the Gorse Shieldbug a familiar sight around gorse and birch. Management of heathlands,

Holmsley bog [GP]

Balmer Lawn

Becton Bunny, Barton-on-Sea [GP]

includes periodic controlled heathland fires, such as burning over-mature heathland, which can be beneficial for wildlife. The bogs are important (including carr = wet woodland) for species richness, yet are vulnerable to changes.

Lawns (grasslands) (in Crown land c.3,000 ha, 11%, part wet lawn but mostly lowland acid grassland) – Popular with tourists and local residents alike, areas of grassland, or 'lawns' are better drained soils, often alongside streams, ditches and ponds and may be used for recreational purposes. The lush vegetation is sought after by grazing animals, but a rich variety of plants grows along the banks. Balmer Lawn, near Brockenhurst is a good example of a 'lawn', which supports a colony of Lesser Marsh Grasshoppers. Notably, during the summer months the endangered Beaulieu Dung Beetle is reliably found in cattle dung at the margins of a pond on Balmer Lawn, its only known site in the British Isles. A very rare weevil *Bagous brevis* is now known only from a pond, again at Balmer Lawn, and possibly one or two other ponds in the New Forest, where it is associated with lesser spearwort, and should be looked for by carefully examining submerged waterside vegetation. Other lawns and grasslands by heathlands and woodlands, support nectar flowers and hence attract insects, including woodland butterflies. The water attracts dragonflies and damselflies.

Coastal areas – There are 42 km of New Forest coastline, which comprise cliffs, shingle spits, saltmarsh and mudflats. Some specialists are wholly or partly dependent on coastal soft cliffs for their survival. Hurst Castle (an area of vegetated shingle) supports the UK's mainland population of the Glanville Fritillary, otherwise only established on the Isle of Wight in Britain, as well as the rare Dew Moth. Craneflies are plentiful. On and near the undercliffs, populations of the rare Grey Bush-cricket occur and the Short-winged Cone-head is present at some coastal sites, such as Lepe and Milford-on-Sea. Grasshoppers are more plentiful than in woodlands, with all three of the UK's small, well camouflaged ground-hopper species present in damp places. The attractive Stripe-winged Grasshopper is found around Barton, but apparently no longer in the New Forest boundary. Shieldbugs and Leatherbugs are likely to be seen on low-growing plants or on the ground. The Bee Killer wasp is occasionally seen busy carrying its prey. Where there is ivy in the vicinity, such as Lymington, Hordle and Barton-on-Sea, to Boscombe and beyond, the attractive Ivy Bee (first resident in the UK in 2001), nests on the undercliffs in huge numbers. Further outside the Forest boundary, the coastal sandy grassland and maritime cliffs of the Bournemouth area have an interesting fauna, with Crucifer Shieldbugs commonly seen. Dibden Bay in the Solent is known for its nationally important assemblage of beetles, bees, wasps and flies. There is always a chance that migrant insects from continental Europe will arrive and stay in the vicinity. In years where the Clouded Yellow butterfly is scarce there are usually a few to be found along the coast either at Keyhaven, Barton or beyond; they usually breed in the Boscombe area.

Other land – About half of the National Park is made up of woods and fields, including agricultural land (with important hedgerows suitable for wildlife), mostly privately owned and often fenced off, to prevent stock roaming freely. One of the better known examples is Roydon Woods Nature Reserve, an estate of nearly 40 square kilometres managed by the Hampshire and Isle of Wight Wildlife Trust, which includes woodlands, heathlands and meadows, also with important wetland habitat. Whilst some insects have difficulty expanding their range, because the Open Forest habitats may be unsuitable, these create pockets of habitat such as grasslands seldom grazed by livestock (except where land is managed), where insects can thrive. Roydon is one of the few sites in the area for the Small Pearl-bordered Fritillary and has a rich insect fauna. Sims Wood (part of the North Solent National Nature Reserve, near Beaulieu) is well known for insect rarities. In the Open Forest, Shirley Holms has a rich butterfly fauna, almost approaching the number of species seen in some of the best known Forest Inclosures. Houses and gardens attract an interesting range of fauna, attracted by the nectar, with plenty of butterflies, bees, flies and other insects; larger houses in the Forest often have the bonus of having several established trees in their gardens. Churchyards attract a wide variety of insects, particularly those with hedgerows and trees, or woodland alongside. Road verges support populations of various insects, as the long grass is not a feature of much of the grazed, surrounding landscape. The very rare Noble Chafer beetle is just as likely to be found on hogweeds or elder flowers by a road verge as hogweed rarely grows elsewhere in the Forest. These sun-loving beetles breed in decaying wood deep within hollowing old trees, most likely in Ancient and Ornamental woodlands, or Inclosures, near to Lyndhurst.

A few hazards

Whilst much of the New Forest can be visited, there are signs warning of nesting birds on the heathlands and bogs. Visitors and naturalists need to exercise care in minimising possible disturbance to other wildlife and avoid damaging the landscape. Besides obvious hazards such as getting lost in the forest (take a good OS map), using a torch (and having spare batteries) at night, not walking in the bogs (risk of falling in) and other aquatic habitats, and being aware of livestock and others around you, including cyclists, a few of the hazards humans may encounter include:

Adders – our only venomous snake, adders are common in the Forest heathlands, also some woodlands and have legal protection. They often bask in the morning and are well camouflaged. There is still evidence of persecution of adders, with some killed by fear or ignorance. In reality these snakes will only bite when provoked. Early shock and collapse are seen in severe cases. However, anyone bitten normally makes an uneventful recovery, but should seek medical attention.

Forestry activities – keep well away from any forestry work and obey any warning signs. On rare occasions, entrances to Inclosures are closed.

Hornets – These ferocious insects have much more venom than wasps and can be seen on forest rides in the daytime, looking for insect prey. Some entomologists run moth traps at night (permission from the Forestry Commission at Lyndhurst is required). Care is needed to try to avoid a hornet sting as several hornets may be attracted to the lights. There is also a risk they may injure themselves inside the moth trap.

Ticks – in rare cases these can cause Lyme disease and to be safe, one should assume any tick bite is potentially infectious. Ticks are found in grassy places and attach themselves to passing animals and people, then find a suitable site to feed by biting through the skin and sucking blood. Wearing a long-sleeved shirt and trousers helps; trouser bottoms can be tucked into shoes or boots. If noticed, ticks can be picked off. Check for ticks during a visit and at the end of the day, particularly armpits and groins, removing ticks as soon as possible, using tweezers or a pet tick remover, available from vets. Use tick collars on pets. More detailed advice is available in a leaflet from the New Forest District Council.

A tick *Ixodes ricinus* waiting for a passing animal or human being (3–3.6 mm, 11 mm when engorged with a blood meal)

Examples of habitats in the New Forest

Ancient woodlands – Denny Wood

LOCATION: South of the Forest, approached from Lyndhurst on the B3056, or from Beaulieu, the entrance, signposted Denny Wood campsite is at SU334069, one can drive past the campsite and there is limited parking alongside the main track, before reaching Denny Lodge. Alternatively park at SU332075 (near another main campsite at Matley Wood), the second gravel entrance coming from Lyndhurst, and also explore nearby Matley, including Matley Bog, which harbours insect rarities. Bird watchers consider Denny Wood a good area for commoner woodland birds, Wood Warbler and Redstart and it is also renowned as a fungi site.
HABITAT: Large area of broadleaved ancient woodland, with plenty of dead and decaying wood.
SUGGESTED ROUTE: Explore off the track, examine dead and decaying wood, go towards Parkhill and Denny Inclosures and if a longer walk is desired, Stubby Copse and Denny Lodge Inclosures, with a good network of tracks and a wide range of habitat. Patience is needed, there can be good numbers of insects attracted to flowers such as hawthorn and brambles, but this type of locality requires time to search habitats. It could be a while before interesting, rarer insects are spotted, it may even be necessary to search diligently over a number of seasons. For example, the endangered ground beetle *Pterostichus aterrimus*, associated with wet humus, was found in a marshy area south of Denny Wood from 1969 to 1973.
HIGHLIGHTS: There will be a wide range of insects, perhaps not many butterfly rarities, but one should see plenty of Silver-washed Fritillaries in July and August and keep an eye out for Purple Hairstreaks flitting high up around oaks. The nectar flowers attract various insects, and beetle specialists have always found rare insects by searching bark and flowers, although some species are nocturnal. Many of the longhorn beetles occur on fallen or standing beech trunks. Stand and watch these and a multitude of insects will reveal themselves. Common and rare species of hoverfly explore hollows and craneflies (including rarities), rest on beech trunks. A wide range of other flies, bees and wasps are also frequently seen, also large ichneumons. Flowers including hawthorn in spring, elderberry and brambles attract many nectar feeding insects, with an ideal combination of nectar and rotting wood in close proximity. Dung attracts colourful dor beetles, including the Minotaur Beetle. Dragonflies and damselflies are sometimes seen, possibly the Emperor Dragonfly, sometimes migrants like the Red-veined Darter are at nearby Matley Bog. Keep an eye out for rarer ground beetles in the heathland bordering the entrance, or around a sandpit. Here, the attractive black and red spider-hunting wasps

Denny Wood, old beech stumps

BELOW
Lesser Stag Beetle
Purple Hairstreak [MH]

and caterpillar-hunting sand wasps look for prey to paralyse and transport to the nest. There is a much larger sandy area to explore though at Parc Pale, close to Lyndhurst. Heathland surrounding the wood is rich in insects, including Silver-studded Blue and Grayling butterflies and Emperor Moth. Many moths are seldom seem in the daytime, but light trapping [permission needed from the Forestry Commission] produces a wide range of species, some uncommon.

Inclosed woodland – Pignal Inclosure

LOCATION: North-east of Brockenhurst, when travelling on the A337 from Lyndhurst or Brockenhurst, take the B3055 to Beaulieu by Balmer Lawn. After ¼ mile, fork left on the forest dirt track, ignore the first car park on the left, at the junction ahead turn left and park on the left at the Standing Hat car park [SU314036], which can be busy at weekends in peak season, as it is popular with walkers and cyclists.
HABITAT: Woodland glades (mixed deciduous and coniferous trees), open areas managed by Forestry Commission keepers, suitable for rarities such as Pearl-bordered Fritillaries.
SUGGESTED ROUTE: Enter the five-bar gate and take the left track, heading north-east and ignore occasional tracks to the side, although these can be explored later. The gravel tracks are mainly straightforward, but after heavy rain, can be muddy immediately before a breeding site for the Pearl-bordered Fritillary, which is reached after approximately 1 km [SU316046]; technically this is just in Parkhill Inclosure. A large area of open habitat is seen on both sides of the track, part heathland and with quite a few gorse bushes adding to the colour in spring. The butterflies are seen sunning themselves and flying in this area from early May (late April in favourable years). At the end of this open area, turn right upon reaching a T-junction, and then turn right at marker post 34 for Brockenhurst, effectively following a rectangular route leading back to Standing Hat car park. The first and last kilometre of this 4-km walk tends to be more productive. This walk can easily be combined with other areas, as Pignal borders other well-known forest Inclosures. At marker post 34 one can turn left (signposted Lyndhurst) to see the Frohawk Ride 200 m on the left, this was named after the well known naturalist F.W. Frohawk in 1996. A frequent visitor to the New Forest, Frohawk had named a female form of the Silver-washed Fritillary after his third daughter, Valezina.
HIGHLIGHTS: The gorse, hawthorn and privet flowers attract various insects, perhaps Rose Chafer beetles. Several species of dragonflies are likely here, also beetles, bees and several species of butterflies. It is the Pearl-bordered Fritillaries that catch the eye, they spread out looking for nectar plants, or may be observed laying eggs on or near dog-violets. Bugles are a particular favourite nectar source and can be found at the edges of open rides. The Green Tiger Beetle should also be readily encountered on the

Pignal Inclosure

BELOW
Rose Chafer
Pearl-bordered Fritillary

ground in damper areas, along with numerous Southern Wood Ants, patrolling on or near their conspicuous, large, mound-like nests. Flowers along the ditches provide nectar for butterflies, beetles and hoverflies, amongst others; there are likely to be several species of longhorn beetles, whose females may also be seen egg-laying in the log-piles, as well as Rose Chafers.

In July and early August Silver-washed Fritillaries appear on the tracks, mainly nectaring on bramble flowers; watch out for the dark female form *valezina*. The White Admiral may also occasionally be seen in July, but is less common than in several other New Forest Inclosures. Commoner species of butterflies should be sighted from April through to September, particularly Meadow Browns, Gatekeepers and Ringlets. Purple Hairstreaks catch the eye high up, flitting around oak trees; with the possibility of rarer species (31 species of butterflies have been recorded since 2000). Dung attracts colourful Dor Beetles, which keep themselves busy disposing of it; whilst these are the commonest dung beetle, the impressive three-horned Minotaur Beetle is sometimes observed. Interesting moths may occasionally be seen, possibly even a nectaring Broad-bordered Bee Hawkmoth in May.

HISTORICAL NOTE: Don Russwurm (1904–2001), a well known collector of butterfly varieties, retired to Brockenhurst in 1959 – Pignal Inclosure was one of his favourite localities, which produced its fair share of interesting varieties.

Heathlands, mires and bogs – Beaulieu Heath, Matley Bog

LOCATION: Various parts of Beaulieu Heath can easily be walked, with car parking available at Hatchet Pond, Crockford and Hawkhill, as well as Hatchet Moor itself, centred on the old airfield, popular today for flying model aircraft (SU358007). Matley Bog is in the south of the Forest, approached from Lyndhurst on the B3056, or from Beaulieu, park at SU332075 (near the campsite at Matley Wood), the second gravel entrance coming from Lyndhurst, and walk to Matley Bog (SU333073), past the heath. This excursion can be combined with a visit to Denny Wood.

HABITAT: Beaulieu Heath is a good example of heathland with occasional scrub and woodland edge, with a rich fauna. Matley Bog, well known since Victorian times, is an ancient woodland bog and perfect habitat for some of the Forest's rarest specialities.

SUGGESTED ROUTE: Try the routes mentioned above, for a better choice of species in a compact area, the heathland in front of Hawkhill Inclosure is productive, or near the old airfield.

HIGHLIGHTS: The heathland, with low-growing heather and gorse, attracts butterflies such as the Silver-studded Blue and Dark Green Fritillary, with Graylings on bare patches. Even White Admirals may

Beaulieu Heath

BELOW
New Forest Shieldbug
Silver-studded Blue [PC]

occasionally be seen at the woodland edge and some commoner species may be seen. Day flying moths include the Emperor and Fox moths.

Hatchet Pond is the largest pond in the Forest, popular with visitors and with an interesting range of insects, including many dragonflies, damselflies and other aquatic life. This fauna also excels further into the heath at Crockford bridge, via streams either side of the bridge. Crockford is one of Britain's best dragonfly sites with 28 species seen in the area, including Hampshire's only Scarlet Darter, found in 2002. Notably, there are many Southern Damselflies, one of our UK's rarest species. There is also a surprising range of butterflies at Crockford, including the rare Grizzled Skipper and Dark Green Fritillary, around 21 species, more than double the number of species at other good heathland sites in the vicinity, although mainly in small numbers.

Matley bog is notable for rarities such as the Large Marsh Grasshopper, New Forest Shieldbug and Bog Bush-cricket, also for the presence of the rare Black Bog Ant in tussocks, which was discovered there in the early 20th century by Horace Donisthorpe.

Lawns – Burley, Burbush area

LOCATION: Park at Burbush Hill car park (SU203018), south of Burley, popular with cyclists and walkers.
HABITAT: A less extensive 'lawn' than Balmer Lawn, with streams, surrounded by various habitats, hedgerows, heathland and nearby ponds (Whitten Pond, SU204013, is one of the best in the Forest to watch and photograph dragonflies and damselflies). Part of the site is a now disused railway line.
SUGGESTED ROUTE: Search around the lawn near the car park and in the immediate vicinity first, and then examine some of the attractive surrounding habitats.
HIGHLIGHTS: Check around the lawn for mainly commoner butterflies, including the delightful Small Copper. Silver-studded Blues and Graylings can be found on nearby heaths. There are plenty of commoner insects around the hedgerows, flies, beetles, shieldbugs, wasps, also Wood Crickets in leaf litter. Using a beating tray has revealed the presence of many 'hidden' insects.

Dragonflies such as Broad-bodied Chaser, Keeled Skimmer and Southern Hawkers are likely, damselflies and other aquatic life are found also, although if interested in these insects, visits to the nearby ponds will be rewarding for these and other species, including Black Darter, and it is usually straightforward to photograph species such as the Brown Hawker and Southern Hawker, on low vegetation.

In nearby areas, rarities such as the Large Velvet Ant and the Mottled Bee-fly may be seen, if fortunate. As in often the case in the Forest, various habitats merge together.

Whitten Pond and feeder stream

BELOW
Brown Hawker
Mottled Bee-fly

Coastal areas – Keyhaven and Pennington Marshes

LOCATION: Keyhaven and Pennington marshes are managed by the Hampshire and Isle of Wight Wildlife Trust (the sea wall and grazed marsh inside the wall form part of Hampshire County Council Nature Reserve) and are easy to find by heading south from Lyndhurst on the A337 through Lymington and Pennington, then turn left on the B3058 to Keyhaven via Milford-on-Sea and head for the public car park opposite the pub (SZ310910). There are other parking options, including taking a left turn before the car park if there are spaces available by the sea wall. Alternatively, take the A337 from Lymington, but at the roundabout take the first exit onto Ridgeway Lane, then sharp right onto Lower Pennington Lane, which is narrow in part (SZ319927) and there are only a few spaces near the gate, in an area popular with birdwatchers and dog walkers. A ferry can be taken from Keyhaven to Hurst Castle, or one can walk.

HABITAT: A large area of saltmarsh and mudflats either side of the Lymington River, an important site for breeding, feeding and roosting birds. Effectively a network of ditches and ponds within the saltmarsh behind a sea-wall, some of the land is fenced off and out of bounds. Nearby are hedgerows and damp meadows, very close to the refuse tip at Efford. Milford-on-Sea is about a mile away. Hurst Castle is a nearby area of vegetated shingle.

SUGGESTED ROUTE: From the Keyhaven car park, take the Coastal Way, a circular trip coastal footpaths bordering the lagoons returning along inland tracks around the Pennington and Keyhaven marshes (such as the track known as the Ancient Highway). It is possible to walk along the Iley Lane towards Efford and check meadows, hedgerows and ponds in the area, or walk to Normandy Marshes. For dragonflies and damselflies try the (lower) Balancing pond (SZ311921), the upper balancing pond (SZ311932) and the ditches along the edges of the lagoons behind the sea-wall.

HIGHLIGHTS: A well known refuge in Hampshire for the Wall butterfly, which flies backwards and forwards on the coastal paths, particularly those less breezy. There are about 26 species of butterflies in the vicinity, notably Green Hairstreaks flitting around gorse bushes, Brown Argus, even the occasional Silver-washed Fritillary. Small Coppers are found in larger numbers than in most parts of the county and Speckled Woods are easily the commonest species. A wide range of moths are found on the site, including migrants.

The meadow alongside Hurst Castle is well known for the Glanville Fritillary and attractive Cream-spot Tiger moths are often common, also the rare Dew Moth. Look around and there are often interesting larvae to find or insects nectaring on the meadow flowers.

Pennington Marshes

BELOW

Blue-tailed Damselfly [PCr]

Cream-spot Tiger [GP]

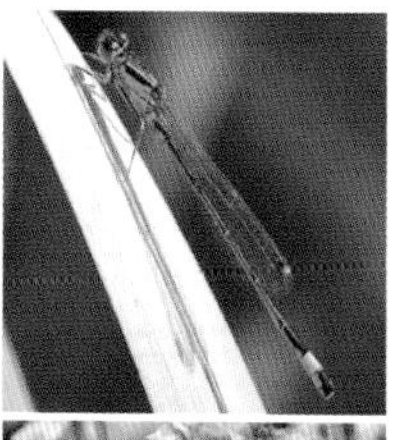

The waters attract about 24 species of dragonflies and damselflies, with rarer species such as the Small Red-eyed Damselfly, Hairy Dragonfly, Scarce Chaser and migrant Red-veined Darter sometimes present. Migrant Hawkers are common. Thousands of Blue-tailed Damselflies can be seen by the sea-wall in the right conditions.

Flies provide plentiful food for the birds and dragonflies, and occasionally interesting beetles are found.

Other areas – Roydon Woods (SU315009)

LOCATION: One mile south-east of Brockenhurst, this site is owned and managed by the Hampshire and Isle of Wight Wildlife Trust. These woods were a gift to the Trust by Peter Barker-Mill. Roydon is accessed from the A337 towards Lymington. The usual entrance for this Site of Special Scientific Interest (SSSI) is near the Filly Inn (SU306015), with off-road parking nearby, for example take the first right and park immediately on the left. Visitors can drive further on the A337 and take the first left after the Filly Inn, signposted Sandy Down, which has limited off road parking, for example at SZ313995, also see http://www.hwt.org.uk/pages/roydon-woods-r.html for other options. It is also worth looking on the scrub areas at Setley, slightly further along the road to Lymington.

HABITAT: A large site of c.400 hectares when one includes subsequent purchases by the owners, such as meadows in the Lymington River Valley together with the contiguous Lymington River Reedbeds. There are several habitats: ancient woodland, pastures, ponds, streams, heaths and the Lymington River.

SUGGESTED ROUTE: Take the various paths in the reserve; a trail guide is available from the Trust. When approaching from the Filly Inn, go straight up the lane alongside, over the cattle grid and after passing cottages, a Roydon Woods sign will be seen. Turn right onto the main track at a gate; walk on the track through the conifers and on the heath turn left on the narrow track, and look out for a damp meadow on the right for the Small Pearl-bordered Fritillary site. Explore the many tracks to find other habitats. Whilst there are conifers in some parts, in others there are fine deciduous trees, including oaks and beeches.

HIGHLIGHTS: There are about 28 species of butterflies in this well spread out area, notably the strongest colony of Small Pearl-bordered Fritillaries in the area. There are usually Silver-studded Blues on the first small area of heathland, Silver-washed Fritillaries and White Admirals on some rides, also Pearl-bordered Fritillaries are occasionally seen. Surveys have shown that there are a wide range of moths

Roydon Woods

BELOW
Small Pearl-bordered Fritillary [GP]
Tanner Beetle [GP]

Southampton Natural History Society meeting at Fawley Inclosure

found on the site, also interesting beetles, including Glow-worms and the huge longhorn, the Tanner Beetle. Snakeflies are occasionally seen (also at Setley, outside the Reserve). Unusual flies are also present.

The waters attract dragonflies and damselflies, although the main pond is fenced off.

Learning more

Organised events are held in and around the Forest, which is a good opportunity to learn more about insects and indeed, plants and animals. Examples of organisations holding events are Butterfly Conservation, Hampshire & Isle of Wight branch, Forestry Commission, Hampshire & Isle of Wight Wildlife Trust, Lymington & District Naturalists' Society and Southampton Natural History Society.

Butterfly watching, Butterfly Conservation meeting, Wootton Coppice Inclosure

MAYFLIES – Order EPHEMEROPTERA

UK: 51 species
New Forest: at least 23 species [45%]

Well known to trout fishermen (who tie artificial mayflies), many people will have seen the weak fluttering of mayflies over rivers, lakes, ponds or streams. They have one or two pairs of densely veined, almost transparent wings (forewings much larger), characteristic short antennae and two or three slender, long, trailing 'tails'. The name Ephemeroptera means 'living for a day' and in some species this is true. However, the larvae are aquatic, spending a year or more under water, feeding on vegetation and small fragments of organic matter. Mayflies are the only insects to moult when fully-winged. When freshly emerged, the non-feeding adults are known as duns and are rather dull, but they moult within a few hours. The mature adults, known as spinners, rest with the wings held vertically above the back and some days there may be hundreds or thousands of these insects flying around in mating 'dances', above the water. The life cycle is one of incomplete metamorphosis (development), so females lay eggs which hatch into larvae, from which eventually an adult emerges. A larva can take about two years to complete its life cycle and may be found by examining the underside of stones in fast-flowing streams; others burrow in the silt or are active swimmers. Mayflies are poorly recorded in the Forest and there is likely to be a higher percentage of species present, although the acid waters of much of the Forest may restrict numbers, as some species have exacting habitat requirements. They are particularly noticed at popular beauty spots in the Forest in spring and summer, such as Balmer Lawn; representative, common species are illustrated, ***Cloeon dipterum*** (6–10 mm) which lacks hindwings, ***Centroptilum luteolum*** (6–7 mm) with large turret-like eyes [both in the family Baetidae], also a ***Leptophlebia*** species (c.12 mm) [family Leptophlebiidae]. *Cloeon dipterum* females are known to lay eggs in ponds 10–14 days after mating, with eggs hatching immediately.

1
2
3

Plate 1
Cloeon dipterum

Plate 2
Centroptilum luteolum

Plate 3
Leptophlebia species

Mayflies like streams such as Crockford

DRAGONFLIES and DAMSELFLIES – Order ODONATA

UK: 45 species, including 2 extinct (Hampshire 34 species, including 1 extinct)
New Forest: 32 species, including 1 extinct [71%]

Adults are large, fast, day-flying predators with amazing aerial skills. They have large eyes, tiny antennae and two pairs of wings, with a complex network of veins. The abdomen is long, slender and often brightly coloured, enabling them to be identified in flight. In fact, some rarely settle, making photography difficult. Immature forms and colour forms may add to confusion, but there are excellent guide books available. The life cycle is incomplete metamorphosis, involving egg, larva and adult. The predatory larvae are aquatic, feeding on insect larvae (including of the same species) and larger larvae eat tadpoles and small fish. The exuviae (larval skin) is often observed clinging onto reeds or waterside vegetation. If fortunate, the observer may see an adult emerging and drying its wings.

Dragonflies and damselflies are popular and local enthusiasts have benefited from a small book *The Dragonflies of the New Forest* by Noelle and Tony Welstead (1984), founder members of the 'New Forest Odonata Study Group', which became affiliated to the British Dragonfly Society. *The Dragonflies of Hampshire* by Taverner, Cham, Hold *et al.* was published in 2004 which included the Southampton Natural History Society's detailed survey.

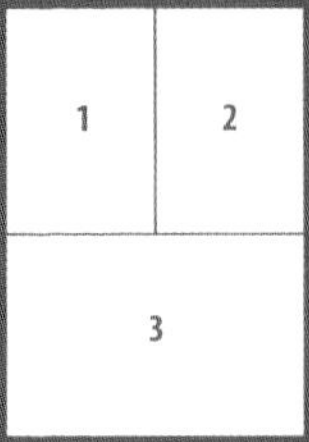

DAMSELFLIES – Suborder Zygoptera

UK: 19 resident species, including 1 extinct (Hampshire 14 species)
New Forest: 14 species [74%]

The slender-bodied damselflies have a weak flight and usually rest with the wings held vertically above the body, although some rest with wings at least partly open. Like small jewels, the Beautiful Demoiselle is an impressive sight alongside streams in spring and summer, hunting for small insects. Damselflies tend to be much commoner at ponds and streams than the larger dragonflies; as such areas can only support a modest population. There may be hundreds of damselflies at some of the Forest streams, where they spread out on vegetation, and males form territories; different species may occupy other zones. Females are eagerly awaited and will often be seen paired, or egg-laying, often the female oviposits in tandem with the male, which prevents rival males mating. Sperm is stored by the female in specialised organs. Fresh adults are known as teneral (not fully mature in colours), which can confuse observers until the normal adult colour is reached after a few days. The flight and colour of individuals helps to identify species. Larvae are carnivorous, often taking one to three years to complete their development under water.

Always a stronghold for damselflies in the New Forest, there are a number of sites where one can expect to see most of the species, sometimes in huge numbers. Good general sites are the Crockford area, with 10 species, well known for numerous Southern Damselflies and the occasional Scarce Blue-tailed Damselfly; Hatchet Pond with up to 10 species; Keyhaven / Pennington (the lower and upper Balancing ponds) several species, including Banded Demoiselle, Red-eyed and Small Red-eyed Damselflies; Puttles Bridge and surrounds (stream further up near Clumber Inclosure), for White-legged Damselflies, also occasional Banded Demoiselle, rare in the Forest. Other good localities include Badminston Gravel pit, Broomy Pond, Eyeworth Pond, Long Pond and Whitten Pond. Just outside the New Forest it is well worth visiting Blashford Lakes, Testwood Lakes and Lower Test Marshes, good for Banded Demoiselle, although the species is abundant alongside the Avon River, Ibsley.

1	2
3	

Plate 1
Recently emerged Beautiful Demoiselle colouring up, still clutching its exuvia, or larval skin

Plate 2
Large Red Damselflies mating in 'wheel' position

Plate 3
Emerald Damselfly feeding [GH]

DEMOISELLES – Family Calopterygidae

Beautiful Demoiselle *Calopteryx virgo* (length: 45–49 mm)
CURRENT STATUS IN THE NEW FOREST: Common
IDENTIFICATION: Large, bright metallic bluish-green male, female metallic bronze-green, with brownish wings, very likely to be seen by the general naturalist or walker.
HABITAT: Common and widespread on Forest neutral to moderately acid rivers and streams, with sandy or gravel beds, from May to September (peaking in June to early July). This species is a regular sight in the Inclosures, Crockford area, Latchmore Brook, Puttles Bridge and elsewhere on the Ober Water. Also found in numerous other Forest sites, the Isle of Wight and mostly west of a line between Liverpool and Folkestone; as well as southern Ireland. Vivid flashes of colour are usually clashes between spiraling males, which have a fluttering flight. Females lay eggs alone, with males standing guard nearby. This species often rests on bank side vegetation and if carefully stalked, is easy to photograph.

Banded Demoiselle *Calopteryx splendens* (length: 45–48 mm)
CURRENT STATUS IN THE NEW FOREST: Rare
IDENTIFICATION: Large, body of male bright metallic blue; band of blue across each wing. The female has a green body, with greenish-yellow wings.
HABITAT: Common near the Forest on the Avon, Test and Itchen rivers (neutral to alkaline sluggish rivers on muddy beds with good growth of vegetation on the riversides). This species is rarely observed in the Forest, although noted near Clumber Inclosure, also Pennington [private site], during May to mid-September. However, hundreds can be observed at Ibsley and Lower Test, also parts of the River Stour. Found on the Isle of Wight, this is a common species throughout most of England (south of the Humber), Wales and Ireland. Sometimes difficult to photograph, they often keep to riverside vegetation in numbers and readily take flight at any perceived danger.

EMERALD DAMSELFLIES – Family Lestidae

Emerald Damselfly *Lestes sponsa* (length: 35–39 mm)
CURRENT STATUS IN THE NEW FOREST: Local
IDENTIFICATION: Slightly larger than other UK damselflies, except for the Demoiselles. Body metallic green; male with blue on both sides of the thorax and the first and last two segments of the abdomen.
HABITAT: Locally common in the Forest on sheltered, well vegetated ponds and bog pools, possibly also ditches from June to September. Good localities include Ashley Hole, Broomy, Long, Rushbush and Whitten Ponds, during mid-June to October. Found on the Isle of Wight although rare, this is a locally common species throughout Britain and Ireland. Often close to waterside vegetation, this species has a very fluttering flight, with wings often held away from the body when resting.

WHITE-LEGGED DAMSELFLIES – Family Platycnemididae

White-legged Damselfly *Platycnemis pennipes* (length: 35–37 mm)
CURRENT STATUS IN THE NEW FOREST: Rare
IDENTIFICATION: Male pale cream to pale blue and to green in the female. The legs are always white, with a black line.
HABITAT: Slow flowing streams with lush and tall marginal vegetation. Good localities include the Ober Water by Puttles Bridge, near Clumber Inclosure and Brinken Wood from mid to late May to August. Found on the Isle of Wight, this is a mainly uncommon species in southern England and a few sites in Wales. Often rests on bog myrtle. The female oviposits in tandem with the male.

1a	3a
1b	3b
2a	4a
	4b
2b	4c

Plates 1a & 1b
Beautiful Demoiselle
a) male
b) female

Plates 2a & 2b
Banded Demoiselle
a) male
b) female

Plates 3a & 3b
Emerald Damselfly
a) male [GH]
b) female [GH]

Plates 4a–4c
White-legged Damselfly
a) male
b) female
c) male close-up

RED AND BLUE / BLACK DAMSELFLIES – Family Coenagrionidae

Large Red Damselfly *Pyrrhosoma nymphula* (length: 33–36 mm)

CURRENT STATUS IN THE NEW FOREST: Common

IDENTIFICATION: Thorax black in both sexes, with red stripes, abdomen red with dark bronze to black on final segments in male; in female yellow band encircling each abdominal segment. There are several female colour forms.

HABITAT: Found in all aquatic habitats from April to September. Widespread on the Isle of Wight and throughout much of Britain and Ireland. The female, clasped by the male, oviposits into floating leaves and stems.

Red-eyed Damselfly *Erythromma najas* (length: 30–36 mm)

CURRENT STATUS IN THE NEW FOREST: Local

IDENTIFICATION: Black species with distinctive red eyes. The male has light blue on the sides of the thorax (in female, yellow), the first and last two abdominal segments.

HABITAT: Found on large ponds and lakes with floating vegetation such as water lilies, from May to September. Pennington, Eyeworth, Long and Whitten Ponds are all good habitats, amongst others. Rare on the Isle of Wight, this species is locally common in southern England and the Welsh Borders. It can be frustrating photographing this species, nearly always on floating vegetation too far away from the camera; only occasionally resting on waterside vegetation. The female oviposits in tandem with the male and may submerge with or without the male.

Small Red-eyed Damselfly *Erythromma viridulum* (length: 26–32 mm)

CURRENT STATUS IN THE NEW FOREST: Local

IDENTIFICATION: Very similar to the larger Red-eyed and sometimes found together. Black species with distinctive red eyes. The male has light blue on the sides of the thorax, the first and last two abdominal segments, but the sides of the second and eight segments are blue, but largely black in the Red-eyed Damselfly.

HABITAT: Only recognised as a British species in 1999, found on large ponds and lakes with floating vegetation, from June to September. Badminston Gravel Pit, a private site at Pennington and Rushbush Pond are good habitats, amongst others. Outside the New Forest, Southampton Boating Lake and Testwood Lakes centre pond are reliable sites. Now spreading on the Isle of Wight and locally common in south-east England. This species is possibly even more difficult to photograph than the Red-eyed Damselfly.

Damselflies habitat, Broomy Pond

1a		
1b	1c	
2a	2b	2c
3		

Plates 1a–1c
Large Red Damselfly
a) mating pair
b) mating pair 'in tandem'; the male prevents other males from mating with the female
c) emerging from exuvia [BV]

Plates 2a–2c
Red-eyed Damselfly
a) male [GH]
b) male, occasionally rest on vegetation by watersides
c) immature female [GH]

Plate 3
Small Red-eyed Damselfly male [GH]

Southern Damselfly *Coenagrion mercuriale* (length: 27–31 mm)
CURRENT STATUS IN THE NEW FOREST: Local
IDENTIFICATION: One of our smallest damselflies, both sexes have slim thoracic stripes and small circular eye-spots with a coloured bar between them—this distinguishes them from similar blue and black damselflies, namely the Common Blue and Azure, although many look for the black 'mercury' sign of the Southern Damselfly, on the 2nd abdominal segment. The female is black with yellow, green or greenish blue eye-spots, bar and thoracic stripes.
HABITAT: Found in sheltered, but often overgrown streams and ditches with acid heathland, from May to about August, sometimes in large numbers. Crockford is widely known as a major locality for this species, but there are a number of other reliable sites, mainly in the southern part of the Forest, which is the stronghold for this rare British insect, thought to enjoy the microhabitat created by trampling of stream margins by livestock. A declining species, now known to occur in mainly smaller colonies in Devon, Dorset (including near Bournemouth airport) and Oxfordshire, on the flood plains of the Test and Itchen rivers in Hampshire, also parts of Wales. Absent on the Isle of Wight. This species is most active in mid-morning to mid-afternoon, easily seen on vegetation by streams at Lower and Upper Crockford and surrounds. The female oviposits in tandem with the male, sometimes when completely submerged.

Azure Damselfly *Coenagrion puella* (length: 33–35 mm)
CURRENT STATUS IN THE NEW FOREST: Common
IDENTIFICATION: A rather bright blue and black species in the male, which has a characteristic "U" shaped mark on the 2nd abdominal segment. Segment eight is blue and segment nine has black markings towards the rear. The female is green or pale blue with black markings.
HABITAT: One of the Forest's commonest species on slow-moving streams, ditches and sheltered ponds, from May to August. Crockford area, Eyeworth and Hatchet Ponds are good places to see them in abundance, also common on the Isle of Wight and throughout Britain, except the northern half of Scotland.

Variable Damselfly *Coenagrion pulchellum* (length: 33–38 mm)
CURRENT STATUS IN THE NEW FOREST: Very rare
IDENTIFICATION: Similar to the Azure Damselfly, but appears a darker blue. The male has a thick black "U" shaped mark on the 2nd abdominal segment. The female is similar to the blue form of the Azure Damselfly.
HABITAT: Believed to still be present on Sowley Pond, a private lake, well vegetated and sheltered. Uncommon in mainland Britain, but commoner in Ireland, between May to August. Absent on the Isle of Wight.

Upper Crockford Bottom, ideal habitat for Southern Damselflies [SF]

1a	2a
1b	2b
1c	3a
	3b

Plates 1a–1c Southern Damselfly
a) male
b) female
c) mating pair

Plates 2a & 2b Azure Damselfly
a) male
b) mating pair

Plates 3a & 3b Variable Damselfly
a) male [GH]
b) female, blue form [GH]

Common Blue Damselfly *Enallagma cyathigerum* (length: 29–36 mm)
CURRENT STATUS IN THE NEW FOREST: Common
IDENTIFICATION: Another blue and black species which can be confused with others; both sexes have conspicuous eye-spots with a coloured bar between them. The male has a variably shaped spot on the 2nd thoracic segment. The female is green or blue with black markings; there is a conspicuous broad arrow-head marking on the 8th abdominal segment.
HABITAT: One of the Forest's commonest species on open ponds, from May to September. Broomy, Eyeworth, Hatchet and Slufters Ponds are good places to see them in abundance, also common on the Isle of Wight and throughout Britain. The sight of several males hovering close by over a pond usually means that submerged females are ovipositing into the vegetation below.

Scarce Blue-tailed Damselfly *Ischnura pumilio* (length: 26–31 mm)
CURRENT STATUS IN THE NEW FOREST: Rare
IDENTIFICATION: A small species, similar to the Blue-tailed Damselfly, the male has blue thoracic stripes and eye-spots. The abdomen is black with blue on part of the 8th and all of the 9th segments. The female is often black with apple green at the sides. In the immature *aurantiaca* form, it is light to bright orange.
HABITAT: Found in the Forest on sheltered bog pools, shallow heathland ponds and slow flowing streams, between June to August. Rather scarce, Latchmoor Brook is a good place to see them, or occasionally at other sites, including Crockford. Rare on the Isle of Wight. Most likely to be observed in southwest counties of England and Wales, but with scattered sites across Britain and Ireland. The female lays eggs on her own, sometimes with the male nearby.

Blue-tailed Damselfly *Ischnura elegans* (length: 30–34 mm)
CURRENT STATUS IN THE NEW FOREST: Common
IDENTIFICATION: A fairly small species, male with black abdomen with blue on 8th abdominal segment, along with thoracic stripes and eye-spots. The female is our most variable species, with five colour forms. In the normal form, it is similar to the male, otherwise can be violet, green, brown or pink.
HABITAT: Prefers brackish or slightly polluted water, but found almost everywhere, between May to September. Crockford area, Eyeworth and Hatchet Ponds are good places to start with. Common throughout Britain and Ireland, including the Isle of Wight.

Small Red Damselfly *Ceriagrion tenellum* (length: 25–35 mm)
CURRENT STATUS IN THE NEW FOREST: Local
IDENTIFICATION: A fairly small species, easy to distinguish from the Large Red Damselfly, with its bronze thorax. The male has an all red abdomen. The female has colour forms varying in the amount of red and black on the abdomen. The normal female has red on the first three and final two abdominal segments, whereas form *melanogastrum* is nearly all black. There is an uncommon red form, *erythrogastrum*.
HABITAT: In the Forest, can be common on sphagnum bogs such as Puttles Bridge, wetter margins of some ponds and streams, from early June to September. Brownloaf, Crockford area and Latchmore Brook are also good sites and the Forest is regarded as a national stronghold for the species, otherwise restricted to heathlands in southern England and west Wales. Absent on the Isle of Wight. Mating pairs remain in tandem while the female oviposits into stems or leaves of mainly submerged plants. Males defend a perch and tolerate other males in the vicinity.

MIGRANTS: Other migrant damselflies have not yet been found in the Forest.

1a	3a
1b	3b
	3c
1c	3d
	3e
2a	4
2b	

Plates 1a–1c
Common Blue Damselfly
a) male
b) female
c) mating pair

Plates 2a & 2b
Scarce Blue-tailed Damselfly
a) male [GH]
b) immature female form *aurantiaca* [GP]

Plates 3a–3e
Blue-tailed Damselfly
a) male
b) immature female form *violacea*
c) immature female form
d) female form *infuscans*
e) immature female form *rufescens*

Plate 4
Small Red Damselfly mating pair [GH]

DRAGONFLIES – Suborder Anisoptera

UK: 26 resident species, including 1 extinct (Hampshire 20 species, including 1 extinct)
New Forest: 18 species, including 1 extinct [69%] (+ at least 1 regular migrant)

The dragonflies are larger and stouter than damselflies, with the hindwing broader than the forewing. Often powerful flyers, appearing to rarely stop, they rest with the wings fully open. Hawkers stay on the wing longest, patrolling their territories much of the day, sometimes stopping to eat a meal. They often catch bees, flies, wasps, butterflies, moths and even damselflies or smaller dragonflies. They are not seen paired as often as damselflies, except in the case of Common Darters. Egg-laying is, however, often observed, with females either ovipositing on their own, in tandem with the male, or with a male on guard. Other dragonflies will attempt to chase them off their territories. Fresh adults are known as teneral (not fully mature in colours). The flight, colour and to some extent behaviour, of individuals helps to identify species. Larvae are carnivorous, as with damselflies often taking up to five years to complete their development under water, depending on species.

Several Forest localities are amongst the best in the country for dragonflies. The Crockford area again stands out, with up to 18 species sighted, including migrants, a good place to see several Golden-ringed Dragonflies patrolling in a small area, and possibly see the egg-laying behaviour. All the other sites mentioned for damselflies are also good dragonfly searching areas. In addition, Ashley Hole and Duckhole Bog are likely sites for the now rare Common Hawker, amongst other species. Photographers will enjoy Whitten Pond, where it is more straightforward than most sites to obtain good images of Hawkers, including egg-laying and mating. The low vegetation in this area helps, as dragonflies often perch low down, particularly in the feeder stream running to the pond. Outside the Forest, another good area is Southampton Common. Photographers need to be out early morning to try to glimpse dragonflies emerging on pond or streamside vegetation, and at least arrive by the flight time of c.9.30am or so, to try to locate and then photograph them at rest. Dragonflies are not uncommon visitors to gardens, particularly those with ponds.

Common Club-tail, now extinct in the Forest [SR]

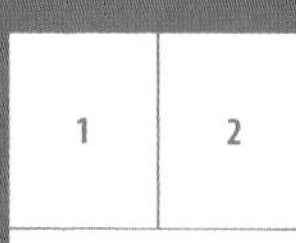

Plate 1
Hornet Robberfly eating Black Darter [GH]

Plate 2
Emperor Dragonfly larva

Plate 3
Migrant Hawker male in flight [PCr]

HAWKER DRAGONFLIES – Family Aeshnidae

Common Hawker *Aeshna juncea* (length: 65–80 mm)

CURRENT STATUS IN THE NEW FOREST: Rare

IDENTIFICATION: One of three similar Hawkers in the Forest, the Common Hawker registers as brown and blue in flight and rather larger than the Migrant Hawker. It only has narrow yellow stripes on the thorax. The male has blue abdominal spots (always rounded), usually yellow in the female.

HABITAT: In heathland with acidic pools and ponds, between June to October, now fairly rarely seen in the Forest, most likely at sites such as Ashley Hole craters and Duckhole Bog, but reported in 'The Dragonflies of the New Forest' in 1984 as common (although not the case in Victorian times). Can be common in parts of western England, Wales, Scotland and Ireland. Sometimes seen hunting woodland rides and streams at dusk. A quick flier, this is one of the most difficult dragonflies to photograph. It may be productive looking for females egg-laying in shallow ponds; males occasionally perch up, usually out of reach!

Migrant Hawker *Aeshna mixta* (length: 56–64 mm)

CURRENT STATUS IN THE NEW FOREST: Local

IDENTIFICATION: Our smallest Hawker, similar to, but looks darker in flight than the Common Hawker. It has a blue band and small yellow triangle on the 2nd abdomen segment. The female abdomen is brown with yellow or green markings.

HABITAT: Breeds at sheltered ponds and lakes with tall marginal vegetation from late July to November. Fairly common in the Forest at coastal sites such as Keyhaven and Pennington, occasional in woodland rides, also found on the Isle of Wight. The stronghold for this species is southern England, but it is increasing its range well into northern England, also Ireland. As the name implies, numbers may be boosted by migration from continental Europe. This species more readily rests than some Hawkers and is not aggressive towards other individuals, sometimes flying in small groups. Whilst hovering, it is easier to obtain in flight photographs than with many species.

Southern Hawker *Aeshna cyanea* (length: 67–76 mm)

CURRENT STATUS IN THE NEW FOREST: Common

IDENTIFICATION: Appears greener in flight than the Common Hawker. Both sexes have a narrow yellow triangle on the 2nd abdomen segment and large yellow spots on the thorax, as well as green bars (blue in male) on 8th and 9th abdominal segments, which readily distinguish this species.

HABITAT: Found on sheltered ponds, slow moving streams, ditches and around gardens from June to November. This species is the commonest New Forest Hawker, often seen in Inclosures and heathlands throughout the Forest, hunting insects, or near water. Plentiful at sites like Whitten Pond, where one can readily observe egg-laying, the females ovipositing in aquatic vegetation or on mud by the waterside. Also common on the Isle of Wight, southern and central England and Wales, but more local elsewhere. The Southern Hawker appears to be inquisitive and flies very close to observers; at times very easy to photograph, as they sometimes readily perch low down.

1a	1b
2a	2b
3a	3b

Plates 1a & 1b
Common Hawker
a) male [JH]
b) egglaying female [JH]

Plates 2a & 2b
Migrant Hawker
a) male
b) female

Plates 3a & 3b
Southern Hawker
a) male
b) female

Brown Hawker *Aeshna grandis* (length: 70–77 mm)
CURRENT STATUS IN THE NEW FOREST: Local
IDENTIFICATION: A large Hawker, easily recognised in flight by the golden brown wings; both sexes are similar.
HABITAT: Breeds on larger lakes and ponds from June to November. In the Forest can be observed at localities such as Holmsley gravel pits, Linford Bottom and surrounds, also Whitten Pond, or occasionally in woodland rides. Outside the Forest, common at Blashford Lakes. Photographing this species is not as straightforward as most dragonflies, but they do periodically settle on low perches such as twigs. Also found on the Isle of Wight, this is a fairly common and widespread species in Britain, though absent from Scotland and much of southwest England.

Emperor Dragonfly *Anax imperator* (length: 66–84 mm)
CURRENT STATUS IN THE NEW FOREST: Widespread
IDENTIFICATION: A colourful large Hawker, with a green thorax and green abdomen in the female, brilliant blue with black markings in the male.
HABITAT: Frequent in the Forest on heathland and garden ponds from late May to September; Eyeworth, Hatchet, Long and Whitten Ponds are good places to start looking. Widespread on the Isle of Wight, southern England and southern Wales; increasing its range northwards, including Ireland. The Emperor is a challenge to photograph, although they often rest on low-growing vegetation near water in some sites, such as on brackens near King's Garn Gutter stream. All too often there is one at a pond in the Forest, flying almost continuously. At Blashford Lakes they often rest on low vegetation in meadows.

Lesser Emperor Dragonfly *Anax parthenope* (length: 62–75 mm)
CURRENT STATUS IN THE NEW FOREST: Very rare
IDENTIFICATION: Smaller and duller than the Emperor Dragonfly, with only the first two segments of the abdomen bright, otherwise brown, although the eyes are green.
HABITAT: Ponds and small lakes. Found at Keyhaven and Blashford Lakes in 2007, a rare migrant, first recorded in 1996 from Gloucestershire. This species is included on the British list, as it has bred in Cornwall and there are records from many parts on England.

Hairy Dragonfly *Brachytron pratense* (length: 54–63 mm)
CURRENT STATUS IN THE NEW FOREST: Rare
IDENTIFICATION: A small Hawker which could be confused with the Common Hawker, but is out earlier in the season. As the name implies, the thorax is hairy.
HABITAT: Mainly found near unpolluted, well-vegetated waters, from early May to early July. This is a rare Forest species, found on the large lake and surrounding ditches at Needs Ore [access by permit], but also seen at Exbury Gardens, Keyhaven and Pennington and, at times, well inland, such as Furzey Pool. Localities in the area include Hengistbury Head. Rare on the Isle of Wight, this uncommon species is widely scattered throughout Britain and Ireland, but is rare in Scotland.

1a	1b
2a	2b
3a	3b

Plates 1a & 1b
Brown Hawker
a) male
b) egglaying female [GH]

Plates 2a & 2b
Emperor Dragonfly
a) male
b) egglaying female [GP]

Plates 3a & 3b
Hairy Dragonfly
a) male [SF]
b) female [SF]

GOLDEN-RINGED DRAGONFLIES – Family Cordulegastridae

Golden-ringed Dragonfly *Cordulegaster boltonii* (length: 74–84 mm)
CURRENT STATUS IN THE NEW FOREST: Common
IDENTIFICATION: Britain's longest species of dragonfly, easy to recognise by its yellow thoracic stripes and yellow-banded abdomen. The female has an ovipositor at the end of her abdomen.
HABITAT: Common in the Forest on heathland streams and ditches from May to October. Also frequent in woodland rides, including Hawkhill Inclosure where they hunt in the meadow near the parking area, as well as heathland outside the Inclosure. One of the best places to observe their behaviour is Crockford, where each male flies up and down the stream or open heathland in its small territory, awaiting a female. Fights between encroaching males are regular. The egg-laying behaviour differs from other Hawkers, the female hovers in an upright position and repeatedly stabs into the streamside mud to deposit her eggs; in good spots she may stay for several minutes before speeding away to another spot. The larval stage lasts up to five years. Occasional on the Isle of Wight, fairly common in southern England, Wales, parts of the north and western Scotland.

EMERALD DRAGONFLIES – Family Corduliidae

Downy Emerald *Cordulia aenea* (length: 47–55 mm)
CURRENT STATUS IN THE NEW FOREST: Local
IDENTIFICATION: Easily recognised by its greenish-black to bronze abdomen and yellowish green eyes.
HABITAT: Occasional in the Forest on tree sheltered ponds and lakes, or clearings, from May to August, usually reliable on Broomy, Hatchet and Slufters Ponds, also Exbury Gardens. This species is scattered from Devon to the highlands of Scotland, although its stonghold is in southeast England. Not easy to photograph, as it is a tireless flier, but they do occasionally settle.

CHASERS, SKIMMERS AND DARTERS – Family Libellulidae

Four-spotted Chaser *Libellula quadrimaculata* (length: 39–48 mm)
CURRENT STATUS IN THE NEW FOREST: Widespread
IDENTIFICATION: Easily recognised by the additional black mark on the centre of the upper part of each wing; rather attractive with golden yellowish veins. Abdominal segments 3–9 are usually edged in yellow.
HABITAT: Fairly widespread in the Forest on bog and heathland pools, ponds and lakes from May to September, reliable on Long Pond, Whitten Pond and many others. Common throughout Britain, although rare on the Isle of Wight. Sometimes found well any from water. Males tend to be aggressive towards other males, also other species entering their territory.

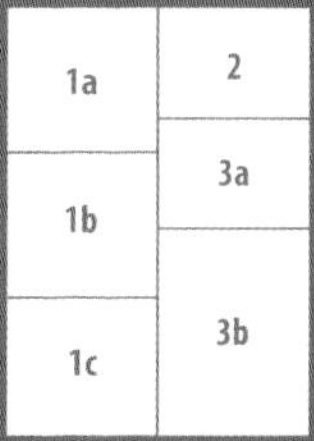

1a	2
1b	3a
1c	3b

Plates 1a–1c
Golden-ringed Dragonfly
a) male
b) female
c) eating a wasp

Plate 2
Downy Emerald male

Plates 3a & 3b
Four-spotted Chaser
a) male
b) form *praenubila* (more extensive black), recently hatched [GH]

Scarce Chaser *Libellula fulva* (length: 40–49 mm)
CURRENT STATUS IN THE NEW FOREST: Rare, but local in Forest surrounds
IDENTIFICATION: When mature, the male has pale blue on the abdomen and blue eyes and black mark at the forewing tip. Before maturing, the male and female look very similar, with orange coloration, black triangular shaped markings on the upper surface of each abdominal segment, also dark bases to the wings.
HABITAT: Prefers river floodplains, slow-moving rivers and gravel pits and may be seen in the Forest from the end of May to late July, with records from Crockford, Pennington and others. Just outside the Forest, found on the Avon at Blashford Lakes, Lower Test and Testwood Lakes; also found in the Bournemouth and Christchurch surrounds and recorded from near Lymington in 2008, Barton-on-Sea in 2010. The Scarce Chaser is scarce in Britain and restricted to six main river localities in Cambridgeshire, Dorset/Hampshire, Kent, Norfolk / Suffolk, Sussex and Wiltshire / Somerset with some evidence of expansion. Absent from the Isle of Wight.

Broad-bodied Chaser *Libellula depressa* (length: 39–48 mm)
CURRENT STATUS IN THE NEW FOREST: Common
IDENTIFICATION: A rather broad, flattened abdomen distinguishes this species, which is likely to be seen by the casual observer. Both sexes have brown eyes and very dark brown wing bases. The males have a powdery blue abdomen with yellow spots along the sides, whilst in females the blue is replaced by golden brown.
HABITAT: In the Forest found at sheltered pools, ponds and streams from early May to September, common at Crockford, other heathland and most Inclosures, including Pignal, Parkhill, Hawkhill, Little Wootton and Wootton Coppice Inclosures, also seen in gardens. Common throughout Britain, including the Isle of Wight. The male defends his territory from a favoured sunlit perch.

Black-tailed Skimmer *Orthetrum cancellatum* (length: 44–50 mm)
CURRENT STATUS IN THE NEW FOREST: Local
IDENTIFICATION: A yellow to brown thorax, lacking stripes. The abdomen is pale powdery blue in the male, with the last three segments black; in the female the abdomen is yellow with attractive black markings unlike those of other species.
HABITAT: Found in larger ponds and lakes with gravel or clay surrounds in the Forest, from mid-May to September. It is fairly common in Badminston gravel pits, Eyeworth and Hatchet Ponds. Also found on the Isle of Wight and fairly common in southern England, parts of Wales and Ireland and increasing its range northwards. This species flies swift and low, skimming the water surface but frequently perches, preferring to rest on bare earth, where they remain very alert.

Keeled Skimmer *Orthetrum coerulescens* (length: 36–45 mm)
CURRENT STATUS IN THE NEW FOREST: Common
IDENTIFICATION: A slender insect, mid to dark brown thorax, with pale stripes. The abdomen is pale powdery blue in the male; golden yellow in the female, with a black central line.
HABITAT: Pools and streams in bogs or damper heathland sites are favoured, from May to September. It is very common at many localities, including Crockford, Hawkhill Inclosure, Latchmore Bottom and Puttles Bridge and a frequent sight in the Forest. Also found on the Isle of Wight but only rather scattered and locally common and in mainly western Britain and Ireland. Likely to be resting on low vegetation with the wings held downwards and forwards, at times it appears that mating pairs are everywhere.

1a	1b	1c
2a	2b	
3a	3b	
4a	4b	4c

Plates 1a–1c
Scarce Chaser
a) male [GP]
b) female [MP]
c) mating pair

Plates 2a & 2b
Broad-bodied Chaser
a) male
b) female

Plates 3a & 3b
Black-tailed Skimmer
a) male
b) female

Plates 4a–4c
Keeled Skimmer
a) male
b) female
c) mating pair [GP]

Common Darter *Sympetrum striolatum* (length: 33–44 mm)
CURRENT STATUS IN THE NEW FOREST: Common
IDENTIFICATION: A slender insect, with brown thorax, with pale stripes dorsally and on the sides. The abdomen is red in the male; yellowish brown in the female, with black side markings.
HABITAT: Found in bog and heathland pools and ponds, also ditches, lakes and streams from late June to November, possibly even into December. It is very common at some localities, including Crockford, Latchmore, Long and Whitten Ponds and is possibly the commonest dragonfly in the Forest. Also common on the Isle of Wight and throughout England, Wales and Ireland. Less common in Scotland. Numbers may be supplemented by migrants from continental Europe. Mating pairs are a frequent sight, the female oviposits in tandem with the male.

Ruddy Darter *Sympetrum sanguineum* (length: 34–39 mm)
CURRENT STATUS IN THE NEW FOREST: Local / Rare
IDENTIFICATION: Slightly smaller than the Common Darter, the male with a much brighter red abdomen, with black marks on segments eight and nine. The female has a yellow abdomen and differs from the Common Darter in having black legs (in the Common Darter these are brown or black with a yellow stripe).
HABITAT: Usually found in ponds, lakes and ditches, sometimes in or near woodland, from mid June to September. Local to borderline rare, but usually seen at Crockford, Emer Bog, Exbury Gardens, Keyhaven, Needs Ore, Pennington and Sheepwash Pond. It is also found on the Isle of Wight. Still uncommon in the west and north of Britain, it is increasing in numbers in the Midlands and Eastern England, also in Ireland. Numbers are possibly supplemented by migrants from continental Europe.

Black Darter *Sympetrum danae* (length: 29–34 mm)
CURRENT STATUS IN THE NEW FOREST: Local
IDENTIFICATION: A small species, the only black dragonfly in the UK. It is the male which has a black abdomen with yellow markings remain along the sides of the thorax and abdomen. The female has a yellow abdomen and brown thorax, with the sides strongly marked in black, on the abdomen mainly towards the tip.
HABITAT: Found in sheltered bog and heathland pools and ponds from late June to October. It is fairly common at some localities, including Beaulieu Road Station, Latchmore Brook, Long Pond and Rushbush Pond. Widespread and common, especially in the north of Britain, more local in eastern and central England, also southern Ireland. Used to occur on the Isle of Wight. Sometimes found well away from water, hunting over heathland.

MIGRANTS: These include the **Vagrant Emperor *Hemianax ephippiger*** (61–70 mm) at Dibden in 1984, but the most frequently seen species, possibly breeding in the Forest and surrounds, is the attractive **Red-veined Darter *Sympetrum fonscolombii*** (33–40 mm), found at Badminston, Keyhaven and Matley Bog, amongst others. The last good year for the **Yellow-winged Darter *Sympetrum flaveolum*** (32–37 mm) was in 1995 when it was found in Holmsley and Wootton, as well as the Forest surrounds, also a **Scarlet Darter *Crocothemis erythraea*** (36–45 mm) was recorded at Crockford in 2002. The **Blue-eyed Hawker *Aeshna affinis*** (57–66 mm) was known from just a single record, in Kent in 1952, but in 2006 four specimens were reported in the south of England, including Little Wootton Inclosure on 6 August.

EXTINCTION: The **Common Club-tail *Gomphus vulgatissimus*** (45–50 mm) used to be abundant on the Ober Water, for example Puttles Bridge and Rhinefield, in the 1930s and 1940s (when it also was found at Linwood), but it declined sharply in numbers and the last specimen was seen in 1970, or briefly on one day in 1988.

1a	1b
2a	2b
3a	3b
4a	4b	5

Plates 1a & 1b
Common Darter
a) male
b) female

Plates 2a & 2b
Ruddy Darter
a) male [GP]
b) female [GP]

Plates 3a & 3b
Black Darter
a) male [GH]
b) female [GH]

Plates 4a & 4b
Red-veined Darter
a) male
b) immature male

Plate 5
Scarlet Darter male [GH]

STONEFLIES – Order PLECOPTERA

UK: 36 species
New Forest: at least 16 species [44%]

A small group of mainly brown insects found in aquatic habitats, the adults have two pairs of wings (shortened in some species), folded flat over the body, or wrapped around the abdomen. The end of the body has two thread-like tails in some species, but absent in most. The long antennae are thread-like, mouthparts are designed for chewing, but some larvae are carnivorous, whilst others feed on aquatic vegetation. Larvae grow to over 30 mm in some species and cling to stones on the stream bed. Most adults do not feed, live for only one or two days, and are likely to be found at rest on vegetation near streams and rivers. There is an incomplete life cycle: egg, larva and adult. Identification to species level can be difficult and normally involves using a microscope to examine genitalia. Species recorded in the Forest include the **Common Black Stonefly *Capnia bifrons*** (c.6 mm, rare), found early in the year, from February to April, rarely in May and several ***Leuctra*** species (4–7 mm, widespread) and ***Nemoura*** species (c.10 mm, widespread).

STICK INSECTS – Order PHASMIDA

UK: 8 species
New Forest: 0 species [0%]

Large insects resembling sticks, with nearly 3,000 worldwide species, mainly in the tropics. The British species are established aliens, with only three introduced New Zealand species well established. The life cycle is incomplete: egg, nymph and adult. These insects rely on camouflage for protection against predators and are nocturnal, feeding on leaves and sometimes flowers. The adults are nocturnal and may be found most months in mild weather, but usually die during colder weather, leaving the eggs to overwinter.

Unarmed Stick-insect *Acanthoxyla inermis* (body length: 90–125 mm)
CURRENT STATUS IN THE NEW FOREST: Not in the Forest, but found in Hampshire in 2009 and may spread across the county
IDENTIFICATION: This is the longest insect in Britain, an unmistakable, stick-like, green or brown species, lacking the thoracic spines present in other *Acanthoxyla* species.
HABITAT: Typically found in gardens, or wasteland, often feeding on bramble or rose. Adults are often seen between June to December, all are females, which reproduce by parthenogenesis (unfertilised eggs hatch into females). Although not yet recorded in the Forest, this New Zealand native species was reported from Rowlands Castle, Hampshire in July 2009, feeding on a low-growing *Cupressus* bush. Since being listed as a new British insect in 1987, this species has become widespread throughout Cornwall, is established in parts of south west Ireland, but only occasional elsewhere in southern England, although quickly becoming our commonest stick insect. Garden centres are often sources of introduction to other areas and once established, the species usually spreads into neighbouring gardens. Females lay about 300 seed-like eggs, dropping them to the ground.

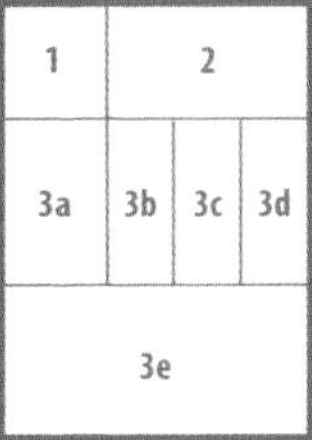

1	2		
3a	3b	3c	3d
3e			

Plate 1
Common Black Stonefly

Plate 2
***Nemoura* species**

Plates 3a–3e
Unarmed Stick-insect
a) habitat
b) female, green form
c) female, lateral view, green form
d) female, brown form
e) female, brown form, close up

BUSH-CRICKETS, CRICKETS and GRASSHOPPERS – Order ORTHOPTERA

UK: 31 species
New Forest: 27 species (including 4 extinct) [87%]

This group of insects usually has two pairs of wings in adults, although a few lack wings. The antennae are long or short; eyes are large. Most characteristic are the large hind legs, which are modified for jumping. In all cases the life cycle shows incomplete metamorphosis (development), so adults lay eggs which hatch into nymphs; these resemble small adults and shed their skins several times before reaching the adult, breeding stage. The New Forest has always been recognised as outstanding country for Orthoptera and whilst populations have suffered declines and, in a few cases, unexpected extinctions, the Forest is still one of the richest sites in Britain. In particular, the areas of wet and dry heathland are productive, with some of the best localities as reported in Marshall and Haes (1988), quoted from west to east, Broad Bottom; Vales Moor; Castle Hill to Church Moor; Holmsley Bog and Goatspen Plain; Wilverley Bog and Denny Bog (Shatter Ford Bottom); Woodfidley Passage; Crockford Bridge; and Needs Ore.' In 1985, Tony and Noelle Welstead privately published distribution maps of Orthoptera from the New Forest and surrounds, covering the period from 1980–1985. The one British representative of Wingless Camel-crickets [Rhaphidophoridae] has not yet been recorded in Hampshire.

BUSH-CRICKETS – Family Tettigoniidae

UK: 11 species
New Forest: 10 species (including 2 extinct) [92%]

Often large, recognised by a bulky appearance, with antennae often exceeding body length. Females have a blade-like ovipositor, in some species as long as the body. The length given below is from head to end of abdomen, so females are much longer if the ovipositor is included. Whilst some species are nocturnal, many sing by day and night. A courtship display is part of a pre-mating process in which song (stridulation) plays an important role. Eggs of some species may take one, two or more years to hatch. In the field, a bat detector set to a frequency suitable for Orthoptera, is useful to help detect these insects.

Oak Bush-cricket *Meconema thalassinum* (body length: 13–17 mm)
CURRENT STATUS IN THE NEW FOREST: Common
IDENTIFICATION: Small, rather delicate-looking long-winged insect, pale green with a yellowish stripe along the back.
HABITAT: Found in woods, hedges and gardens, where they feed on small insects, in late July to about November. In the Forest found almost anywhere, the trees around Balmer Lawn, near Brockenhurst are a good area, also plentiful at Keyhaven. Eggs are laid in crevices in bark or under mosses or lichens. Common throughout southern England and the Midlands, becoming scarcer in the north. Occasional in Wales and southern Ireland. Whilst this species may be seen in the daytime, it is more active at night and usually plentiful on nocturnal searches, often resting on deciduous tree trunks, or fences. Attracted to light, the species sometimes enters houses.

1a	1b
1c	1d
2a	
2b	

Plates 1a–1d
Speckled Bush-cricket mating sequence
a) meeting up [GP]
b) mating [GP]
c) transfer of spermatophore (sperm package) [GP]
d) separation [GP]

Plates 2a & 2b
Oak Bush-cricket
a) male
b) female

Dark Bush-cricket *Pholidoptera griseoaptera* (body length: 11–21 mm)
CURRENT STATUS IN THE NEW FOREST: Widespread
IDENTIFICATION: Almost wingless insect, dark brown with yellow underside.
HABITAT: Found in wasteland, hedgerows, woodland edges and rides, thickets on undercliffs and scrub on the edges of saltmarshes and dunes; generally absent from heathland. Adults are found from July until about November, feeding on vegetation or on small insects. In the Forest found almost anywhere there are brambles, for example the rides in Wootton Coppice Inclosure, also fairly common in the Forest surrounds. Eggs are laid into rotting wood or bark crevices. Common in southern England, rarer north of the Midlands, with isolated populations in northern England, southern Scotland and south-east Ireland. Usually straightforward to find in the daytime or dusk, by listening for them singing and carefully searching vegetation.

Grey Bush-cricket *Platycleis albopunctata* (body length: 18–28 mm)
CURRENT STATUS IN THE NEW FOREST: Very rare, mainly in Forest surrounds
IDENTIFICATION: Variable in colour, long-winged, usually greyish brown.
HABITAT: A mainly coastal species, inhabiting coarse grass and scrub on sand dunes, shingle banks and warm cliffs, where they feed on herbs, grasses and flowers, as well as small insects, from July to October. Recorded from Linwood, near Ringwood; another strong colony was found in the Ringwood area, 14 km inland, in 1998 until the site was redeveloped. Just outside the Forest, readily found on the undercliffs at Barton-on-Sea, Hordle, Boscombe and Southbourne, around Chewton Bunny and Hengistbury Head. The song is difficult to hear. Mainly found on the southern coast of England (including the Isle of Wight) and parts of coastal Wales; rarely inland. This species should be carefully looked for on low vegetation on undercliffs; they readily hide in thick vegetation when disturbed.

Bog Bush-cricket *Metrioptera brachyptera* (body length: 11–21 mm)
CURRENT STATUS IN THE NEW FOREST: Widespread
IDENTIFICATION: Green or brown short-winged species, with bright green underside. Hind part of pronotum with a cream side band. Short-winged (brachypterous), with only vestigial hind-wings and short fore-wings. A rare fully winged form *marginata* occurs, with brownish-black wings.
HABITAT: Found in damp heathland, often on cross-leaved heath, where it mainly eats vegetation, feeding on buds, seeds and flowers. Usually seen from July to about November. In the Forest used to be decidedly local (Burr, 1900, who recorded it from near Lyndhurst), but is widespread in suitable habitat and found at places like Badminston Common, Fritham, Hinchelsea, Holmsley, Matley and Wilverley Bogs and Roydon Woods, reflecting the Forest's position as one of the strongholds for this species. Also recorded from some heathlands in the Bournemouth surrounds and the Isle of Wight. Commoner in the south of England, but also found in Wales and scattered colonies to south-west Scotland. Eggs are inserted into vegetation using the ovipositor.

1a	2a
1b	2b
1b	2c
1c	3

Plates 1a–1c
Dark Bush-cricket
a) male [GP]
b) female [GP]
c) female

Plates 2a–2c
Grey Bush-cricket
a) male
b) female
c) female nymph [GP]

Plate 3
Bog Bush-cricket
female [PCr]

Roesel's Bush-cricket *Metrioptera roeselii* (body length: 13–26 mm)
CURRENT STATUS IN THE NEW FOREST: Rare
IDENTIFICATION: One of our most attractive species. Usually short-winged, dark brown and yellow, sometimes green. There is a cream-coloured margin around the sides of the pronotum, and three pale yellow spots on the sides of the thorax. The fully winged form *diluta* may be seen in hot summers.
HABITAT: Found in coarse, ungrazed grassland and scrub, coastal grassland and lush meadows, also dry downland and road verges, mainly feeding on grass and other vegetation, but will eat small insects. In the Forest found at Warren Farm and Needs Ore Point near the coast, also further inland at Poundhill and Wootton Coppice Inclosures from late July to early November. Also found in the surrounds including the Southampton area, Bournemouth mainly in the Stour valley; rare on the Isle of Wight. This species is expanding its range from south-east England, has spread towards the Midlands and to Yorkshire. Also found in west Wales and south-east Ireland. The loud song often reveals the presence of this species, which is often well hidden but sometimes sits for some time on the top of brambles or other vegetation.

Long-winged Cone-head *Conocephalus discolor* (body length: 16–22 mm)
CURRENT STATUS IN THE NEW FOREST: Widespread
IDENTIFICATION: Slender green (occasionally brown) insect with long brown wings and brown stripe along the back. The female has a long, almost straight ovipositor. An occasional extra-long winged form exists, with wings reaching the end of the ovipositor or beyond in the female.
HABITAT: Found in coarse dry and damp grassland of various types, including downland, woodland edge, reedbeds, heathland and bogs, where they feed on grasses, also small insects, from August to November. In the Forest found in many places, plentiful around Brockenhurst, including Roydon Woods, also Keyhaven, Lepe Country Park, Pig Bush and most places where it is damp, such as Matley Bog. Also widespread in the Forest surrounds, inland and on the coast, including the Isle of Wight. Females bite a hole in hollow stems of grass, reed or rush, inserting an egg with their ovipositor. First recorded in Britain in the 1930s, they have spread from the south-east, particularly rapidly during the 1990s, to occupy all of southern England, part of the Midlands and south Wales. Often heard, they are well camouflaged but a walk through grassland will reveal their whereabouts.

Short-winged Cone-head *Conocephalus dorsalis* (body length: 11–18 mm)
CURRENT STATUS IN THE NEW FOREST: Local
IDENTIFICATION: Slender green insect (rarely brown) with short brown wings, reaching only half length of the abdomen and brown stripe along the back. The female has a long, upward curved ovipositor, which is a good way to distinguish it from the Long-winged Cone-head, particularly if it is a long-winged form *burri*.
HABITAT: Found on salt marshes amongst grasses and reeds, or inland in damp places, such as reed beds and bogs, where they feed mainly on seed heads, buds and flowers of rushes, sedges or grasses, from July to October. In the Forest, Lepe Country Park is a good site, where they are, however, vastly outnumbered by Long-winged Cone-heads. Emery Down, Exbury Gardens, Needs Ore, Holmsley, Matley and Wilverley Bogs are other sites. Just outside the Forest, recorded at Sturt Pond at Milford-on-Sea, also Testwood Lakes and on the Isle of Wight. Found in southern England, absent or becoming scarcer towards the north. Also in Wales and southern Ireland. Searching the main foodplants in the daytime is often productive, but to confuse matters, they are often found with the similar Long-winged Cone-head.

1a	2a
	2b
1b	3a
1c	3b

Plates 1a–1c
Roesel's Bush-cricket
a) male [GP]
b) female [GP]
c) female form *diluta*

Plates 2a & 2b
Long-winged Cone-head
a) male extra-long winged form [GP]
b) female

Plates 3a & 3b
Short-winged Cone-head
a) male [GP]
b) female [GP]

Speckled Bush-cricket *Leptophyes punctatissima* (body length: 9–18 mm)
CURRENT STATUS IN THE NEW FOREST: Widespread
IDENTIFICATION: A small, green short, reduced-winged species with a brown stripe on the back and conspicuous tiny dark speckles over the whole body. The ovipositor is broadened and upturned.
HABITAT: Open woodland, scrub, gardens and hedgerows where they feed on vegetation, including brambles, from late July to about November. In the Forest found almost anywhere, for example in Deerleep and Pignal Inclosures, also at Keyhaven, but normally in fairly small numbers. Widespread throughout southern England and Wales, becoming scarcer in the north, but reaching Scotland; also found in parts of Ireland. Eggs are laid in the bark of trees or shrubs. A bat detector is useful to help find this species, which has also dropped into a beating tray on several occasions.

Two extinct species, Great Green Bush-cricket and Wart-biter, of particular interest in the Forest may be rediscovered or reintroduced.

Great Green Bush-cricket *Tettigonia viridissima* (body length: 40–55 mm)
CURRENT STATUS IN THE NEW FOREST: Extinct, local in surrounds
IDENTIFICATION: Stunning, very large green long-winged insect, with a brown stripe along the back.
HABITAT: Found in bramble scrub, nettle beds, hedgerows and other vegetation, including on coastal undercliffs, feeding on a range of plants and insects, from late July to about November. This species may once have been within the Forest boundary, with records from around Fordingbridge and Ringwood, and one assumes it would have been found all along the coast. The Victoria County History for Hampshire (1900) records it from Hampshire, merely stating that 'it is familiar to every one who has collected in our southern counties.' No longer found in the Forest, but in the vicinity it is reliable at Mudeford Woods, also Purewell Meadows and Stanpit Marsh, both near Christchurch, Canford Heath, Hengistbury Head in Dorset and beyond, and widely distributed on the Isle of Wight. This is a fairly common species along the south coast of England and parts of south Wales, but uncommon inland. The loud rattling song can be heard from afternoon to evening, but these insects are superbly camouflaged. Walking through the grass may disturb them, or checking at dusk by torchlight. Eggs are laid in the ground where they overwinter.

Wart-biter *Decticus verrucivorus* (body length: 30–38 mm)
CURRENT STATUS IN THE NEW FOREST: Extinct
IDENTIFICATION: A large, robust, dark green long-winged but flightless insect, with black marks on the pronotum and wings.
HABITAT: Found on chalk downland slopes, or heathland with heathers, sedges and grasses, feeding on herbs and insects, including grasshoppers, from July to September. Malcolm Burr (Victoria County History, 1900) states that the species 'is one our rarest and handsomest Orthoptera. Curtis records its capture by Bingley at Christchurch, and by J.C. Dale in the New Forest.' A population was well known at Godwinscroft, near Bransgore around the mid to late 1800s. It was also recorded from Ventnor, Isle of Wight, in 1940 and St Boniface Down in 1951. In Purbeck, Dorset, it was first reported from near Corfe Castle in 1923, with sporadic reports from Stoborough and Slepe Heath, now possibly extinct in Dorset. A rare species in England, now restricted to managed reserves in Wiltshire, East Sussex and Kent, possibly a single heathland colony in Dorset.

1a	1b
2a	2b
3a	3b

Plates 1a & 1b
Speckled Bush-cricket
a) male
b) female

Plates 2a & 2b
Great Green Bush-cricket
a) male [GP]
b) female

Plates 3a & 3b
Wart-biter
a) male [AB]
b) female [AB]

It is expected that the Southern Oak Bush-cricket will spread into the Forest.

Southern Oak Bush-cricket *Meconema meridionale* (body length: 11–17 mm)
CURRENT STATUS IN THE NEW FOREST: Not yet reported, but occasional in surrounds
IDENTIFICATION: Small, rather delicate-looking short-winged insect, pale green with a yellowish stripe along the back (apart from the wings much the same as the Oak Bush-cricket).
HABITAT: Found in woods and gardens, where they feed on small insects, from mid August to November. First noted in Surrey in 2001, spreading in southern England including Hampshire; Boscombe, Dorset, in 2009 and Bournemouth in 2010. Worth searching for at night, on deciduous tree trunks and branches.

Other Bush-crickets may occasionally be encountered, such as the rare migrant **Sickle-bearing Bush-cricket *Phaneroptera falcata*** (24–36 mm) found in Gary Palmer's New Milton garden on 12 September 2006.

CRICKETS – Families Gryllidae (True Crickets) and Gryllotalpidae (Mole Crickets)

UK: 5 species
New Forest: 4 species (including one extinct) [80%]

Antennae shorter than bush-crickets and thread-like. As they are adapted to running and burrowing, the hind legs are less proficient at jumping. Many people will have seen and heard crickets in a pet shop or garden centre that supplies live food for reptiles, but may not be familiar with our other native crickets. True crickets take more than one year to mature after hatching, so may overwinter as nymphs and/or adults. There is only one mole cricket species in Britain.

House Cricket *Acheta domesticus* (body length: 14–20 mm)
CURRENT STATUS IN THE NEW FOREST: Occasional
IDENTIFICATION: Sandy brown with two dark bars across the head.
HABITAT: This successful species may be found in some heated buildings, such as private homes, hotels and factories, but most likely at large rubbish tips and land-fill sites. Originally a native of North Africa and the Middle East, now cosmopolitan and may be found throughout Britain and Ireland, assisted by the fact it is readily available from pet shops and garden centres and likely to escape. Feeds on a wide range of animal and vegetable matter, wherever they can also find warmth.

Field Cricket *Gryllus campestris* (body length: 17–23 mm)
CURRENT STATUS IN THE NEW FOREST: Extinct, recent reintroduction attempts on the Forest border failed
IDENTIFICATION: Large, robust, shiny black species with a deep yellow band behind the thorax, lacking hindwings.
HABITAT: Short turf on free draining soils with mixed herbs and patches of bare soil. Extinct in the New Forest, they were present on the west Solent coast until the early 1960s, when the expansion of Hythe and Fawley destroyed their habitat. Reintroduction attempts near Fawley in the mid 1990s had limited success and they died out by the end of 2000. There are records from another reintroduction site at Arreton Down, Isle of Wight from 1999. Always rare in Britain, this species feeds on herbs and grasses, persisting naturally at one protected site in Sussex, and reintroduced to others in Sussex, Surrey and north Hampshire.

1a	3
1b	4a
2	4b

Plates 1a & 1b
Southern Oak Bush-cricket
a) male [MS]
b) female [MS]

Plate 2
Sickle-bearing Bush-cricket male [GP]

Plate 3
House Cricket [SR]

Plates 4a & 4b
Field Cricket
a) male
b) female

Wood Cricket *Nemobius sylvestris* (body length: 7–12 mm)
CURRENT STATUS IN THE NEW FOREST: Widespread
IDENTIFICATION: Small, dark species with lighter brown pronotum; wings short.
HABITAT: The Forest is the stronghold for this species. This species was first found by J.C. Dale at Lyndhurst, in 1820. The high pitched trilling song is often heard from May to October, in sunny glades in the Forest, in various habitats, particularly Inclosures, Ancient and ornamental woodlands, churchyards and gardens. For example, they are common in Pignal Inclosure and Roydon Woods, feeding on dead vegetable matter. This species is distributed in southern England from Devon to Surrey, including the Isle of Wight. It is recorded from the southern half of Ringwood Forest, on Avon Heath and nearby, as well as Nea Meadows, Christchurch. They often hide and when heard should be searched for hiding underneath leaf litter or fallen bark. Searching bark and leaf litter at night by torchlight is also very productive. Adults may be found all year in warm weather, but most likely to be seen in summer. The life cycle is about two years and they may over winter as nymphs and/or adults.

Mole Cricket *Gryllotalpa gryllotalpa* (body length: 35–46 mm)
CURRENT STATUS IN THE NEW FOREST: Very rare
IDENTIFICATION: Brown with patches of golden-brown velvet-like hair on the thorax and abdomen; wings full length; fore legs modified for digging.
HABITAT: Damp grassland, well drained water meadows and flood plains. Recorded widely across Britain up to the mid twentieth century but never in numbers. Burr (Victoria County History, 1900) referred to it as a 'local insect', stating 'It is not uncommon in the New Forest (Jeffreys), and in the Isle of Wight (Welsford).' Since the 1960s short-lived colonies have been recorded from the northern edge of the New Forest in a small meadow on the Hampshire / Wiltshire border, and at Sholing, near Southampton (up to 1977). In Dorset a specimen was recorded at Wareham in 1991 and Corfe Common in the 1990s. Accidentally imported specimens (not necessarily this species), occur in Britain in most years. Elusive and more likely to be dug up by keen gardeners (song being rarely heard) than seen, a small population has persisted near Brockenhurst since 2003. The Forest is currently the only known site for this species in Britain, which should be looked for on warm spring or early summer nights, the male stridulates from the burrow entrance; the life cycle is about three years and they mainly feed on larvae and worms.

Other crickets may be encountered; photographs are included of the **Jamaican Field Cricket *Gryllus assimilis*** (20–23 mm) and **Tropical House Cricket *Gryllodes supplicans*** (13–18 mm), which are commonly sold as reptile or amphibian food in pet shops. The **Southern Field Cricket *Gryllus bimaculatus*** (17–23 mm) is an occasional fully-winged importation and not to be confused with *Gryllus campestris.*

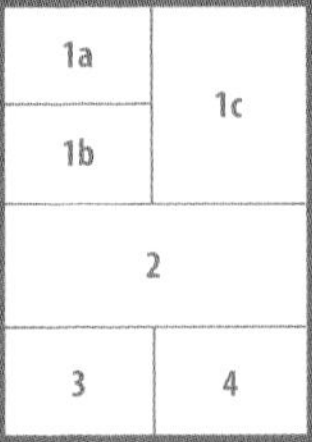

1a	1c
1b	
2	
3	4

Plates 1a–1c
Wood Cricket
a) male
b) female
c) nymph

Plate 2
Mole Cricket [GP]

Plate 3
Jamaican Field Cricket
female [GP]

Plate 4
Tropical House Cricket
female [GP]

GROUND-HOPPERS – Family Tetrigidae

UK: 3 species
New Forest: 3 species [100%]

Small grasshopper-like insects with short antennae, with the pronotum extending backwards over the top of the abdomen, sometimes beyond. The forewings are reduced to small scales. These well camouflaged insects are active in the day, where they can be found in damp areas with bare ground, where they feed on algae, lichen and mosses; they are good swimmers, even underwater. Ground-hoppers take more than one year to mature after hatching, so nymphs and/or adults may overwinter, hence may be found all year in warm weather, particularly on undercliffs. Unlike grasshoppers, the Ground-hoppers do not sing.

Cepero's Ground-hopper *Tetrix ceperoi* (body length: 8–13 mm)
CURRENT STATUS IN THE NEW FOREST: Rare
IDENTIFICATION: This species has very long wings extending well beyond the end of the abdomen, also lacks a high keel on the pronotum. May be confused with the similar Slender Ground-hopper, but the shape of the head and smaller distance between the eyes of no more than 1.5 times the width of an eye in Cepero's Ground-hopper, should assist with identification.
HABITAT: Found in damp, open, sunny spots, such as seepages on undercliffs, sand dunes and river banks. Adults are found all year, but the new generation of adults appears in late July. In the Forest only recorded from bare peat by streams in Marlborough Deep and Crockford Bridge, but outside the boundary, commoner on the undercliffs in Barton-on-Sea, Hordle and beyond; occasional on the Isle of Wight. This scarce species is mainly confined to parts of the southern coasts of England and Wales.

Slender Ground-hopper *Tetrix subulata* (body length: 9–14 mm)
CURRENT STATUS IN THE NEW FOREST: Rare
IDENTIFICATION: This species is similar to Cepero's Ground-hopper, with very long wings extending well beyond the end of the abdomen, also lacks a high keel on the pronotum. The difference shape of the head and longer distance between the eyes of up to 1.8 times the width of an eye in the Slender Ground-hopper, should assist with identification.
HABITAT: Found in damp areas on bare mud or short vegetation, close to ponds or streams, also on chalk undercliffs. In the Forest reliable at Marlborough Deep, also found at Crockford Bridge and Sway. Just outside the Forest, recorded from Testwood Lakes, also the Southampton surrounds; past records from Lymington and Isle of Wight are worth checking. This fairly common species is found throughout much of southern and central England and south Wales, but more sparsely distributed elsewhere. Also found in parts of Ireland.

Common Ground-hopper *Tetrix undulata* (body length: 8–11 mm)
CURRENT STATUS IN THE NEW FOREST: Widespread
IDENTIFICATION: This robust species is easy to recognise from its short wings and short pronotum about reaching or just exceeding end of the abdomen. A rare long-winged form occurs, but the keel on the pronotum is conspicuous.
HABITAT: Found on damp or dry bare earth in woodland rides and edges, sand dunes, quarries and heathlands. Adults are found all year. Widespread in the Forest, examples include Acres Down, Cadnam Common, Marlborough Deep, Matley Bog, Crockford Bridge, Fritham, Ivy Wood, and Wootton Coppice Inclosure and outside the boundary, common on the undercliffs in Barton-on-Sea, Hordle and beyond. Our commonest British Ground-hopper, widely distributed throughout much of Britain. Needs looking for carefully on bare ground and soon enough, one will jump out of the way.

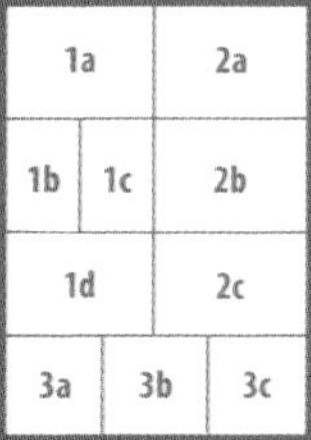

1a		2a
1b	1c	2b
1d		2c
3a	3b	3c

Plates 1a–1d
Cepero's Ground-hopper
a) green form [GP]
b) black and white form, lateral view [GP]
c) black and white form [GP]
d) head [GP]

Plates 2a–2c
Slender Ground-hopper colour forms
b & c) [GP]

Plates 3a–3c
Common Ground-hopper colour forms
b) [GP]

GRASSHOPPERS – Family Acrididae

UK: 11 species
New Forest: 10 species (including 1 extinct) [91%]

Grasshoppers have large hind legs for jumping. The short antennae readily distinguish grasshoppers from Bush-crickets. They are found in grassy areas, often heard, not seen—unless walking through the grass. The similarity of some species may make them difficult to identify in the wild, without close examination, a situation not helped by the range of colour forms sported by most species. Grasshoppers hatch in spring, develop and mature in the same year, lay eggs, die.

Large Marsh Grasshopper *Stethophyma grossum* (body length: 21–36 mm)
CURRENT STATUS IN THE NEW FOREST: Local
IDENTIFICATION: Britain's largest grasshopper, yellowish green to olive brown. Lower margin of hind femora vivid red. A plum coloured form is sometimes observed in females, which are considerably larger than males.
HABITAT: Found in wet, acid places such as quaking bogs and marshes, usually with sphagnum mosses, purple moor-grass, cross-leaved heath and scrub present. Adults appear from mid-July to early November. In the Forest most likely to be found in small numbers in Acres Down, Duckhole, Hinchelsea, Holmhill, Matley, Red Hill and Wilverley Bogs, including alongside Wootton Coppice Inclosure. This local species now appears to be confined to bogs in the New Forest and Dorset, also parts of Ireland. The eggs are laid in the base of grass tufts. Often found near the edges of quaking bogs; due to the terrain, great care is needed when searching for them and when disturbed, they can fly some distance.

Stripe-winged Grasshopper *Stenobothrus lineatus* (body length: 15–23 mm)
CURRENT STATUS IN THE NEW FOREST: Very rare
IDENTIFICATION: Brightly coloured, often green and brown with red on the abdomen. Gently incurved side keels on the pronotum. White line and elongated spot on the forewing.
HABITAT: Found in grasslands on chalk and limestone, heathland and sand dunes, in mid-July to October. In the Forest there are records from Kings Garn Gutter and Linwood from the 1970s and possibly still present in the area, likely to be unrecorded in places. This species can be observed just outside the Forest at Barton Common, Hordle undercliff and Avon Heath Country Park, near Ringwood, amongst others. Scarce in the Isle of Wight but generally widespread in parts of southern and eastern England, scarcer in the far south-west.

Woodland Grasshopper *Omocestus rufipes* (body length: 12–20 mm)
CURRENT STATUS IN THE NEW FOREST: Local
IDENTIFICATION: Dark greyish brown species; underside of the abdomen and sometimes top is red in the male. The tips of the palps (mouthparts) are almost white. Females are all brown or sometimes with green forewings and upperside of head and pronotum.
HABITAT: Found in woodland edges, rides and clearings, also grassland and scrub nearby, including heathland, in June to mid-October. In the Forest found in Beaulieu Heath—in front of Hawkhill Inclosure, Brook, Burley area, Fritham and many others. Outside of the Forest, frequent in Hurn, Ringwood and Wareham Forests in Dorset. Found throughout southern England, with the New Forest one of the strongholds, but absent from the Isle of Wight.

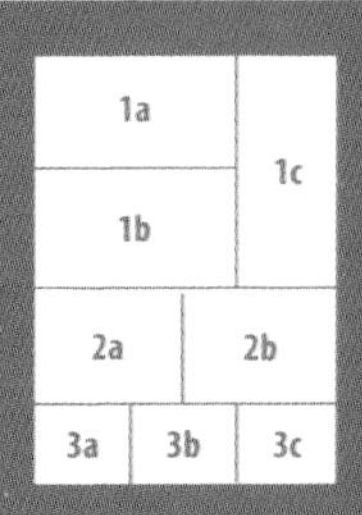

Plates 1a–1c
Large Marsh Grasshopper
a) male [GP]
b & c) female

Plates 2a & 2b
Stripe-winged Grasshopper
a) male [GP]
b) female [GP]

Plates 3a–3c
Woodland Grasshopper
a & b) male
c) female, green form

Common Green Grasshopper *Omocestus viridulus* (body length: 14–23 mm)
CURRENT STATUS IN THE NEW FOREST: Local / rare
IDENTIFICATION: Usually green or green and brown or purple sides, with gently incurved side keels on the pronotum.
HABITAT: Associated with long grass, damp meadows and woodland rides from July to November. In the Forest, this species has declined and is now very scattered, recorded in small numbers from sites including Crockford, Denny Wood, Holmsley and Parkhill Inclosure. Also found in some surrounding areas, such as north of Bournemouth and Poole, Cranemoor Common, also on the Isle of Wight. Whilst seemingly widespread in Britain and Ireland, there has been a decline in some populations.

Field Grasshopper *Chorthippus brunneus* (body length: 15–25 mm)
CURRENT STATUS IN THE NEW FOREST: Widespread
IDENTIFICATION: Often brown, but variable, striped and mottled forms with parts of the body varying from buff through orange or even purple; the underside of the body is rather hairy. Sharply incurved pronotal side keels.
HABITAT: Found in short turf or stony ground, particularly in dry, sunny spots, such as downland and coastal grassland, from June to December. Only occasional on heathland in the Forest, but generally widespread, plentiful at Keyhaven and surrounds, Brockenhurst area, Denny Wood, Fritham, Gibbet Wood, Matley Wood and many others. Also frequently found outside the Forest, including Barton-on-Sea, Boscombe, Southbourne and the Isle of Wight; widespread throughout much of England and Wales, also Ireland.

Heath Grasshopper *Chorthippus vagans* (body length: 13–21 mm)
CURRENT STATUS IN THE NEW FOREST: Rare
IDENTIFICATION: Dark, greyish brown. The pronotum has incurved side-keels and dark wedge-shaped markings. End of abdomen may be orange or orange-red tinged, also hind femora, which otherwise have two dark bands.
HABITAT: Found in dry heathland, typically with bare ground, close to heather and dwarf gorse (on which they feed), from late June to early October. In the Forest with a restricted distribution, reliable around the Burley area, including Broad Bottom, Castle Hill, Church Moor and Vales Moor. Close to the Forest, recorded from several areas, including Avon Heath Country Park, Canford Heath, Ringwood Forest, Sopley Common and Town Common near Christchurch. A scarce species, restricted to heaths in Dorset and the New Forest.

1a	3a
1b	
2a	3b
2b	3c

Plates 1a & 1b
Common Green Grasshopper
a) female
b) female, dark form [GP]

Plates 2a & 2b
Field Grasshopper
a) male
b) female [GP]

Plates 3a–3c
Heath Grasshopper
a) male [GP]
b) female [SR]
c) egglaying female

New Forest bog, habitat of the Large Marsh Grasshopper and several other species

Meadow Grasshopper *Chorthippus parallelus* (body length: 10–23 mm)
CURRENT STATUS IN THE NEW FOREST: Widespread
IDENTIFICATION: Green, sometimes with brown wings, although a striking pinkish purple form occurs. The short-winged female is easily recognised, but in form *explicatus*, it is long-winged. The pronotal side-keels are slightly incurved in this species. Some adult females are a vivid pinkish purple.
HABITAT: Found in coarse grassland, particularly in ungrazed areas in various habitats, including downland, heathland, woodland rides, saltmarshes and sand dunes, from June to about November. In the Forest, this is possibly the commonest grasshopper, found almost anywhere in suitable habitat, plentiful in the Keyhaven area, heathlands, and bogs, also around the various campsites, commonest where there is no grazing. Plentiful around the area also, abundant at Barton Common. This is a common species throughout much of Britain, including the Isle of Wight.

Lesser Marsh Grasshopper *Chorthippus albomarginatus*
(body length: 13–23 mm)
CURRENT STATUS IN THE NEW FOREST: Local
IDENTIFICATION: Pale brown or light green, less brightly coloured than the Meadow Grasshopper. The side keels of the pronotum are almost parallel.
HABITAT: Found in grassland by water, saltmarshes, sand dunes, flood meadows and damp clearings in woods, often with sedges present. However, it also occurs in drier land, including roadside verges, from mid-July to about October. Found occasionally in parts of the Forest, including Balmer Lawn, Holmsley, Keyhaven and Pennington area and Wootton Coppice Inclosure. Outside the Forest, there are scattered records, including Eling, Hengistbury Head, Lower Test, Lymington, Sturt Pond in Milford-on-Sea, Southampton area and the Isle of Wight. This species is found in southern and eastern England, as far north as Yorkshire; also parts of Wales and southwest Ireland.

Mottled Grasshopper *Myrmeleotettix maculatus* (body length: 12–19 mm)
CURRENT STATUS IN THE NEW FOREST: Widespread
IDENTIFICATION: A variably mottled species with 12 described colour forms. Clubbed antennae in the male and the thickened antennal tips of the female help to distinguish them. The side keels of the pronotum are deeply indented.
HABITAT: Found in sunny dry open grassland with short turf and some bare ground, such as railway lines, heathland and coastal dunes, from mid-June to about October. In the Forest found in many areas, including Brook, Burley surrounds, Cadnam Common, Matley Bog and Wood, also Pignal Inclosure. Widespread in the Forest surrounds, including Hengistbury Head and the Isle of Wight. Common and widespread throughout Britain and much of Ireland, but scarce or not reported from some inland areas.

One species, Rufous Grasshopper, is now thought to be extinct in the Forest.

Rufous Grasshopper *Gomphocerippus rufus* (body length: 14–22 mm)
CURRENT STATUS IN THE NEW FOREST: Extinct, local in Hampshire
IDENTIFICATION: The clubbed, white-tipped antennae are conspicuous.
HABITAT: Coarse grassland, usually in south facing slopes on chalk downland, but occasionally on woodland edge, scrub and cliffs, from late July to November. In the Forest, there is a 1961 record from Wilverly Walk; records from the surrounds are also from around this period, but the species is still sparsely distributed on downland in Hampshire, such as Noar Hill.

1a	2a	3a
		3b
1b	2b	3c
1c		3d
1d	2c	4a
		4b

Plates 1a–1d Meadow Grasshopper
a) male (beneath) and female
b) mating pair [GP]
c) female, purple and green colour form [GP]
d) female, purple form [GP]

Plates 2a–2c Lesser Marsh Grasshopper
a) male [GP]
b) female, green form [GP]
c) female, brown form [GP]

Plates 3a–3d Mottled Grasshopper
a) female brown and white form [GP]
b) female red and green form [GP]
c) female orange ochre form [GP]
d) female form

Plates 4a & 4b Rufous Grasshopper
a) male
b) male, pale form

EARWIGS – Order DERMAPTERA

UK: 7 species (including 1 extinct)
New Forest: 3 species (including 1 extinct) [43%]

Easily recognised by the large pincers at the end of the abdomen, these insects are often seen by gardeners, as they eat flower buds or young plants. However, they are found almost everywhere, feeding on plant or animal material. Earwigs vary from having fully developed wings beneath flap-like forewings, to having reduced wings, absent in some species. These mainly nocturnal insects have an unusual behaviour, in that females guard their young until they are able to fend for themselves. Even the eggs are carefully kept clean.

Lesser Earwig *Labia minor* (Body length: 4–7 mm)
CURRENT STATUS IN THE NEW FOREST: Local
IDENTIFICATION: A small dull yellowish brown species, with blackish head. The hindwings extend beneath the forewings.
HABITAT: Found all year in dung-heaps, compost and rubbish-tips in urban and rural areas, also in generally in rotting and decaying vegetation. In the Forest recorded from Hampton Ridge and Keyhaven Marshes, but possibly fairly widespread. Not uncommon in the Forest surrounds, including the Isle of Wight. This is a widespread British species, but with few records in Scotland and Ireland. A regular visitor to lights at night.

Common Earwig *Forficula auricularia* (Body length: 10–16 mm)
CURRENT STATUS IN THE NEW FOREST: Common
IDENTIFICATION: A shiny, dark chestnut brown species with yellowish legs. The large hindwings project beneath the forewings. The pincers are large and robust, almost straight in the female, strongly curved in the male.
HABITAT: Found all year in most habitats, but less common in arable farmland and dry heathland. Common throughout the Forest, the Isle of Wight and throughout Britain, there can be few individuals who do not recognise this species. Particularly on the coast males are occasionally found with much longer pincers and this is possibly dependant on food availability during development. Mating occurs in autumn when they retreat to cells dug out in the soil. In winter the male leaves, or is ejected, and soon dies. Females lay 30–50 eggs and keep them clean until they hatch in early spring. Initially the young earwigs stay in the nest, but disperse later, becoming adult by about July. Females may live long enough to rear a second brood.

EXTINCTIONS: The **Giant or Tawny Earwig *Labidura riparia*** (12–26 mm) was recorded in the New Forest by Sharp in 1909. Whilst this record may be doubtful, it was first recorded at nearby Christchurch in 1808 and was known at Pokesdown, near Bournemouth, until the early 1930s. There are other, possibly doubtful, records from the southern coast, including the Isle of Wight.

Lesne's Earwig is well worth looking for in the New Forest.

Lesne's Earwig *Forficula lesnei* (Body length: 6–7 mm)
CURRENT STATUS IN THE NEW FOREST: Not recorded, but found in the surrounds
IDENTIFICATION: A small, pale species, with hindwings absent or greatly reduced.
HABITAT: Found from July to October in most habitats, including grassland, woodland, scrub and coastal marshes. This species is sometimes found in hollow stems of umbellifers. Whilst not yet observed in the Forest, this is possibly an oversight as it has been recorded in nearby Hythe, Lord's Wood and West Wood in the Southampton area and is also present, but scarce in the Isle of Wight. This species has a scattered British distribution.

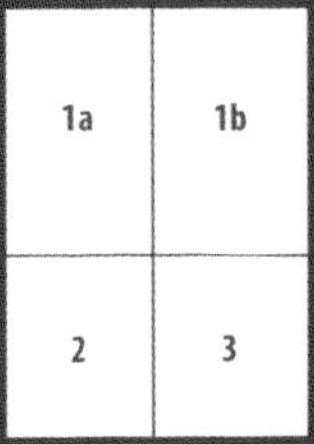

1a	1b
2	3

Plates 1a & 1b
Common Earwig
a) male
b) female

Plate 2
Lesser Earwig [MG]

Plate 3
Lesne's Earwig [CO]

COCKROACHES – Order BLATTODEA

UK: 9 species
New Forest: at least 3 species [33%]

Generally regarded as pests by many, but that tends to apply to the larger, introduced species, particularly unwanted finds in kitchens. All three of our smaller native species are harmless and are found in the Forest. These flat-bodied insects have long antennae and are equipped to run fast. The forewings are leathery and cover the membranous hindwings. The native species live in warm, sunny places among low vegetation, scavenging on decaying plants or eating small insects. After mating, females are sometimes seen with an ootheca (egg pod) protruding from the end of the abdomen, until it is released in leaf litter and tussocks after a few days. Whilst sometimes observed on flowers or vegetation, they are nervous and winged species can fly well or move rapidly. They can be carefully searched for in leaf litter; sunny spots on cliffs are a good place to start searching, or in a woodland clearing.

Dusky Cockroach *Ectobius lapponicus* (body length: 7–11 mm)

CURRENT STATUS IN THE NEW FOREST: Widespread
IDENTIFICATION: Light brown, often with dark brown pronotum in male. Females are darker and rather broad. The male is winged, whilst the female forewings are slightly reduced, not reaching the end of the abdomen.
HABITAT: Found from May to September in Inclosures and other woodland, typically in low scrub and bramble where the life cycle takes two years. Recorded from Crockford Bridge, Holmsley Bog and Inclosure, King's Garn Gutter, Mark Ash Wood, Roydon Woods and many others. Locally common mainly in central southern England, with the New Forest a major site for the species, but rare on the Isle of Wight. Males readily fly and on sunny days may be observed basking on the top of grass stems. An occasional visitor to moth traps.

Tawny Cockroach *Ectobius pallidus* (body length: 8–10 mm)

CURRENT STATUS IN THE NEW FOREST: Widespread
IDENTIFICATION: Golden yellowish-brown, both sexes winged and can fly well.
HABITAT: Found from late June to October in woodland rides and clearings, often associated with pine litter, also heathlands where there is short or recently burnt heather, as well as the coast and gardens. The life cycle takes two years. In the Forest, recorded from Bolderwood, Burbush, Markway Inclosure, Stanswood Valley near Fawley and Stoney Cross amongst others. A widespread species in southern England, including the Isle of Wight and Bournemouth; there are also isolated populations elsewhere, including Wales and eastern England.

Lesser Cockroach *Ectobius panzeri* (body length: 5–8 mm)

CURRENT STATUS IN THE NEW FOREST: Widespread
IDENTIFICATION: Small, dark brown. The flightless female is easily recognised by its short, truncate forewings. In both sexes there is a speckled pattern on the pronotum.
HABITAT: Found from July to early October on sparse vegetation with large amounts of bare ground on sea cliffs, sand dunes and shingle beaches. However, inland records are on the increase, including under heather in warm, sheltered dry heathland and occasionally woodland. The life cycle takes one year. Recorded from Acres Down, Beaulieu area, Brockenhurst area, Burbush, Crockford Bridge, Denny Bog, Keyhaven, Vales Moor and others. Outside the Forest reliable at Barton-on-Sea undercliffs; rare on the Isle of Wight. This locally common species is mainly confined to southern and eastern coasts of England or slightly inland, with scattered populations in Wales, Lundy and the Scilly Isles. An occasional visitor to moth traps, colonies are often small and difficult to locate.

It is likely that other cockroaches are present in the area from time to time. Most people in the UK who have an infestation in the kitchen are likely to have **German Cockroach *Blattella germanica*** or **Common or Oriental Cockroach *Blatta orientalis*.**

1a	3a
1b	
2	3b

Plates 1a & 1b
Dusky Cockroach
a) male
b) female

Plate 2
Tawny Cockroach

Plates 3a & 3b
Lesser Cockroach
a) male
b) female

LICE and BOOKLICE – Order PSOCODEA

UK: 650 species
New Forest: estimated 390 species [60%]

A group of small insects comprising 99 book / barklice (Psocoptera) and c.551 flattened, wingless parasitic lice (Phthiraptera), although there is no consensus of opinion merging them into a single order. The parasitic lice total is a conservative figure, as the group is difficult to study; what is known is that British birds (588) and some mammal species (45) often have two or more species of lice attached to them, feeding on feathers, hair or blood. New species can easily turn up on migrant birds and zoo animals. The **Head Louse *Pediculus humanus*** (1–3 mm) is the most commonly known species associated with humans, particularly young children. Head-to-head contact is by far the most common route of lice transmission. Species usually need to be mounted on a microscope slide for examination in order to identify them. Because of limited studies on these insects, the New Forest figure is a conservative estimate. The booklice and barklice (or barkflies) are generally referred to as psocids; they are small, soft-bodied with large eyes. The antennae are long, forewings are larger then hindwings, but wings are absent in some species. These insects live on trees, grazing on algae, lichens or fungi from bark. Some species live indoors, including the well known book louse. About 30 species are recorded as pests of stored products. The life cycle is incomplete: egg, larva and adult. Easily beaten from trees, or spotted on bark, there are several widespread species in the Forest and surrounds (1.5–7 mm), including ***Mesopsocus immunis***, ***Loensia fasciata*** and the largest, ***Psococerastis gibbosa***.

THRIPS – Order THYSANOPTERA

UK: 157 species
The UK total is based on Collins (2010) and excludes 19 non-established species i.e. isolated populations known to have survived only for a short time, mainly in greenhouses.
New Forest: estimated 63 species [40%]

Thysanoptera means 'fringed wings', this order of small insects are nearly all winged (with fringes); most British species are less than 2 mm long, although one reaches 7 mm. Some species, including ***Frankliniella occidentalis*** are considered pests of ornamental flowers under glass and indoor crops including tomato and cucumber and are subject to chemical and other control. The potential future combination of certain species of thrips with an introduced tospovirus is a major concern. The antennae are short, mouthparts piercing—a single needle-like lance used for piercing, then sucking sap from fungal or plant material, including flowers. The life cycle involves egg, two larval stages, pre-pupa and one or two non-feeding pupal stages and adult. The pupal stages cannot feed but have legs. Fertilised eggs hatch into females and unfertilised eggs into males. Thrips are sometimes seen in large numbers such as in thundery weather, but are otherwise only occasionally seen, although widespread. They are probably more often noticed on flowers, but occur in many places including under bark, in grass and leaf litter. This order is under-recorded in the New Forest [and Hampshire] and the number of species is estimated, based on the fact that some species have a limited distribution range and few host plants.

1	2
3	4
5	6

Plate 1
Head Louse [VS]

Plate 2
Loensia fasciata

Plate 3
Mesopsocus immunis

Plate 4
Psococerastis gibbosa

Plate 5
***Aeolothrips* species** [BV]

Plate 6
Probably *Thrips flavus* [BV]

BUGS – Order HEMIPTERA

UK: 2,000 species
New Forest: estimated 1,200 species [60%]

Even entomologists tend to call insects 'bugs', but Hemiptera are the 'true' bugs. Whilst different in appearance, the groups all have piercing mouthparts (the rostrum), designed for sucking juices from plants or sometimes animals; they vary in size from under 1 mm to the 27 mm cicada, or water stick insect, 40 mm but including its tail. Many gardeners are familiar with aphids, which are serious agricultural pests, damaging crops and some transmit viral diseases. However, most bugs are harmless and often rather colourful; they are divided into three main groups, suborder Heteroptera, meaning 'different wings' (forewings tough and leathery; hindwings membranous, all wings folded flat over their backs, except for flight) and the suborders Auchenorrhyncha and Sternorrhyncha [= Homoptera, meaning 'uniform wings' (forewings either toughened tough and leathery; hindwings membranous, all wings folded flat over their backs, except for flight)]. The Heteroptera include land and water bugs. Amongst the larger species, the shieldbugs (stinkbugs) and leatherbugs (also known as squashbugs) are particularly well studied, plant bugs less so. Assassin bugs feed on other invertebrates, but bed bugs prefer animals, including humans. Water bugs include the water scorpion and water boatman, often seen on ponds. The other suborders comprise the Auchenorrhyncha with short antennae: cicadas (only one species in Britain), froghoppers and planthoppers. The Sternorrhyncha have long antennae: aphids, scale insects and the like. The life cycle is one of incomplete metamorphosis (development), adults laying eggs which hatch into nymphs, which develop into winged adults. Bugs are not well recorded in the Forest and there is likely to be a much higher percentage of species present. Some species are elusive and it is easiest to either examine vegetation closely, particularly in fields and hedgerows, using a beating tray or sweep net. Water bugs can be examined in a tray and returned to the water via a small net. A selection of species is shown from some families likely to be encountered in the Forest and surrounds.

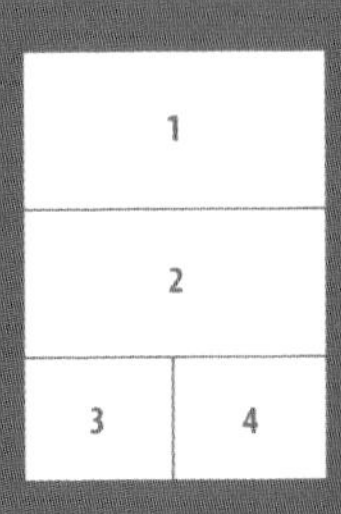

Plate 1
Ornate Shieldbug mating pair

Plate 2
***Metatropis rufescens* mating pair**

Plate 3
Heath Assassin Bug mating pair

Plate 4
Common Pond Skater mating pair, short-winged form [GP]

Wheelers Bay, Isle of Wight, warm coastal habitat for various sun loving bugs on flowers (including Ornate Shieldbug), as well as Glanville Fritillaries.

Suborder Heteroptera

FLATBUGS – Family Aradidae

UK: 7 species
New Forest: at least 3 species [43%]

Flatbugs are small, almost flattened, broad bugs found under bark, under recorded in the Forest and surrounds. The attractively coloured nymphs of the winged **Common Barkbug *Aneurus laevis*** (4–5 mm, local) sometimes congregate beneath bark of deciduous trees infected by fungi.

SHIELDBUGS (see Families below)

UK: 36 species (28 species in Hampshire)
New Forest: at least 20 species [56%]

Shieldbugs or stinkbugs have a conspicuous shield-like shape when adult, with a triangular plate (scutellum) between the wingcases. They look something like beetles and are sometimes confused for them, but have sucking mouthparts (called a rostrum) instead of mandibles, which resemble the needle of a syringe, and when not being used the rostrum is held beneath the head and thorax. Many species feed on vegetation, whilst others are predatory; most overwinter as adults and may change colour; the variability within species and similarity between some may confuse. Nymphs moult several times before reaching the adult, breeding stage. As a defensive reaction, shieldbugs have glands in their thorax between the first and second pair of legs which produce a foul smelling liquid. In the field specimens may be spotted on vegetation, but a sweeping net or beating tray, is useful to help find these insects. Photographing these insects requires care, to ensure that features such punctures on the body, are in sharp focus.

KEELED SHIELDBUGS – Family Acanthosomatidae

KEY FEATURE: Tarsi two-segmented

Hawthorn Shieldbug *Acanthosoma haemorrhoidale*

(body length: 12–16 mm)
CURRENT STATUS IN THE NEW FOREST: Common
IDENTIFICATION: Very brightly coloured, mostly apple green covered with dark punctures. Broad lateral extensions of the pronotum, marked with red, whilst the pronotum and scutellum have a broad, reddish brown border. The abdomen is red-tipped.
HABITAT: Woodland, scrub, hedgerows, parks, also gardens and churchyards, particularly on hawthorn, also dogwood, hazel, holly, oak and others. Common throughout the Forest and surrounds, also in Britain and Ireland, although scarce in Scotland. Adults are mainly found in March to November, with a peak in September.

Juniper Shieldbug *Cyphostethus tristriatus* (body length: 8–11 mm)

CURRENT STATUS IN THE NEW FOREST: Widespread
IDENTIFICATION: Green species with curved and conspicuous pinkish-red markings.
HABITAT: Man-made habitats such as churchyards, gardens and parks. Widespread in the Inclosures such as Fawley, where lawson's cypress is planted, although related plants are sometimes productive. Juniper was historically the sole foodplant of this species. Recorded in the Southampton area. Common in southern Britain, probably expanding its range. Adults are found in March to October, most often between April to July.

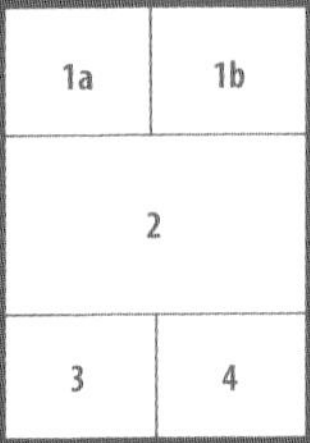

1a	1b
2	
3	4

Plates 1a & 1b
Common Barkbug
a) nymphs and adults [CT]
b) adult

Plate 2
Spiked Shieldbug with prey, a Small Copper caterpillar

Plate 3
Hawthorn Shieldbug

Plate 4
Juniper Shieldbug

1	3a
2	3b
	4

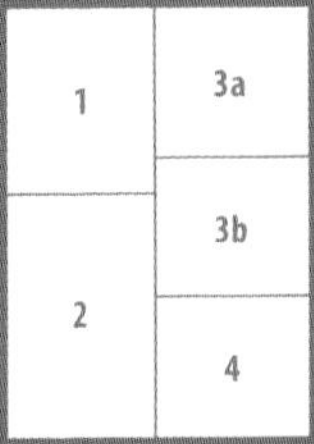

Plate 1
Birch Shieldbug

Plate 2
Parent Shieldbug

Plates 3a &3b
Tortoise Shieldbug
b) unusual colour form

Plate 4
Scarce Tortoise Shieldbug [SR]

Birch Shieldbug *Elasmostethus interstinctus* (body length: 8–12 mm)
CURRENT STATUS IN THE NEW FOREST: Common
IDENTIFICATION: Green covered with dark punctures (lateral extensions of the pronotum, not marked with red as in the Hawthorn Shieldbug), whilst the pronotum and scutellum have a broad, reddish brown and blackish border.
HABITAT: Deciduous or mixed woodlands, gardens and parks, wherever birch, hazel, aspen, oaks and sallow grow, amongst others. Widespread in the Inclosures and open Forest and surrounds. Common throughout Britain, with adults mainly found in March to November, peaking between August to October.

Parent Shieldbug *Elasmucha grisea* (body length: 7–9 mm)
CURRENT STATUS IN THE NEW FOREST: Local
IDENTIFICATION: Variably coloured, often reddish species with a black and white connexivum. There are usually one or more obvious black patches on the scutellum.
HABITAT: Deciduous, coniferous or mixed woodlands, also churchyards, gardens and parks on birch or alder. Although occasionally found in localities including Mark Ash, this species is commoner in the Forest surrounds, including the Southampton area and generally widespread throughout much of Britain. Adults are found in late March to November, peaking between August to October. The female affords her offspring protection by sitting over the eggs for two the three weeks before they hatch, in addition to guarding the young larvae.

TORTOISE SHIELDBUGS – Family Scutelleridae

KEY FEATURES: tarsi three-segmented; smaller, usually triangular, plate behind pronotum (scutellum) extends to end of abdomen

Tortoise Shieldbug *Eurygaster testudinaria* (body length: 9–11 mm)
CURRENT STATUS IN THE NEW FOREST: Common
IDENTIFICATION: The ground colour and intensity of the markings are variable. Ground colour ranges from grey to almost plain pale to very dark brown, to dull greenish with or without spots and markings. This species is distinguished from the slightly smaller and much rarer Scarce Tortoise Shieldbug by the slight central depression at the front of the head. In addition, the 2nd antennal segment is only slightly longer than the 3rd.
HABITAT: Dry and damp tall grasslands, on the foodplants of grasses, sedges and rushes. In the Forest, either in Inclosures or patches of long grassland anywhere, where they sit near the tips of grasses, beautifully camouflaged. Local in southern England, Wales and Ireland. Adults are found in May to early October, with a peak in August.

Scarce Tortoise Shieldbug *Eurygaster maura* (body length: 8–10 mm)
CURRENT STATUS IN THE NEW FOREST: Rare
IDENTIFICATION: Variable, sometimes virtually identical to the Tortoise Shieldbug, except for the shape of the head, which is smoothly rounded and lacks a central depression. In addition, the 2nd antennal segment is at least twice as long as the 3rd. If there are still doubts over identification, examination of the genitalia is the only practical means of confirming identification.
HABITAT: Sunny grasslands, on the foodplants of grasses and cereals. In the Forest recorded from Denny Lodge Inclosure and Pig Bush. Rarer than the Tortoise Shieldbug, with scattered records in southern England.

BURROWING SHIELDBUGS – Family Cydnidae

KEY FEATURES: tarsi three-segmented; Tibiae with strong spines

Cow-wheat Shieldbug *Sehirus biguttatus* (body length: 5–6 mm.
CURRENT STATUS IN THE NEW FOREST: Rare
IDENTIFICATION: Blackish or bluish-black with a pale border and white dot in the centre of the wing cases. The tibiae are spiny.
HABITAT: Sunny parts of woodland rides, edges or clearings, where the foodplant common cow-wheat grows. In the Forest, recorded from the Stubbs Wood area, adults are found from April to about August, but may be under recorded. A scarce and declining species recorded in parts of southern England and the Midlands, which should be looked for at ground level around and under the host plant. Absent on the Isle of Wight, but recorded from Lord's Wood, Southampton.

Pied Shieldbug *Tritomegas (Sehirus) bicolor* (body length: 5.5–8 mm)
CURRENT STATUS IN THE NEW FOREST: Rare
IDENTIFICATION: Black with white patches on the wing cases.
HABITAT: On or around the foodplants, white dead-nettle and black horehound, particularly in spring. In the Forest only recorded from South Gorley in 2010, adults are found from April to about August, but may be under recorded. A fairly widespread species in southern and central England and Wales, becoming scarce further north. Absent on the Isle of Wight, but recorded from the Southampton area, including Eastleigh.

TYPICAL SHIELDBUGS – Family Pentatomidae

KEY FEATURES: tarsi three-segmented; tibiae lacking strong spines

Bishop's Mitre Shieldbug *Aelia acuminata* (body length: 8–10 mm)
CURRENT STATUS IN THE NEW FOREST: Local
IDENTIFICATION: A large, striped insect with a pointed head and ridged pronotum.
HABITAT: Dry tall grasslands, on fine grasses. In the Forest easily overlooked, but recorded from Beaulieu and Denny Lodge Inclosure; fairly common in the Forest surrounds, including Bournemouth and Southampton areas and the Isle of Wight. Widespread and sometimes common in southern and central England and Wales, scarcer further north. Adults are found in May to September, with a peak in late May to early June.

Small Grass Shieldbug *Neottiglossa pusilla* (body length: 5–6 mm)
CURRENT STATUS IN THE NEW FOREST: Local
IDENTIFICATION: Small, shiny pale brown, insect with paler margins to the pronotum and abdomen, and a pale central stripe down the pronotum and scutellum; the latter with two white spots at the front margin. The short head is rather flattened at the front.
HABITAT: Mainly dry or damp grassland with fine grasses. In the Forest, recorded from Denny Lodge Inclosure. In the surrounds found in Chandler's Ford, Hythe, also parts of Southampton and the Isle of Wight. Local, but widely distributed in southern England. Adults are found in May to September, with a peak in June.

Woundwort Shieldbug *Eysarcoris venustissimus* (body length: 5–7 mm)
CURRENT STATUS IN THE NEW FOREST: Local
IDENTIFICATION: Shiny, with dark metallic copper coloured area, while the connexivum is marked with black and white.
HABITAT: Hedgerows, edges of woods, grassland and nettle beds, particularly on hedge woundwort or white dead-nettle (also black horehound). In the Forest, should be searched for on the foodplants, including in Brockenhurst and South Gorley. Common in the Southampton area, also southern and central England and Wales. Adults are found in April to October, with a peak in May.

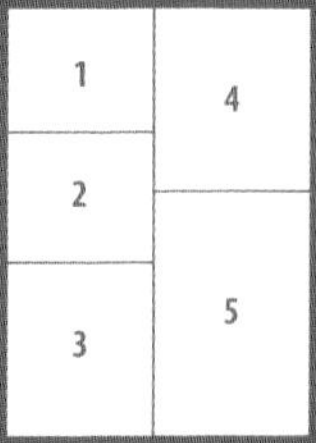

1	4
2	5
3	

Plate 1
Cow-wheat Shieldbug
[TB]

Plate 2
Pied Shieldbug

Plate 3
Bishop's Mitre Shieldbug

Plate 4
Small Grass Shieldbug

Plate 5
Woundwort Shieldbug mating pair

New Forest Shieldbug *Eysarcoris aeneus* (body length: 4–6 mm)
CURRENT STATUS IN THE NEW FOREST: Local
IDENTIFICATION: Dull greenish-grey insect, with two distinctive pale, oval spots at the front corners of the scutellum.
HABITAT: Damp heathland, bogs, or acid grassland, woodland rides and clearings, wherever the foodplants grow, such as heather and possibly slender St John's-wort. In the Forest reliable at Matley Bog and several other heathland sites; in one woodland Inclosure, they are sometimes found in grasses, well away from heather. The New Forest is the stronghold for one of Britain's rarest shieldbug species, with few records from southern England (rare on the Isle of Wight), the Midlands and Wales. Adults are most likely to be seen in May or late August to September. There is a possible association with ants, including *Lasius fulva.*

Green Shieldbug *Palomena prasina* (body length: 12–14 mm)
CURRENT STATUS IN THE NEW FOREST: Common
IDENTIFICATION: Large, green in the spring and summer; finely punctured with dark marks. They become a darker bronze-brown prior to hibernation in winter.
HABITAT: Woodlands, hedgerows, parks, gardens feeding on a variety of broad-leaved trees and shrubs. The commonest species in and around the Forest, often seen resting on plants, such as bramble. Common in southern and central England, Wales and Ireland, but scarcer further north. Adults are found in March to November.

Hairy Shieldbug *Dolycoris baccarum* (body length: 10–13 mm)
CURRENT STATUS IN THE NEW FOREST: Common
IDENTIFICATION: Large, distinctive purple-brown and greenish insects, noticeably covered with long hairs. The antennae and connexivum are banded black and white. During the winter, the ground colour changes to dull brown.
HABITAT: Woodland, grasslands with shrubs, also churchyards, gardens and parks. Common in the Inclosures with meadows, including Hawkhill and likely to be encountered almost anywhere. Often associated with birch, bramble, gorse, hawthorn and rose. Common throughout Britain, becoming scarcer in northern Scotland. Adults are found in late March to November, with peaks in May and August to early September.

Gorse Shieldbug *Piezodorus lituratus* (body length: 10–13 mm)
CURRENT STATUS IN THE NEW FOREST: Common
IDENTIFICATION: Large insect with two adult colour forms. Adults emerging and mating in the spring are mainly green, whereas the new generation appearing in the late summer have purple-red markings on the pronotum and corium.
HABITAT: Heathland, scrub and commons where there is gorse or broom. In addition, sometimes beaten from birch and hawthorn, amongst others. Whilst found in the Inclosures where gorse grows, this species is mainly found on the open heathlands, such as Beaulieu Heath. Common throughout Britain and Ireland where gorse and broom flourish. Adults are found in March to October, with peaks early and later in the season.

1	3
2a	4a
2b	4b

Plate 1
New Forest Shieldbug

Plates 2a & 2b
Green Shieldbug
a) adult
b) nymph

Plate 3
Hairy Shieldbug

Plates 4a & 4b
Gorse Shieldbug
a) spring form
b) summer form

Red-legged Shieldbug *Pentatoma rufipes* (body length: 12–14 mm)
CURRENT STATUS IN THE NEW FOREST: Common
IDENTIFICATION: Large brown insect with has orange legs and slightly hooked projections at the front of the pronotum. The pale spot at the tip of the scutellum varies from orange to cream, but the presence distinguishes it from related species.
HABITAT: Mainly deciduous trees, but occasionally on pines, in woodland, woodland edge, churchyards, gardens and parks. Plentiful on birch, hawthorn, maple, oak, sycamore and on shrubs, including bramble. One of the Forest's commonest species, widespread in the Inclosures and open forest, likely to be seen almost anywhere. Widespread throughout Britain, with adults mainly seen in July to November, with a peak in August; nymphs overwinter.

Spiked Shieldbug *Picromerus bidens* (body length: 10–14 mm)
CURRENT STATUS IN THE NEW FOREST: Common
IDENTIFICATION: Large brown species, could be mistaken for the Red-legged Shieldbug, except for the characteristic thorn-like extensions to the pronotum.
HABITAT: Woodland clearings and rides, also heathlands. Widespread throughout the Forest, hunting for suitable prey, often around brambles or common heather. Common in southern and central England, Wales and Ireland, although less frequent further north. Adults are found in July to early December.

Bronze Shieldbug *Troilus luridus* (body length: 10–12 mm)
CURRENT STATUS IN THE NEW FOREST: Local
IDENTIFICATION: Similar to the Red-legged Shieldbug, but easily distinguished from this species by an orange band on the penultimate antennal segment, mottled brown legs and the scutellum lacks an orange tip, in addition to more rounded extensions to the pronotum.
HABITAT: Mainly in coniferous plantations and deciduous woodland. Often associated with birch, hazel, holly, oak, Douglas fir and larch, searching for suitable prey. Occasional in the Forest, recorded at Bramshaw Wood, Cadnam and Half Moon Common, Denny and Hollands Wood and Shatterford. Widespread in southern and central, also parts of northern England and Wales, also Ireland. Adults are found in March to November, with peaks in April to May, then late August to early September.

Heather Shieldbug *Rhacognathus punctatus* (body length: 7–10 mm)
CURRENT STATUS IN THE NEW FOREST: Rare
IDENTIFICATION: Dark brown, heavily mottled metallic bronze-brown over a pale orange/reddish background, often with a pale midline on the pronotum. The legs are banded pale to orange/red.
HABITAT: Heathland, including damper areas amongst sphagnum moss, or vegetation around the edges, where they predate heather beetles and other beetles. Recorded from Matley Bog and Park Hill and in the Forest surrounds from the Southampton area (Lord's Wood Plantation) and Town Common, north of Christchurch. Local or rare, with scattered records in Britain, very rare in Ireland. Adults are mainly found in April to July, occasionally later.

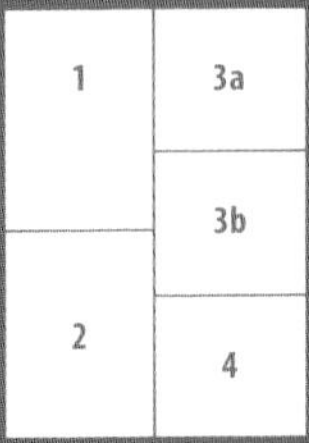

1	3a
	3b
2	
	4

Plate 1
Red-legged Shieldbug

Plate 2
Spiked Shieldbug

Plates 3a & 3b
Bronze Shieldbug
a) adult
b) nymph

Plate 4
Heather Shieldbug

Blue Shieldbug ***Zicrona caerulea*** (body length: 6–7 mm)
CURRENT STATUS IN THE NEW FOREST: Local
IDENTIFICATION: Easily recognised, dark species, due to its bluish green metallic sheen and a dark wing membrane.
HABITAT: Low vegetation, including nettles, in heathland, marshes, grassland and woodland rides which support populations of its prey, mainly leaf beetles. Not common in the Forest, it should be searched for on the ground or low vegetation possibly on sandy areas, such as Hatchet Pond surrounds and Holmsley. In the Forest surrounds, it has been recorded from the Southampton area, Totton and Testwood Lakes, and is widespread throughout Britain, particularly in the north, although absent from Ireland. Adults are mainly seen in March to July, occasionally later.

Possible finds in the surrounds of the Forest, or even with more detailed searches in the Forest, include the following species.

Southern Green Shieldbug ***Nezara viridula*** (body length: 11–15 mm)
CURRENT STATUS IN THE NEW FOREST: Not in Forest, rare in surrounds
IDENTIFICATION: Similar to the Green Shieldbug, except for the 3–5 white spots along the front edge of the scutellum and by the two dark marks at its corners. It lacks the dark punctures present on the Green Shieldbug.
HABITAT: Found to be breeding in the UK in the London area in 2003, this African native is occasionally imported to the UK in food produce and has been recorded from various sites in south-east England since 2003 (including Southampton, 2005), where they feed on various foodplants including vegetables such as beans and tomato.

Crucifer Shieldbug ***Eurydema oleracea*** (body length: 6–7 mm)
CURRENT STATUS IN THE NEW FOREST: Possibly present, local in surrounds
IDENTIFICATION: Often bluish black, can be metallic green, blue or violet, usually with red or white spots and markings; the latter change from red to orange or white to cream, following overwintering as adults and are reversed once adults feed in spring.
HABITAT: Woodland edge, waste ground, farmland, gardens and coastal sites. Feeds on crucifers, including horse radish, wild radish and hedge mustard. Sea radish is widely used in the Bournemouth area, where the species is common. Also well distributed in Southampton and Isle of Wight and recorded from near Godshill right on the Forest border. Local in parts of southern and central England. Adults are mainly seen from April to November, with a peak in May to early June.

Ornate Shieldbug ***Eurydema ornata*** (body length: 7–9 mm)
CURRENT STATUS IN THE NEW FOREST: Not in Forest, rare in surrounds
IDENTIFICATION: An attractive scarlet and black species with distinctive patterning.
HABITAT: So far mainly coastal grassland and scrub, feeding on members of the cabbage family, including cress, radish and cabbages. Adults overwinter. A recent arrival in the UK, but now established in parts of Dorset and Hampshire; it may also appear at other places in south England. Can be frequent on wallflowers and sea radish in Ventnor, Isle of Wight (first recorded in 2006), scarcer on sea radish on coastal cliffs in the Boscombe area. Adults are likely from May to late in the year.

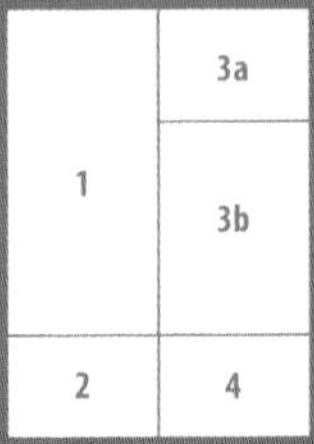

1	3a
	3b
2	4

Plate 1
Blue Shieldbug and flea beetle prey [SR]

Plate 2
Southern Green Shieldbug [TB]

Plates 3a & 3b
Crucifer Shieldbug
a) orange winter form
b) mating pair

Plate 4
Ornate Shieldbug

Other species in the Forest surrounds include the **Bordered Shieldbug *Legnotus limbosus*** (3.5–5 mm), **Heath Shieldbug *Legnotus picipes*** (3–4 mm) and **Forget-me-not Shieldbug *Sehirus luctuosus*** (7–9 mm), all in the Southampton area. The **Down Shieldbug *Canthophorus (Sehirus) impressus*** (6–7 mm) has been recorded at Martin Down and the Isle of Wight; it appears to be restricted to chalk downlands, where the foodplant bastard toadflax grows [all Cydnidae]. The **Knobbed Shieldbug *Podops inuncta*** (5.5–6 mm) is recorded from Barton-on-Sea, Southampton area, Gosport and the Isle of Wight, amongst others. The **Vernal Shieldbug *Holcostethus vernalis*** (9–10.5 mm) was recorded in Boscombe in 2007 and the Southampton area (2005/6) [all Pentatomidae]. The **Scarab Shieldbug *Thyreocoris scarabaeoides*** (3–4 mm) has been recorded in the Isle of Wight [Thyreocoridae].

STILTBUGS – Family Berytidae

UK: 9 species
New Forest: at least 4 species [44%], with others in the immediate surrounds, including Isle of Wight

A small group of elongate bugs with stilt-like legs. ***Metatropis rufescens*** (9–11 mm, local) is an unmistakable woodland species, feeding on enchanter's nightshade.

GROUNDBUGS – Family Lygaeidae

UK: 86 species
New Forest: estimated 52 species [60%]

A group of mainly dark brown or black species which are mostly terrestrial. Several are commonly associated with heather throughout the forest: ***Macrodema micropterum*** (2.5–3.5 mm), ***Scolopostethus decoratus*** (3.5–4 mm) and ***Kleidocerys ericae*** (3.5–4.5 mm). Two common arboreal species include the **Birch Catkin Bug *Kleidocerys resedae*** (4.5–5.5 mm) which is abundant on Birch trees and the broad-bodied **Pine-cone Bug *Gastrodes grossipes*** (6–7 mm) on Scots pine. The dark long-legged ground bug ***Rhyparochromus pini*** (7–8 mm, local) is occasionally seen in the Forest, for instance in New Copse Inclosure. The strangely shaped ***Megalonotus dilatatus*** (5–6 mm, rare) is found in dry, often sandy places and has been recorded in Fawley. ***Henestaris laticeps*** (5–6 mm, local) is a coastal species feeding on buck's horn plantain, easily recognised by having eyes on long stalks, occasionally found in coastal parts of the Forest, Barton-on-Sea and Isle of Wight. The **Nettle Groundbug *Heterogaster urticae*** (6-6-7 mm, widespread) is associated with nettles. ***Pachybrachius luridus*** (4–5 mm, rare) inhabits sphagnum bogs.

Denny Wood sandpit and sandy paths, ideal habitat for groundbugs

1	2	3	
4	5	6	7
8		9	
10	11	12	
13	14	15	

Plate 1
Bordered Shieldbug [TB]

Plate 2
Heath Shieldbug

Plate 3
Forget-me-not Shieldbug [SR]

Plate 4
Down Shieldbug

Plate 5
Knobbed Shieldbug and eggs

Plate 6
Vernal Shieldbug

Plate 7
Scarab Shieldbug [TB]

Plate 8
Metatropis rufescens

Plate 9
Kleidocerys ericae

Plate 10
Gastrodes grossipes

Plate 11
Rhyparochromus pini

Plate 12
Megalonotus dilatatus

Plate 13
Henestaris laticeps

Plate 14
Heterogaster urticae

Plate 15
Pachybrachius luridus
[TB]

SPURGEBUGS – Family Stenocephalidae

UK: 2 species
New Forest: 0 species [0%]

Dicranocephalus medius (8–11 mm, not in Forest; rare in surrounds) has been observed on spurge at Blashford Lakes and could turn up in the Forest on wood spurge or leafy spurge in woodland clearings. These insects are seldom recorded possibly because they rest low down, often on the ground, beneath the foodplant.

LEATHERBUGS – Family Coreidae

UK: 11 species
New Forest: at least 5 species [45%]

The leatherbugs or squashbugs are similar to shieldbugs, but are generally narrower in body shape with the abdomen expanded laterally. They mainly feed on fruit and seeds and only one species is likely to be seen by the casual observer, the other species usually require specialised searching for. Some species are best searched for on bare dry ground, others on vegetation.

Box Bug *Gonocerus acuteangulatus* (body length: 11–14 mm)

CURRENT STATUS IN THE NEW FOREST: Local
IDENTIFICATION: Brown with a narrow abdomen and pale legs; edge of pronotum pointed.
HABITAT: Varied, including woodland edge, hedgerows, gardens, parks wherever the foodplants (berried shrubs including box, bramble, hawthorn, rose and others) grow. Adults are active from April to November and they are most likely to be seen in late July to October. Found at Bartley, Beaulieu, Brockenhurst and Pennington in 2010, the species is rapidly increasing its range and is well established in the Southampton area and the Isle of Wight. In 1990 this species had only spread 10 km from Box Hill, Surrey.

Dock Bug *Coreus marginatus* (body length: 10–12 mm)

CURRENT STATUS IN THE NEW FOREST: Common
IDENTIFICATION: Mottled brown, the abdomen broad and rather diamond-shaped. The second and third antennal segments are red.
HABITAT: Varied, including hedgerows, wasteland, roadside verges, damp and dry grassland, heathland, woodland rides and gardens wherever the foodplants (members of the dock family, amongst others) grows, preferably along with bramble and other fruits, which they also feed on. Adults are active from May to November, with peaks in May and August to September, when sometimes many congregate on shrubs and trees.

Other leatherbugs are seldom recorded in the Forest. **Falléns Leatherbug *Arenocoris falleni*** (6–7 mm, rare) is recorded from Shepherds Gutter, Great Wood in 1979 and the **Denticulate Leatherbug *Coriomeris denticulatus*** (7–9 mm, rare) from Fawley and common in the Southampton area. The latest species to arrive in Britain in 2007, the **Western Conifer Seed Bug *Leptoglossus occidentalis*** (15–20 mm, rare) has already been recorded in Pennington in October 2010, also the Forest surrounds, including the Isle of Wight. Other than Dock Bug, all species require further surveys and it is likely that other species exist in the Forest. Some species are present in the Forest surrounds, including the vicinity of Bournemouth and Southampton. The **Rhombic Leatherbug *Syromastus rhombeus*** (9–11 mm) is found in the Gosport area, **Dalman's Leatherbug *Spathocera dalmanii*** (5–6.5 mm) in Boscombe, Southampton (Lord's Wood) and Hayling Island. The **Slender-horned Leatherbug *Ceraleptus lividus*** (9–11 mm) has been recorded in the Southampton area, also Boscombe and the **Boat Bug *Enoplops scapha*** (10–12 mm) on the Isle of Wight.

1		2
3	4	5a
6		5b
7		8

Plate 1
Dicranocephalus medius

Plate 2
Box Bug

Plate 3
Dock Bug

Plate 4
Falléns Leatherbug [SR]

Plates 5a & 5b
Denticulate Leatherbug
a) adult
b) nymph

Plate 6
Western Conifer Seed Bug [SR]

Plate 7
Rhombic Leatherbug [SR]

Plate 8
Boat Bug

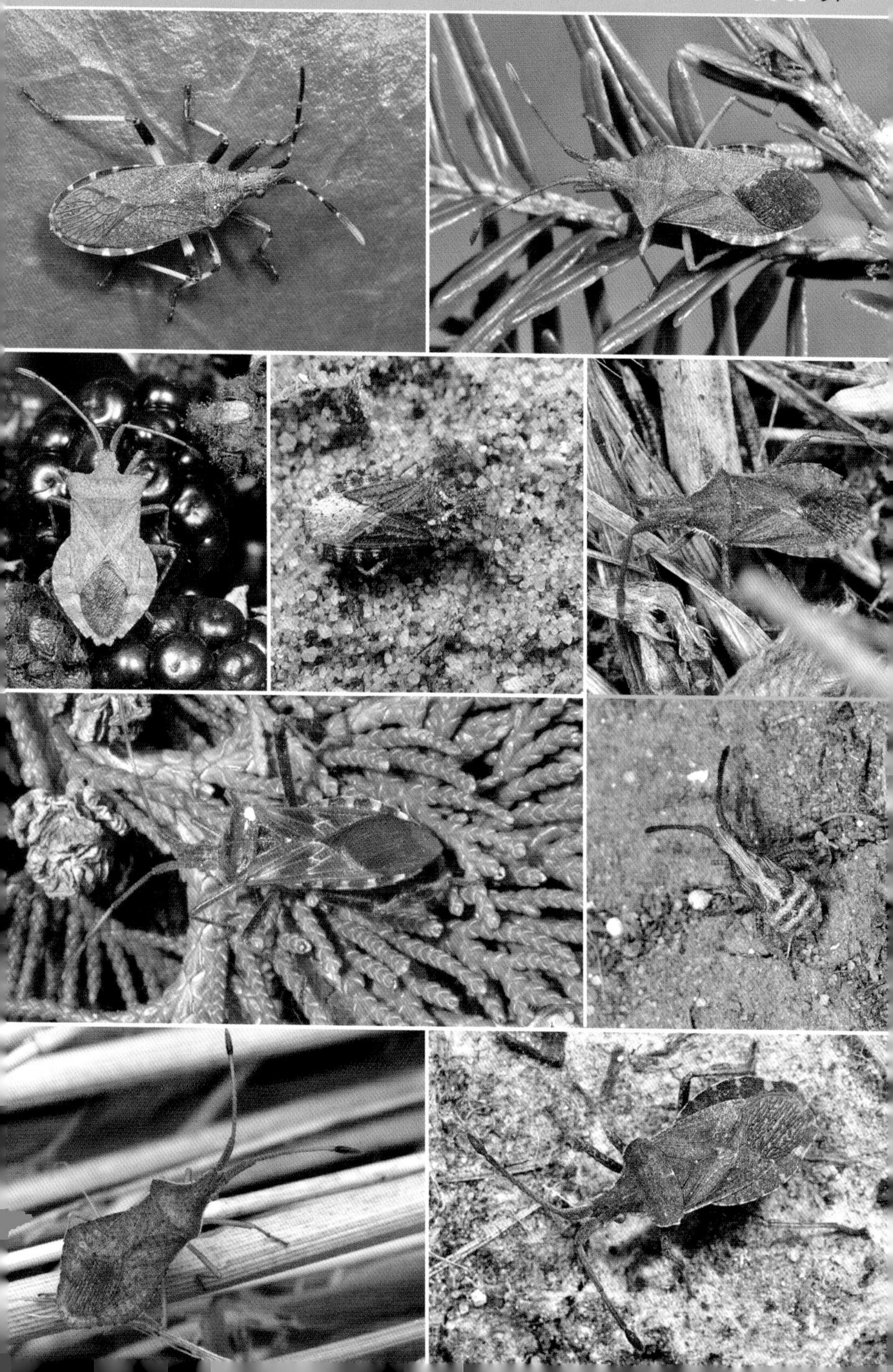

BROAD-HEADED BUGS – Family Alydidae

UK: 1 species
New Forest: 1 species [100%]

The large brownish black bug ***Alydus calcaratus*** (10–12 mm, local), with long narrow wings, is the only British representative of this family. Found in dry heathlands, mainly in July to September, this species is easily recognised in flight, having a bright orange patch on the abdomen. In the Forest it should be searched for at localities like Badminston Common; also found in the Forest surrounds, including Southampton and Bournemouth areas. The larvae resemble ants and develop in ants nests.

RHOPALID BUGS – Family Rhopalidae

UK: 11 species
New Forest: at least 6 species [55%]

Mainly seed or fruit feeders with conspicuously shaped antennae, sometimes known as scentless plant bugs. The attractive red and black ***Corizus hyoscyami*** (9 mm, rare, local in surrounds) is mainly coastal, but is increasingly being seen inland. Recorded from Holidays Hill Inclosure in 2006 and Brockenhurst in 2010, also the Southampton area, Gosport and Isle of Wight amongst others; mainly seen May to September in grassland, scrub, woodlands and gardens. There are four British *Rhopalus* species, all hairy. The commonest species ***Rhopalus subrufus*** (7–7.5 mm, local, common in surrounds) is found on low vegetation in scrub and woodland clearings. The darker ***Rhopalus maculatus*** (7.5–8 mm, rare) occurs in different habitat in damp heath, feeding on marsh thistle and marsh cinquefoil; it has been recorded in few places in the Forest, including Matley Bog, as well as Southampton (Lord's Wood). Females of the usually short-winged, rather conspicuous bug ***Myrmus miriformis*** (6–10 mm, widespread) are always green, whilst males are green or brown; they live in dry or damp grassland, feeding on grasses and unripe seeds.

LACEBUGS – Family Tingidae

UK: 24 species
New Forest: estimated at least 12 species [50%]

A group of attractive, small plant feeding species with lace-like edges to the pronotum and wings. The **Spear Thistle Lacebug *Tingis cardui*** (3–4 mm, common) is easy to find on spear thistle heads, whilst ***Physatocheila dumetorum*** (2.5–3 mm, widespread) can be found on lichen covered trees, including hawthorn; adults overwinter.

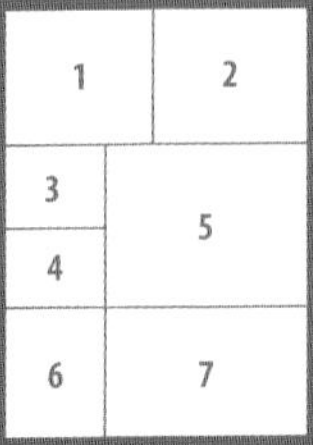

1	2
3	5
4	
6	7

Plate 1
Alydus calcaratus

Plate 2
Corizus hyoscyami

Plate 3
Rhopalus subrufus

Plate 4
Rhopalus maculatus [SR]

Plate 5
Myrmus miriformis
mating pair

Plate 6
Spear Thistle Lacebug

Plate 7
Physatocheila
dumetorum **about to fly**

PLANT OR CAPSID BUGS – Family Miridae

UK: 222 species
New Forest: estimated 133 species [60%]

Where wings are present, these bugs have soft forewings, with a prominent triangular area, often a different colour than the rest of the body. This is by far the largest family of bugs in Britain, a wide variety of often attractive species, to be found in meadows and woods; some are coastal specialists. Most feed on fruits, leaves and seeds, although some eat aphids and other prey. The commonest and best known species are the **Common Green Capsid *Lygocoris pabulinus*** (5–6.5 mm), ***Miris striatus*** (9–11 mm, a predator of small insects on oak and hawthorn), ***Capsus ater*** (5–6 mm, found in grasslands; note the swollen second antennal segment) and the **Meadow Plant Bug *Leptopterna dolabrata*** (8–8.5 mm, a grassland species whose females are usually short-winged). A small selection of other common Forest species is shown.

DAMSEL BUGS – Family Nabidae

UK: 12 species
New Forest: at least 6 species [50%]

These predatory brown bugs differ from assassin bugs by having a four-segmented beak; the 2nd antennal segment is always the longest. There are several common species in the Forest, most often seen by beating or sweeping, but may be spotted on the ground or, in the case of the short-winged **Tree Damsel Bug *Himacerus apterus*** (8–12 mm, widespread), the only damselbug to live mainly in trees. The **Ant Damsel Bug *Himacerus mirmicoides*** (7–8 mm, common) is found on low vegetation and has rather longer wings than *H. apterus*. The **Grey Damsel Bug *Himacerus major*** (7.5–9 mm, local) has a rather different appearance, with full length wings and is found in grassy habitats including coastal areas. The **Heath Damsel Bug *Nabis ericetorum*** (8–12 mm, common) is a mainly heathland species, often found amongst heather. There are other similar, closely related species.

Sweeping for bugs in a wide ride, Denny Lodge Inclosure

1	2	3
4a	4b	5
6	7	8
9	10	11
12	13	14

Plate 1
Common Green Capsid

Plate 2
Miris striatus

Plate 3
Capsus ater

Plates 4a & 4b
Meadow Plant Bug
a) male
b) female

Plate 5
Capsodes gothicus
(c.6 mm)

Plate 6
Deraeocoris ruber
(6–8 mm)

Plate 7
Dryophilocoris flavoquadrimaculatus
(6–7 mm)

Plate 8
Heterotoma planicornis
(4.5–5.5 mm)

Plate 9
Harpocera thoracica
(c.6 mm)

Plate 10
Pantilius tunicatus
(8–10 mm)

Plate 11
Tree Damsel Bug

Plate 12
Ant Damsel Bug

Plate 13
Grey Damsel Bug

Plate 14
Heath Damsel Bug [GP]

FLOWER BUGS – Family Anthocoridae

UK: 32 species
New Forest: estimated 19 species [60%]

These predatory bugs feed on aphids for much of the year, ***Anthocoris nemorum*** (3–4 mm, common) is likely to be found on low vegetation. The commonest of several similar species, the delicate-looking *A. nemorum* feeds on aphids, psyllids, mites and other small animals and sometimes leaves; it can pierce human flesh.

ASSASSIN BUGS – Family Reduviidae

UK: 7 species
New Forest: at least 4 species [57%]

The predatory assassin bugs have a three-segmented beak; the 1st antennal segment is the longest. Not often found in the Forest, one of the commonest British species is the usually short-winged, **Heath Assassin Bug *Coranus subapterus*** (9–12 mm, local), which can be found by careful searching on the ground in open parts of heathland from July to October, where it hunts for insects and spiders. Vales Moor is a good area to find them and long-winged forms are likely at this site. Both the adults and larvae stridulate loudly if disturbed and should be handled with care, as they can pierce human skin.

PONDSKATERS and ALLIED BUGS

UK: 20 species
New Forest: at least 15 species [75%]

Ponds and streams often have an interesting range of bugs, the pondskaters [Gerridae] have legs adapted for rowing on the water surface and are predators, detecting vibrations. They sometimes fly to lights at night. The **Common Pondskater *Gerris lacustris*** (8–10 mm, common) is often seen in numbers on ponds and other waters; on occasions, larger species including ***Aquarius paludum*** (14–16 mm, local) may also be observed. The similar **River Pondskater *Aquarius najas*** (13–17 mm, local) is nearly always wingless and lacks the yellow line at the side of the pronotum in *paludum*. This group also includes the water measurers (Hydrometridae) and water crickets (Veliidae).

WATER BUGS

UK: 44 species
New Forest: at least 29 species [66%]

There are several families of these aquatic bugs. The water scorpions (Nepidae) have a long tail to distinguish them from other families. The two species are well worth looking for, firstly the flat, broadened, but harmless **Water Scorpion *Nepa cinerea*** (18–22 mm, widespread), a predator in shallow, muddy water, which often eats tadpoles and small fish. It breathes by pushing its tail to the surface and is common. The elongate **Water Stick-insect *Ranatra linearis*** (30–35 mm, rare) is recorded near Hatchet Pond and elsewhere and most likely to be seen when flying in warm weather. Underwater they often remain still within vegetation waiting for prey to approach. The water boatmen (Notonectidae, example ***Notonecta glauca*** (c.15 mm, common) sometimes known as Backswimmers) and Corixidae (example **Common Water Boatman *Corixa punctata*** (12–13.5 mm, common)) include common species likely to be seen under the water surface in any pond.

1	2a	2b
3	4	
5	6	7
8		9
		10

Plate 1
Anthocoris nemorum
piercing human flesh

Plates 2a & 2b
Heath Assassin Bug
a) typical form
b) long-winged form

Plate 3
Common Pond Skater
long-winged form

Plate 4
Aquarius paludum
with mayfly prey [GH]

Plate 5
Water Measurer
Hydrometra stagnorum
(9–11.5 mm)

Plate 6
Water Cricket
Velia caprai
uncommon winged form
(5–5.7 mm) [CO]

Plate 7
Water Scorpion

Plate 8
Water Stick-insect
large nymph

Plate 9
Notonecta glauca

Plate 10
Common Water
Boatman

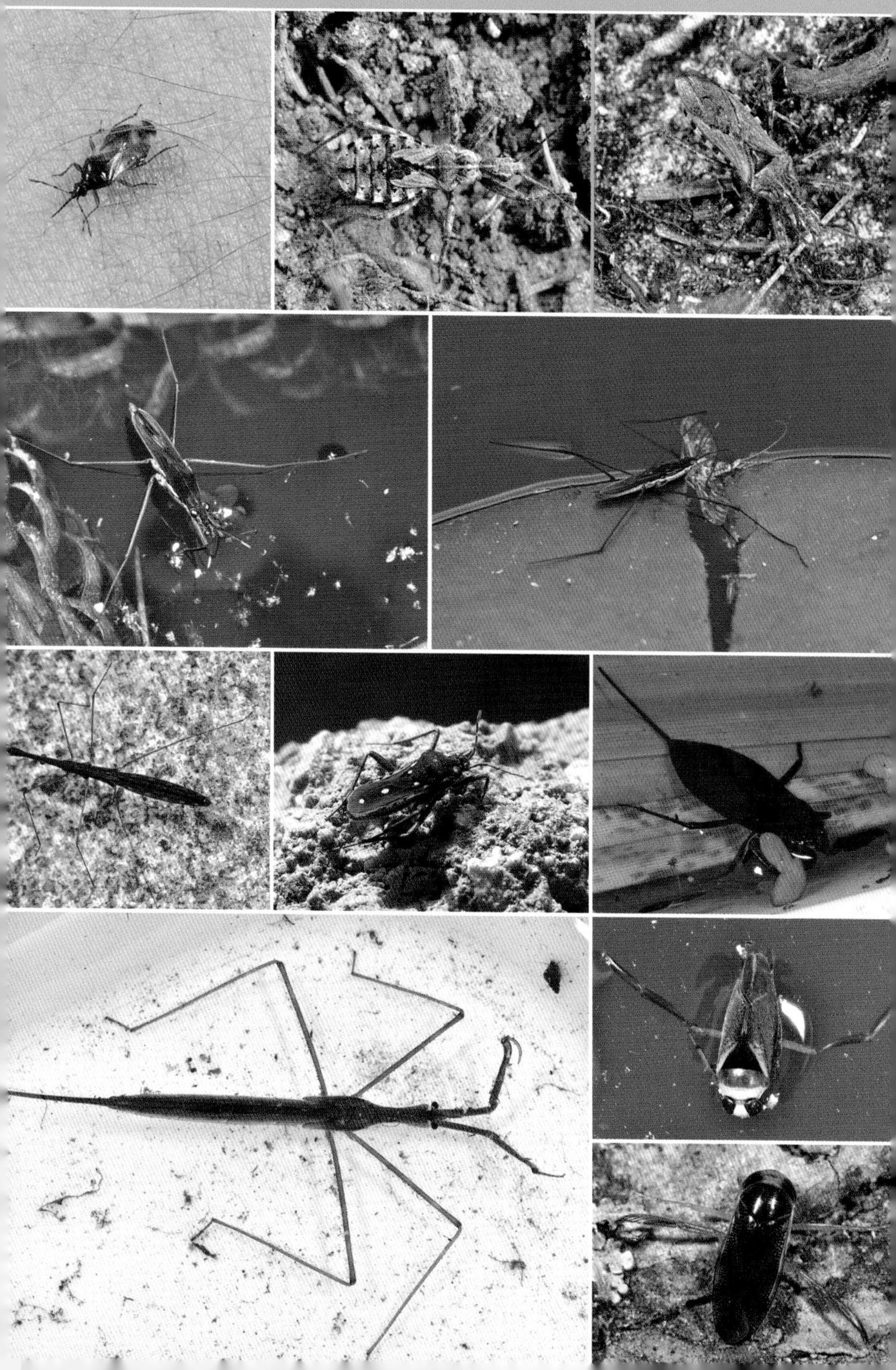

Suborder Auchenorrhyncha

CICADAS – Family Cicadidae

UK: 1 species
New Forest: 1 species [100%]

There are about 2,500 worldwide species of cicada (popular as food for humans in some countries), bugs with large eyes wide apart on the head and often transparent, well-veined wings. Under-studied in some countries, many remain unclassified. Well known from the long life cycle of some species. Many visitors taking trips to the Mediterranean often wonder where the constant noise originates from. However, our only cicada, has always been rare and has a high-pitched song which can usually only be heard by persons under the age of 40.

New Forest Cicada *Cicadetta montana* (body length: 16–27 mm)
CURRENT STATUS IN THE NEW FOREST: Very rare
IDENTIFICATION: Black with large transparent, heavily veined wings. Abdomen with gold rings.
HISTORY: First found at Pennington Common in 1812 but always hard to find in the New Forest (also occasionally recorded in Surrey from 1864 to 1936). Colonies had been found near Brockenhurst and elsewhere in the New Forest until 1941. A colony was found in 1962 in the old woods between Brook and Fritham. The late Jim Grant made extensive studies on the species in this area until his death in 1990. In total there have been records from 26 different localities within the Forest, the last definite sighting reported from Denny Wood in 1991, with occasional singing heard elsewhere up to 1994 and a probable adult sighting in 1992. Ongoing searches for this species continue.
HABITAT: Swinton (1885) stated 'The male, usually beaten in June from blossoming Hawthorn in the New Forest, is provided with instruments of music, and the female, more terrestrial, is often observed wandering with a whirring sound among bracken wastes, where she is thought to deposit her ova.' Pinchen and Ward (2002) produced a detailed account of habitat requirements from literature available and further research on the species. Adults are found from late May to mid July, preferring warm, sunny south-facing and sheltered woodland rides or clearings with mixed ground flora and early successional scrub. Adults feed on twigs (oaks, birches, beech, hawthorn, small-leaved lime and bracken) and should be searched for in scrub, or bracken, or possibly on the ground. Males may be higher up, particularly when singing and a bat detector may help pick out a rasping sound. Very much weather dependant, males start to sing when the temperature exceeds 20°C, from around 10.30am, reaching a peak at 2pm or so and stop around 6pm, or in the slightest cooling breeze. After mating, females lay 200–300 eggs in stems of bracken, oak, birch and small-leaved lime. The twigs bear scars forming a distinctive 'W' shape in the wood. Eggs hatch in 50–125 days and nymphs feed underground on roots, taking 6–8 years to mature. Prior to emerging in spring, nymphs make their way to the surface, where they construct a small chimney-like turret from soil and saliva. The top of the turret is removed when the nymph climbs out to moult for a final time to become an adult. The nymphal skin is left clinging to nearby vegetation and is worth looking for, as a sign of the presence of this species. Suitable habitat in the Forest is limited due to heavy grazing of the ground flora, but there is still a reasonable chance that this elusive species still survives in isolated small colonies somewhere in the forest. Any records or possible sightings should be reported to Natural England.

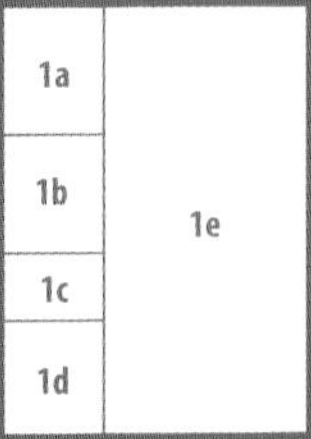

1a	1e
1b	
1c	
1d	

Plates 1a–1e
New Forest Cicada
a) burrow [JG]
b) egglaying [JG]
c) eggs [JG]
d) nymphal skin [JG]
e) female [JG]

2 cm 3 4 5 6 7 8 9
1 INCH

FROGHOPPERS – Families Aphrophoridae and Cercopidae

UK: 10 species
New Forest: at least 5 species [50%]

The plant feeding froghoppers have leathery wings folded back over the body, with short bristly antennae; they can jump well and the so called 'cuckoo-spit' or white froth surrounding a nymph, is a familiar sight on stems, including in gardens. The **Common Froghopper *Philaenus spumarius*** (5–7 mm, common), has remarkably variable colour forms. The **Alder Spittelbug *Aphrophora alni*** (9–10 mm, common) is found on a wide range of trees and bushes. The vivid **Red-and-black Froghopper *Cercopis vulnerata*** (9–11 mm, widespread) is also familiar in Forest rides; the nymphs feed on roots underground.

LEAFHOPPERS – Family Cicadellidae

UK: 276 species
New Forest: estimated 166 species [60%]

A large family of often slender, jumping plant-feeding bugs, which can also fly well. The forewings are often softer than those of froghoppers; hind legs have a series of bristles. The **Rhododendron Leafhopper *Graphocephala fennahi*** (8–10 mm, common) is often noticed; relatively few insects feed on rhododendron leaves, but in June to November these insects (introduced from the USA in the early 1900s) are a colourful sight throughout the Forest wherever rhododendron grows, sometimes with several congregating on one leaf. The most stunning leafhopper is probably the large, grey **Eared Leafhopper *Ledra aurita*** (13 18 mm, local) with ear-like lobes. Superbly camouflaged in wooded areas, particularly oaks, it is most likely to be beaten from vegetation or occasionally attracted to light in May to September. As a defensive strategy, in addition to playing dead, they can stridulate loudly. A selection of other common Forest species is shown.

TREEHOPPERS – Family Membracidae

UK: 2 species
New Forest: 1 species [50%]

The pronotum extends horn-like, back over the body. The **Horned Treehopper *Centrotus cornutus*** (c.10 mm, local) occurs in April to August on herbs and shrubs in woodland rides and clearings.

Wootton Coppice Inclosure, good for froghoppers and leafhoppers

1	2	3
4	5a	5b
6	7	8
9	10	11
9	12	13

Plate 1
Common Froghopper

Plate 2
Alder Spittlebug mating pair

Plate 3
Red-and-black Froghopper

Plate 4
Rhododendron Leafhopper [GP]

Plates 5a & 5b
Eared Leafhopper b) front view

Plate 6
***Errastunus ocellaris* (3–4 mm)**

Plate 7
***Allygus mixtus* (6–7 mm)**

Plate 8
***Cicadella viridis* (6–8 mm)**

Plate 9
***Eupelix cuspidata* (5.5–7 mm)**

Plate 10
***Iassus lanio* (6.5–8 mm)**

Plate 11
***Linnavuoriana decempunctata* (3.5 mm)**

Plate 12
***Zygina rubrovittata* (2.5 mm)**

Plate 13
Horned Treehopper

LACEHOPPERS – Family Cixiidae

UK: 12 species
New Forest: at least 7 species [58%]

One of several similar species, ***Cixius nervosus*** (6.5–8.5 mm, common) is a distinctive strongly-veined species, found in the Forest on deciduous trees and shrubs in May to October. ***Pentastiridius leporinus*** (5.5–7.5 mm, local) is associated with grasses in saltmarshes or occasionally wet heathland in June to August.

PLANTHOPPERS – Family Delphacidae

UK: 76 species
New Forest: estimated 42 species [55%]

One of the distinctive species in this family is ***Conomelus anceps*** (4 mm, common), found in damp meadows and woodlands.

ISSID PLANTHOPPERS – Family Issidae

UK: 2 species
New Forest: 1 species [50%]

The very distinctively shaped ***Issus coleoptratus*** (c.9 mm, local) is found on bushes and deciduous trees in gardens or other habitats in June to November, but the species is easily overlooked. In the Forest, recorded from Beaulieu and Brockenhurst; there are scattered records from the Forest surrounds, including the Isle of Wight.

Suborder Sternorrhyncha

Aphids, whitefly, scale insects, jumping plant lice, mealybugs and others, all with long thread-like antennae, including most of the serious pests of gardens, as well as agricultural land. Aphids feed on the phloem sap of plants and are well known to gardeners. The various species are rather under-studied, with most only 2–3 mm long.

Pentastiridius leporinus **saltmarsh habitat, near Beaulieu**

1		2
3		4
5a	5b	5c
6	7	8

Plate 1
Cixius nervosus

Plate 2
Pentastiridius leporinus

Plate 3
Tachycixius pilosus
(4.5–5.5 mm)

Plate 4
Conomelus anceps

Plates 5a–5c
Issus coleoptratus
c) nymph

Plate 6
***Cinara* species [aphid] (c.5 mm, on Scots pine)**

Plate 7
***Uroleucon* species [aphid] (1.5–2 mm, on thistle)**

Plate 8
Woolly Aphid
Eriosoma lanigerum
(c.1 mm, on / near apple trees) [BV]

LACEWINGS and ANTLIONS – Order NEUROPTERA

UK: 69 species
New Forest: at least 37 species [54%]

Graceful, fluttering delicate-looking soft-bodied insects; the adults have two pairs of wings, often with cross-veins, giving a lace-like appearance. The wings are held roof-like over the body at rest. The long antennae are thread-like, mouthparts are designed for biting or chewing. Many adults are predators on small insects such as aphids, also the fierce-looking larvae, of which a few species are aquatic. There is a complete life cycle: egg, larva, pupa and adult. The lacewings are small to fairly large, ranging from 3 mm to 30 mm in wingspan, one species of antlion is found in East Anglia, and the tiny Coniopterygidae, or wax flies resemble whiteflies. Lacewings are attracted to light and are common in gardens, in addition to woodlands, hedgerows and meadows. Many lacewing species are similar in appearance and require examination of genitalia. However, they can broadly be divided into green and brown species. Amongst the green species (Chrysopidae), ***Chrysopa perla*** (wingspan c.15 mm, common) is found in a range of habitats from April to September. It has a bluish tinge and extensive black markings on the head. ***Chrysopa carnea*** (c.15 mm, common) is plainer. Eggs can sometimes be seen on vegetation hanging onto threads. The brown species (Hemerobiidae) include common ***Hemerobius*** species (8–12 mm). The only member of the family Osmylidae, is the **Giant Lacewing *Osmylus fulvicephalus*** (wingspan c.25 mm, with body length c.13 mm, local), usually found near shady woodland streams, where it spends much of the day under shaded bridges or beneath overhanging vegetation. At night, it makes slow flights over the water surface. The main flight season is from May to early August.

1	2
3	4
5	6
7	8

Plate 1
Lacewing larva, a ferocious hunter

Plate 2
Lacewing larvae often camouflage themselves with drained skins of victims and other material

Plate 3
Chrysopa perla

Plate 4
Chrysopa carnea

Plate 5
Hemerobius humulinus

Plate 6
Hemerobius stigma

Plate 7
Giant Lacewing

Plate 8
Sisyra fuscata
(c.8 mm)

South Gorley meadow and hedgerow, home to lacewings, the rare Scarlet Malachite beetle and many other insects

ALDERFLIES – Order MEGALOPTERA

UK: 3 species
New Forest: at least 2 species [67%]

Robust looking dark-bodied insects; two pairs of wings sculptured with network of black veins. The antennae are thread-like. There is a complete life cycle taking about two years: egg, larva, pupa and adult. Larvae are aquatic, found in lakes, ponds, large rivers and streams, where they feed on insect larvae and worms and crustaceans. The greyish egg masses are usually laid on emergent vegetation. There is no specific connection with alder, except they may settle on trees at the water's edge. Adults fly in sunny weather, often resting on waterside vegetation. ***Sialis lutaria*** (c.20 mm, wingspan 22–34 mm, widespread) is the commonest species in the Forest and surrounds near static and moving water, where it is found from early April to early August, individuals only living for two to three days. Species are distinguished by genitalia of males and the anal plate of females. ***Sialis fuliginosa*** (c.20 mm, widespread) is associated with flowing water, mainly seen between May to July. All British species belong to the family Sialidae.

SNAKEFLIES – Order RAPHIDIOPTERA

UK: 4 species
New Forest: 3 species [75%]

Easily recognised by the elongate pronotum, held upright to resemble a snake about to strike out. These slender insects have a blackish body and two pairs of black-veined wings; females have a long ovipositor, used to deposit eggs in cracks of bark. There is a complete life cycle taking over two years: egg, larva, pupa and adult. Mouthparts are designed for biting and chewing, with both larvae and adults predatory; the larvae feed on other insect larvae under the bark of trees and adults on aphids and other small insects. Adults, 10–15 mm long, are best looked for on trunks of oak and pine trees, or nearby from early May; in sunny weather they fly around nearby low vegetation. The following species have been locally recorded from the Forest: ***Subilla confinis*** (found low down on trees in coniferous plantations), ***Atlantoraphidia maculicollis*** (most frequently seen on the ends of pine branches on sunny days in early May) and ***Phaeostigma notata*** (around oaks mainly in late May to June), observed several times around Setley and Brockenhurst. All British species belong to the family Raphidiidae.

Sialis lutaria [SC]

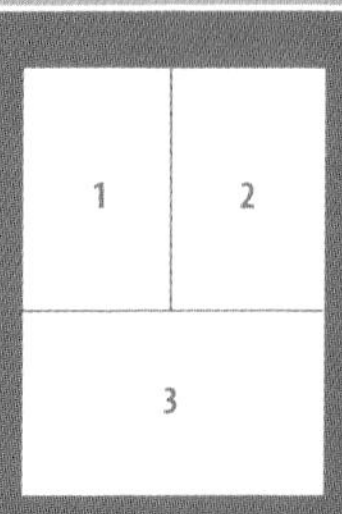

Plate 1
Sialis lutaria

Plate 2
Male snakefly attacked by Southern Wood Ant

Plate 3
***Phaeostigma notata* female**

BEETLES – Order COLEOPTERA

UK: 4,000 species
New Forest: estimated 2,600 species [65%] based on major samples of Families

Whilst the largest order of insects (c.370,000 worldwide), beetles are only the third largest order in Britain, well behind Hymenoptera and Diptera. Some species are as little as 1 mm in length whereas the well known Stag Beetle *Lucanus cervus* reaches up to 75 mm. Coleoptera means 'sheath-winged insects' after the hardened forewings (known as elytra), which cover the membranous hindwings (where present) and usually the whole abdomen, although a small number of beetles completely lack wings. The biting jaws can tackle most food; some are predators, whilst others eat live or dead plants, live and rotting wood, dead animals and dung. The colourful ladybirds are well known in controlling aphid populations, hence are of economic importance. Dung beetles are well known for their ability to dispose of animal dung and work overtime on this in the Forest! In all cases the life cycle is one of complete metamorphosis (development), so adults lay eggs which hatch into larvae, taking the form of fast-running predators, plant feeders or grubs with or without legs, concealed in their foodplants. The larva forms a pupa, before the adult emerges. Some larvae damage timber, particularly longhorns. The New Forest has always been recognised as being productive for rarer Coleoptera and is one of the richest sites in Britain for them. It has been estimated that the Forest supports at least 55% of Britain's saproxylic beetles i.e. those species dependant on the fungal decay of dead woody tissues, mainly in the ancient woodlands, with only Windsor Forest comparable. Even so, many of the rarer species have not been recorded in the Forest for at least 25 years, although the New Forest LIFE project provided impetus for significant beetle recording between 1999–2002. Even in Victorian times 3,500 species of beetles were known in Britain, with 'at least two-thirds in Hampshire', with the New Forest the 'entomologist's paradise' (Victorian County History, 1900). Coleopterists visit many sites, with Denny Wood particularly well worked over the years. The Coleoptera are probably second only to Lepidoptera (butterflies and moths) in terms of popular interest to naturalists, yet without a popular field guide covering all families, except for Linssen's 1959 two volume *Beetles of the British Isles*, although even this is not recommended for species identification. Some of the most well known Families or more interesting species are discussed in the text.

Rose Chafers attracted to Southern Wood Ant nest

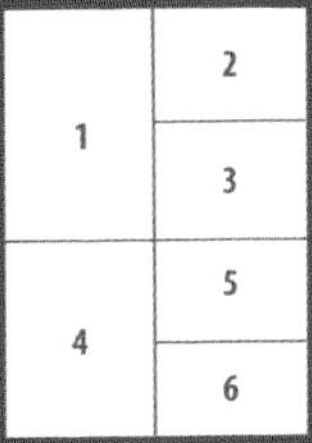

1	2
	3
4	5
	6

Plate 1
Stag Beetle male reflection [CP]

Plate 2
Noble Chafer

Plate 3
Black-headed Cardinal egglaying [GP]

Plate 4
Golden-haired Longhorn Beetle hatched adult and pupa [CT]

Plate 5
Mint Leaf Beetle eggs

Plate 6
Bloody-nosed Beetle mating pair

Suborder Adephaga

GROUND BEETLES – Family Carabidae

UK: 350 species
New Forest: at least 225 species [64%]

As their name implies, Ground Beetles are usually found at ground level, under stones, in leaf litter, or simply running across a track. Many species are carnivorous. The brightly coloured Green Tiger Beetle flies strongly in bright sunlight. With their large eyes, most Ground Beetles are effective hunters at night and although most species are black in colour, many exhibit a range of colours from gold to green. The New Forest is an important area for Ground Beetles but on account of their predominantly nocturnal habits they may be difficult to find. Many collectors employ pitfall traps, in which containers, often glass jars, are buried in the ground with their opening flush with the surface. The best guide for identification of species is that by Luff (2007). Bramshaw, Brinken and Denny Woods are well known areas for these species, but there are many under-studied areas. A small selection of other species is discussed.

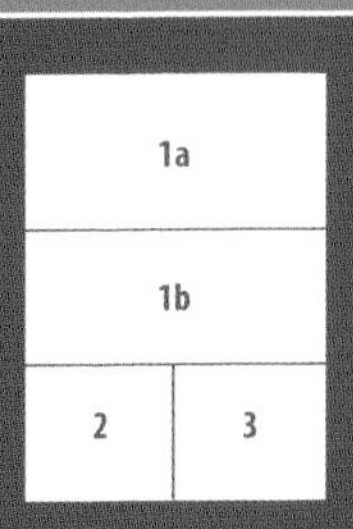

Plates 1a & 1b
Green Tiger Beetle
a) [GP]
b) mating pair

Plate 2
Heath Tiger Beetle [GP]

Plate 3
Cliff Tiger Beetle [JW]

Subfamily Cicindelinae

The tiger beetles have huge eyes and jaws and are active in the day, being fast-moving hunters. In the Forest, the **Green Tiger Beetle *Cicindela campestris*** (12–17 mm, common) is frequently found in sunny weather from March to October, but only in numbers up to July, favouring open, dry habitats such as heathland, but also in some woodland rides. The dark brown **Heath Tiger Beetle *Cicindela sylvatica*** (14–18 mm, very rare) has been recorded in Denny and Hollands Woods and vicinity. It is mainly found on sandy heathland from late May to September and is now confined to Dorset, Hampshire and Surrey. The **Cliff Tiger Beetle *Cylindera germanica*** (9–12 mm, not in Forest, rare in some coastal areas) probably now only occurs on certain partly vegetated clay undercliffs of Devon, Dorset and Hampshire. The species rarely flies, unlike related species. There are old records from Barton-on-Sea and it is still found locally on the Isle of Wight from May to September.

Heath Tiger Beetle with prey [CT]

Subfamily Carabinae

The vast majority of the Carabidae belong to this subfamily, including the large, attractive ***Carabus*** species. Most likely to be seen are the copper, green, purple, blue or black ***Carabus arvensis*** (16–22 mm, widespread) on heaths, the similar ***Carabus granulatus*** (16–23 mm, local), ***Carabus nemoralis*** (20–26 mm, local) and the **Violet Ground Beetle *Carabus violaceus*** (20–30 mm, widespread), which is easily confused with the equally common ***Carabus problematicus*** (20–28 mm, widespread). If very fortunate, the striking metallic green and copper ***Carabus nitens*** (13–18 mm, rare) may be seen running across tracks; it should be looked for in wet heathland and is widely distributed in the Forest, but with few recent records. A caterpillar hunter, ***Calosoma inquisitor*** (16–22 mm, rare) is another seldom recorded Forest species, found in old oak woodlands. Much sought after is **Kugelann's Ground Beetle *Poecilus kugelanni*** (12–14 mm, rare), with head and pronotum coppery red and its wingcases metallic green. It is found around sand pits such as at Denny Wood and Parc Pale, mainly between April to July, studies show that adults live for two years, a few individuals for three, or even four years. The related ***Poecilus cupreus*** (11–13 mm, common) could be confused with it, but is a mainly bright coppery green species (rarely bluish, purple or black). By coincidence, a marshy area very close to Denny Wood was the last known British home of ***Pterostichus aterrimus*** (13–15 mm), recorded from 1969 to 1973. The metallic green ***Drypta dentata*** (7–8.5 mm, not in Forest, rare in surrounds) is a coastal species recorded in Dorset and the Isle of Wight. Various common black ***Bembidion*** (c.3–6 mm) or ***Pterostichus* species** (c.5–21 mm) may be found by checking underneath rocks or logs. A selection of other species is shown.

1	2	3
4	5	6
7	8	9
10	11	12
13	14	15

Plate 1 ***Carabus arvensis*** **green form** [GP]

Plate 2 ***Carabus granulatus***

Plate 3 ***Carabus nemoralis***

Plate 4 **Violet Ground Beetle**

Plate 5 ***Carabus problematicus***

Plate 6 ***Carabus nitens*** [TD]

Plate 7 ***Calosoma inquisitor*** **normal & dark form** [CT]

Plate 8 **Kugelann's Ground Beetle** [GP]

Plate 9 ***Poecilus cupreus*** **mauve form**

Plate 10 ***Drypta dentata*** [CT]

Plate 11 ***Abax parallelepipedus*** **(17–22 mm)**

Plate 12 ***Anchomenus dorsalis*** **(6–8 mm)**

Plate 13 ***Lebia chlorocephala*** **(6–8 mm)**

Plate 14 ***Elaphrus cupreus*** **(8–9.5 mm)** [TP]

Plate 15 ***Cychrus caraboides*** **(14–19 mm)**

Lifting logs or stones may reveal the presence of ground beetles, such as *Nebria brevicollis* (11–14 mm)

WATER BEETLES – Family Dytiscidae

UK: 118 species
New Forest: at least 82 species [69%]

The water beetles have always been popular, they are adapted for life in the water, and some are aggressive predators, whilst others feed on vegetation. The **Great Diving Beetle *Dytiscus marginalis*** (26–32 mm, widespread) is the commonest of six UK *Dytiscus* species, with a yellow underside. The **Black Belly *Dytiscus semisulcatus*** (22–30 mm, local) is the second commonest UK species, with a black underside. The **Brown Diving Beetle *Agabus brunneus*** (9–9.5 mm, rare) is only found in the Forest, including Linford Brook and Widden Bottom, and a few sites in Cornwall and Dorset, where it prefers shallow, fast-flowing streams. A selection of other Forest water beetles is shown, including ***Helophorus*** [Helophoridae]. Other water beetle families include Gyrinidae, the whirligig beetles.

Suborder Polyphaga

CARRION or BURYING BEETLES – Family Silphidae

UK: 21 species
New Forest: at least 11 species [52%]

Scavenging, carnivorous beetles with conspicuous clubbed antennae in several species, which are thought to track down dead bodies of birds, mammals and reptiles by smell and fly in to bury or dispose of carcasses. Also known as sexton beetles, some similar ***Nicrophorus*** species (12–22 mm) have vivid warning colours and are separated by the extent / pattern of the orange bands in the case of ***N. interruptus*, *N. vespillo*** and ***N. vespilloides***. ***Nicrophorus humator*** (15–30 mm, local) is, however, easy to recognise, as it is all black with orange tipped antennae; whilst ***Necrodes littoralis*** (15–25 mm, local) could be confused with *humator*, it lacks the clubbed antennae. ***Oiceoptoma thoracicum*** (12–15 mm, local) is easily recognisable by its orange pronotum and adults and larvae of this species feed on other insects in dung and carrion. ***Thanatophilus rugosus*** (8–12 mm, local) is similar but completely black, with beautiful markings. ***Silpha*** species are adapted to eat snails, notably the almost rounded ***S. atrata*** (10–16 mm, common), the more elongate ***S. tristis*** (13–17 mm, local) and ***S. laevigata*** (12–18 mm, rare), the latter lacking raised longitudinal lines on the elytra; when disturbed it tucks its head beneath the thorax and remains motionless for up to a few minutes. The caterpillar hunting ***Dendroxena quadrimaculata*** (12–15 mm, local) is easily recognised by four black spots on the brown wingcases and is likely to be found in ancient woodland, including Denny Wood.

Hister unicolor (5–8 mm, widespread) [Histeridae], a round shining species which feeds on small insects in dung

1	2	3
4	5	6
7	8	9
10	11a	11b
12	13	14
15	16	17

Plate 1
Water Beetle larva

Plate 2
Great Diving Beetle male [GP]

Plate 3
Black Belly female

Plate 4
Brown Diving Beetle

Plate 5
Lesser Diving Beetle *Acilius sulcatus* (16–18 mm) [GP]

Plate 6
***Helophorus griseus* (2.8–3.8 mm)**

Plate 7
***Nicrophorus interruptus* part covered with mites** [GP]

Plate 8
Nicrophorus vespillo [MP]

Plate 9
Nicrophorus vespilloides

Plate 10
Nicrophorus humator

Plates 11a & 11b
Necrodes littoralis
a) [MP]
b) attracted to dead mammal [CT]

Plate 12
***Oiceoptoma thoracicum* on dead grass snake** [RR]

Plate 13
Thanatophilus rugosus

Plate 14
Silpha atrata

Plate 15
Silpha tristis

Plate 16
Silpha laevigata

Plate 17
Dendroxena quadrimaculata

ROVE BEETLES – Family Staphylinidae

UK: c.1,080 species
New Forest: estimated 700 species [65%]

This is a large family of elongate beetles; often black, some with reddish patches or wingcases, which are easily recognised by their short wingcases, leaving much of the abdomen visible. However, the wings are folded beneath the wingcases, so they still fly well. They range in size from under 1 mm in length to 30 mm. The best known species is the large, all-black **Devil's Coach-horse *Ocypus olens*** (20–30 mm, common), found in the Forest in woods, gardens, heathland and hedgerows, whose startle display includes raising the abdomen, scorpion-like and the male opens its large jaws. They feed on invertebrates at night, but like other rove beetles, are sometimes conspicuous in the daytime, walking on paths. Many species prey on insects in or near dung. Also likely to be seen in the Forest is ***Paederus littoralis*** (7–9 mm, common), with metallic bluish wingcases and reddish pronotum and much of the abdomen. The large ***Staphylinus caesareus*** (17–22 mm, local) commoner than believed, and the similar ***Staphylinus erythropterus*** (14–18 mm, local) are occasionally observed, both with attractive reddish wingcases. By comparison, ***Scaphidium quadrimaculatum*** (4.5–6 mm, local) is not a typical rove beetle shape. The **Hornet Rove Beetle *Velleius dilatatus*** (to 26 mm, rare) occurs in hornets nests in old trees and has been found attracted to moth lights or at the sap of 'Goat Moth' (*Cossus*) trees. Several specimens of ***Planeustomus flavicollis*** (c.2 mm) were collected during the Natural History Museum's long-term soil biodiversity project at Whitley Wood in 2003; previously known in the UK from only two specimens, the last record in 1912 (New Forest, by D. Sharp).

Denny Wood, 'Goat Moth' tree, used by Hornets and home to Hornet Rove Beetle, also Devil's Coach-horse

1a		2
		3
1b		4
5	6	7
8a		8b

Plates 1a & 1b
Devil's Coach-horse
a) male rears up, scorpion-like in defence
b) female

Plate 2
Paederus littoralis

Plate 3
Staphylinus caesareus

Plate 4
Staphylinus erythropterus

Plate 5
Scaphidium quadrimaculatum

Plate 6
***Philonthus* species (c.12 mm)**

Plate 7
***Lordithon lunulatus* (5–7 mm)**

Plates 8b & 8b
Hornet Rove Beetle
a) on hornets nest
b) hornet interaction

STAG BEETLES – Family Lucanidae

UK: 3 species
New Forest: 3 species [100%]

Named after the stag-like mandibles of the males, which vary considerably in length between individuals of the same species. Females are usually smaller than the males, with smaller mandibles. Insect collectors are keen on tropical species of these showy insects, with the largest specimens attracting higher prices, particularly in Japan, where they are also popularly kept as pets. The larvae feed for several years on rotting wood, gardeners can assist by leaving rotting tree stumps, or fallen timber in the garden, rather than tidying up or stump-grinding.

Stag Beetle *Lucanus cervus* (body length: male 35–75 mm, female 28–45 mm)
CURRENT STATUS IN THE NEW FOREST: Local
IDENTIFICATION: Unmistakable, Britain's longest beetle, rather bulky; mainly black, with large stag-like mandibles in the male, which have a reddish sheen. The wing covers may be chestnut brown. The larvae are cream, up to 8 cm long with an orange head.
HABITAT: Now mainly in parts of south and south-east England, rarer or extinct elsewhere; also is becoming rarer in mainland Europe and protected in several countries. Adults are usually found in late May to the end of August in gardens, wooded parks and woodland, near decaying tree stumps (apple, elm, lime, beech and oak). The New Forest is one of the strongholds for this species; adults (mainly males) are often attracted to lights at night, or sap. Searching around lights in early morning in areas like Brockenhurst in June may result in the sight of several lying on, or walking on nearby pavements (some injured after collisions with motor vehicles).
NOTE: Although looking rather fearsome, males are quite harmless; the females can, however, give quite a nip if handled. The size of the antlers appears to have little influence on mating success. Males fly to females after dusk, often in numbers, which may result in rarely observed fights between rival males. The antlers are used in these fights, with the winner throwing the loser onto the ground; several efforts may be made before a male has the right to mate with a female. Whilst fighting, they risk another male walking away with the prize. The female lays eggs singly, near rotting wood and the life cycle takes three to four years, the larvae living in the stumps. The female may either die underground after laying its eggs, or around ground level. Noisy in flight, stag beetles are sometimes rather clumsy landing; if they land upside down or topple over, they struggle to right themselves. During the brief time in the adult stage (a few weeks), they are sometimes seen feeding on sap oozing from trees. In European folklore, the stag beetle was a symbol of evil and bad luck; medieval peasants believed they summoned thunderstorms. Vehicles contribute to death of these insects, as well as people accidentally treading on adults on the pavement; other predators include foxes and hedgehogs, also magpies, which eat the abdomen and leave the rest.

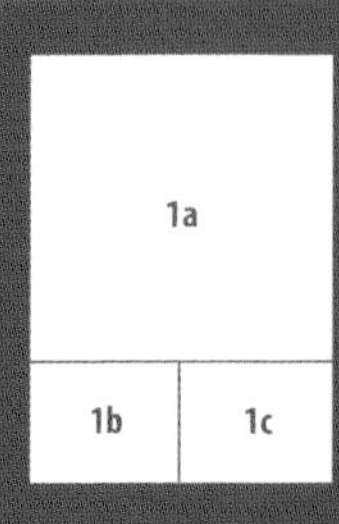

Plates 1a–1c
Stag Beetle
a) male
b) female [GP]
c) female

Lesser Stag Beetle *Dorcus parallelipipedus* (body length: 18–32 mm)
CURRENT STATUS IN THE NEW FOREST: Common
IDENTIFICATION: As implied by the common name, a much smaller, species than it's better known relative, although again males have larger mandibles than females, although only a fraction of the size of *Lucanus cervus*. Both sexes are black.
HABITAT: Widespread and locally common in much of the UK, except Ireland, Scotland and West Wales; also widespread in Europe. Sometimes found in company with *Lucanus cervus*, but known to prefer decaying drier wood, above soil level. In the New Forest may be attracted by lights, or encountered on or near decaying or rotting wood. This species is much more frequently seen in Inclosures and ancient woodland than the Stag Beetle, particularly in July and August, more commonly at night.

Rhinoceros Beetle *Sinodendron cylindricum* (body length: 10–15 mm)
CURRENT STATUS IN THE NEW FOREST: Local
IDENTIFICATION: A much smaller, black species, only the male with a horn-like projection on its head. The common name is not to be confused with the mainly tropical Rhinoceros Beetles in the Scarabaeidae, subfamily Dynastinae.
HABITAT: Widespread and locally common between May to October in parts of the UK, associated with mature woodland, often bores in dead heartwood of beech or oak, also pine. In the New Forest it is seldom noticed, but may be attracted by lights, spotted on or near rotting wood. Unlike the other stag beetles, it is sometimes observed in flight in the daytime. Recorded from Bramshaw, Brinken, Denny, Mark Ash, Parkhill and Sloden Woods, amongst others.

DOR BEETLES – Family Geotrupidae

UK: 7 species
New Forest: 6 species [86%]

The last few segments of the antennae are clubbed. Dor beetles are very efficient dung feeders, well known for their strength in burying food for the larvae and very likely to be encountered whilst walking along woodland rides anywhere in the Forest. Most are likely to be ***Geotrupes stercorarius*** (15-26 mm, common), which is black with a bluish or purple sheen and ridged wingcases. This species is found from April to October but has peaks and lows. The fierce looking glossy black **Minotaur Beetle *Typhaeus typhoeus*** (12–20 mm, local) is essentially a lookalike with horns, which is occasionally seen in most months; the female is equipped with very short horns and this species prefers rabbit droppings. ***Anoplotrupes stercorosus*** (12–19 mm, widespread) is a smaller, smoother, more bluish species. The other dor beetle species ***Geotrupes spiniger*** (16–26 mm, rare), ***Trypocopris pyrenaeus*** (12–20 mm, rare, prefers dung on sandy heaths) and ***Trypocopris vernalis*** (12–20 mm, rare, sandy heaths, prefers fox and sheep dung) are occasionally found in the Forest, but accurate identification requires close examination.

1a		2a	
1b		2b	
3a			3b
4a	4b		5
6	7		8

Plates 1a & 1b
Lesser Stag Beetle
a) male
b) hibernating

Plates 2a & 2b
Rhinoceros Beetle
a) male, showing horn [TM]
b) female [CT]

Plates 3a & 3b
Geotrupes stercorarius

Plates 4a & 4b
Minotaur Beetle
a) male
b) female

Plate 5
Anoplotrupes stercorosus [GP]

Plate 6
Geotrupes spiniger [JW]

Plate 7
Trypocopris pyrenaeus [JW]

Plate 8
Trypocopris vernalis [JW]

SCARAB BEETLES – Family Scarabaeidae

UK: 78 species.
New Forest: at least 45 species [58%]

The last few segments of the antennae are expanded into flaps, which form a club or fan in the chafers. The dung beetles are very efficient dung feeders. Chafers are vegetations, with some species regarded as pests. Dung beetles are very likely to be encountered in the Forest, sometimes settling close by and chafers are seen in gardens. Keen coleopterists (people who study beetles) carefully go through dung to locate species; one of the rarest British species is the **Beaulieu Dung Beetle *Aphodius niger*** (4–5 mm, rare), which is dependent on cattle dung trodden into the water's edge, mainly at Balmer Lawn, Brockenhurst and other temporary pools. Larger species much more likely to be found in the Forest are the two-tone ***Aphodius fimetarius*** (5–8 mm, widespread) and all-black ***Aphodius rufipes*** (9–13 mm, widespread), which feed on dung of large herbivores and are sometimes attracted to moth lights. Some of the chafer beetles are also attracted to light, notably the **Cockchafer *Melolontha melolontha*** (20–30 mm, common), which is large and easily recognised, rather noisy in flight in May to June whilst finding leaves to feed on; the **Summer Chafer *Amphimallon solstitiale*** (15–20 mm, widespread) is a smaller version. This and the **Garden Chafer *Phyllopertha horticola*** (7–12 mm, local) are often seen in gardens, the brown ***Serica brunnea*** (8–10 mm, widespread) in lightly wooded areas. The **Welsh Chafer *Hoplia philanthus*** (8–9 mm, local) is also occasional on flowers. The grubs of chafers feed on roots of grasses and many other plants and sometimes occur in huge numbers, although the life cycle may take up to four years. An attractive sun-loving green species is the **Rose Chafer *Cetonia aurata*** (14–21 mm, common), which is often seen on flowers such as bramble, elderberry, gorse, hogweed and rose, in gardens and throughout the Forest habitats between May to September. The larvae feed in the rotting wood of old stumps and have a little-known association with ants. The author has several times observed adults being carefully transferred to entry points in wood ants nests and it is presumed the larvae help keep the nest clean. The **Noble Chafer *Gnorimus nobilis*** (15–20 mm, very rare) is mainly recorded in the Brockenhurst and Lyndhurst area, usually on elderberry or hogweed flowers in late June to July, invariably flying with Rose Chafers, and sometimes lives for several weeks. The larvae develop in decaying old trees, possibly oak and beech in the Forest, but often in old orchards elsewhere in England, where it has a very restrictive distribution. The **Dune Chafer *Anomala dubia*** (12–15 mm, rare) recorded from Parc Pale in late June, prefers sandy ground. It is also found around sand dunes outside the Forest, for example at Hengistbury Head.

Beaulieu Dung Beetle [CT]

1	2a	2b
3a	3b	4
5	6	7
8a	9a	10a
8b	9b	10b

Plate 1
Aphodius fimetarius

Plates 2a & 2b
Aphodius rufipes
a) adult
b) pupa [CT]

Plates 3a & 3b
Cockchafer
a) adult
b) larva

Plate 4
Summer Chafer [CT]

Plate 5
Garden Chafer

Plate 6
Serica brunnea

Plate 7
Welsh Chafer

Plates 8a & 8b
Rose Chafer
b) being tended by Southern Wood Ants

Plates 9a & 9b
Noble Chafer
b) covered in elderberry pollen

Plates 10a & 10b
Dune Chafer
a) male
b) female

JEWEL BEETLES – Family Buprestidae

UK: 14 species
New Forest: at least 10 species [71%]

Whilst they may fly in sunshine or be spotted on a flower, buprestids are seldom seen at random unless searched for by beating or sweeping; these colourful little jewels have large eyes and are usually metallic. In Asia the wingcases of some species are made into popular jewelry. The larvae are woodborers and can damage trees, including oaks. British species include uncommon species 2.5–19.5 mm long, well represented in the Forest in areas such as Denny and Mallard Woods, also Inclosures. Larvae feed in woody or herbaceous stems, including oak and hawthorn. ***Anthaxia nitidula*** (4.5–7.5 mm, extinct?) has been recorded in Brockenhurst (Balmer Lawn) and Lyndhurst area, but not since 1958 and may now be extinct. It should be looked for on flowers, especially bramble and rose, in woodland clearings between mid May and the end of July. Perhaps it is still found on 'celandine and whitethorn' as reported in the Victoria County History for Hampshire (1900) for 'one of the greatest prizes among the British beetles'. In the Forest, older woods such as Denny, Mallard and Matley should be checked for buprestids, also Inclosures. The metallic dark green or bluish **Oak Jewel Beetle *Agrilus biguttatus*** (9–11 mm, rare) is one of these species, found in May to July.

CLICK BEETLES – Family Elateridae

UK: 73 species
New Forest: at least 38 species [52%]

Slender and often fairly drab beetles with an amazing ability to jump and right themselves, making a clicking sound in the process; it may take more than one flip to land the correct way up. Many species are plain brown or black, or mottled, but some species have attractive orange or red patches. The larvae (wireworms) are liquid feeders, some associated with wood are predators; others feed on roots. Several attractive red and black sun-loving *Ampedus* species are found in the Forest, including ***A. quercicola*** (9–11 mm, widespread), sometimes seen on posts or fences. Stumps or fallen trees attract the conspicuously black-tipped ***A. balteatus*** (7.5–10 mm, widespread). Largely red are ***A. pomonae*** (8–10.5 mm, local) and the larger ***A. cinnabarinus*** (12–14.5 mm, local), whilst ***A. sanguinolentus*** (9–11.5 mm, local) has a black central patch. The smaller ***Calambus bipustulatus*** (6.3–8.5 mm, rare) only has red blotches on the wingcases. Some species are more likely to be seen at night on logs, including ***Aplotarsus incanus*** (7–8.5 mm, widespread), ***Dalopius marginatus*** (6–8 mm, widespread) and one of Britain's longest click beetles, ***Stenagostus rhombeus*** (15–24 mm, widespread).

1		2
3 / 6	4	5
7	8	9
10	11	

Plate 1
Anthaxia nitidula

Plate 2
Oak Jewel Beetle [TP]

Plate 3
Ampedus quercicola

Plate 4
Ampedus balteatus

Plate 5
Ampedus pomonae

Plate 6
Ampedus cinnabarinus

Plate 7
Ampedus sanguinolentus

Plate 8
Calambus bipustulatus

Plate 9
Aplotarsus incanus

Plate 10
Dalopius marginatus

Plate 11
Stenagostus rhombeus

SOLDIER BEETLES – Family Cantharidae

UK: 41 species
New Forest: 32 species [78%]

Cantharids are soft-bodied, brightly coloured species, c.7–13 mm which in the Forest can be abundant in meadows, roadside verges, woodland clearings and rides on angelica, hogweed and other flowers, although they can also eat other insects. The larvae are predators in soil, litter or dead wood. A selection of common Forest species is shown.

GLOW-WORMS – Family Lampyridae

UK: 3 species
New Forest: 1 species [33%]

Large soft-bodied nocturnal beetles, with a wingless female, which emits a yellowish-green light from the end of her abdomen. This attracts the smaller winged males. The larvae feed on snails. The **Glow-worm *Lampyris noctiluca*** (10–20 mm, widespread) is mainly found in June and July. The smaller **Lesser Glow-worm *Phosphaenus hemipterus*** (7–10 mm, only in Forest surrounds) is an extremely rare species, but recorded in the Forest surrounds at Bursledon Nature Reserve near Southampton since 2007.

NET-WINGED BEETLES – Family Lycidae

UK: 4 species
New Forest: at least 1 species [25%]

Bright soft-bodied beetles rare in Britain, with long, thick, serrate antennae. The larvae inhabitat well decayed wood. ***Platycis minutus*** (5–8 mm, local) are found in soft, moist decaying beech and are seldom observed, but when they are, may swarm. They are most likely to be observed at Bolderwood, Denny and Eyeworth Woods and surrounds for a few days in August to September; adults fly to nearby flowers, around tree trunks or logs.

FLAT BEETLES – Family Trogossitidae

UK: 5 species
New Forest: 1 species [20%]

This small group includes the tortoise-like ***Thymalus limbatus*** (5–7 mm, local) which live beneath loose bark on decaying broadleaved timber, particularly oak. They may be found in New Copse Inclosure and elsewhere on felled timber.

CHEQUERED BEETLES – Family Cleridae

UK: 14 species
New Forest: at least 6 species [43%]

Most cleroids are attractive predators, associated with wood. Examples of species seen occasionally are ***Opilo mollis*** (8.5–13 mm, local), predators of *Anobium* beetle larvae and the **Ant Beetle *Thanasimus formicarius*** (7–10 mm, local), a mimic of the wood ant, which predate a wider range of beetles. ***Tillus elongatus*** (6–9 mm, local) usually predate larvae of anobiid beetles, particularly *Ptilinus pectinicornis* in beech.

1 / 2	3	4
5a	5b / 5c	5d / 5e
6a	6b	7
8	9	10

Plate 1
***Cantharis* species (c.10 mm)**

Plate 2
***Cantharis rustica* (11–14 mm)**

Plate 3
***Rhagonycha fulva* (7–10 mm) on hogweed**

Plate 4
***Malthodes marginatus* (4–5 mm)**

Plates 5a–5e
Glow-worm
a) male about to fly
b) male
c) female [CT]
d) female light [RH]
e) larva

Plates 6a & 6b
Platycis minutus
a) mating pair [PMG]

Plate 7
Thymalus limbatus

Plate 8
Opilo mollis [CT]

Plate 9
Ant Beetle

Plate 10
***Tillus elongatus* female**

SOFT-WINGED FLOWER BEETLES – Family Malachiidae

UK: 14 species
New Forest: at least 9 species [64%]

Soft bodied sun loving beetles, often seen on flowers. The **Common Malachite *Malachius bipustulatus*** (5–8 mm, common) is an attractive common green beetle with a conspicuous large red spot at the end of each wingcase. Found in woodland rides and meadows near woodlands in April to July, the larvae are partly predators, in the holes of wood borers, although they also feed on their excreta and larval skins. The Forest is well known as one of the few sites in Britain for the stunning **Scarlet Malachite *Malachius aeneus*** (c.8 mm, rare) recorded at the edge of the Forest in North and South Gorley in grassy areas near thatched cottages, obtaining pollen from grasses or flowers, usually in June; they also eat slow moving invertebrates. The larvae are predators. It is believed that this species prefers old agricultural practices, such as the ecosystem that develops in old straw and hay, similar to changes in thatch. A selection of other Forest species is shown.

LADYBIRDS – Family Coccinellidae

UK: 46 species
New Forest: at least 33 species [72%]

Most British species look like the typical brightly coloured spotted beetles known to practically everyone, varying only in the number of spots and colour. Most are common and variably coloured, overwintering as adults, sometimes in houses or outbuildings. They can spread rapidly, as discovered when the invasive **Harlequin Ladybird *Harmonia axyridis*** (6–8 mm, common) arrived in Britain in 2004; this may impact on numbers of our native species in future, as the Harlequin continues its rapid spread throughout much of Britain and is now the commonest species in the Forest. The aphid-eating ladybirds are well known gardeners friends. Ladybirds occur throughout the Forest. Generalists using a wide range of habitats include the **2-spot Ladybird *Adalia bipunctata*** (3–6 mm, common) and **7-spot Ladybird *Coccinella septempunctata*** (5–8 mm, common) which are amongst the Forest's most frequently seen ladybirds, whereas the rare **Scarce 7-spot Ladybird *Coccinella magnifica*** (6–8 mm, rare) is always close to nests of *Formica* species of ants. A selection of other Forest ladybird species is shown overleaf. These are often found to be common or widespread when specifically searched for in the Forest and surrounding area, mainly associated with the following habitats: deciduous woodlands (page 130, Plates 1–4), heathland (page 130, Plates 5–6, both local species), coniferous woodlands (page 130, Plates 7–9, page 131, Plates 1–3) also grasslands and meadows (page 131, Plates 4–10).

1	2	3
4a	4b	5
6a	6b / 6c	7
8	9a	9b

Plate 1
Common Malachite

Plate 2
Scarlet Malachite

Plate 3
Cordylepherus viridis
(c.6 mm)

Plates 4a & 4b
Anthocomus fasciatus
(3–4 mm)
b) about to fly

Plate 5
Anthocomus rufus
(4–5 mm)

Plates 6a–6c
Harlequin Ladybird
a) adult
b) larva
c) pupa

Plate 7
2-spot Ladybird

Plate 8
7-spot Ladybird
mating pair

Plates 9a & 9b
Scarce 7-spot Ladybird
a) mating pair
b) on Southern Wood Ant's nest [CT]

1	2
3	4
5	6
7a	7b
8	9

Plate 1
10-spot Ladybird
Adalia decempunctata
(3.5–4.5 mm)

Plate 2
Cream-spot Ladybird
Calvia quattuordecimguttata
(4–5 mm)

Plate 3
Orange Ladybird
Halyzia sedecimguttata
(4.5–7 mm)

Plate 4
Kidney-spot Ladybird
Chilocorus renipustulatus
(4–5 mm)

Plate 5
Heather Ladybird
Chilocorus bipustulatus
(3–4 mm)

Plate 6
Hieroglyphic Ladybird
Coccinella hieroglyphica
(4–5 mm) [SR]

Plates 7a & 7b
Eyed Ladybird
Anatis ocellata
(7–9 mm)
b) unusual form

Plate 8
Cream-streaked Ladybird
Harmonia quadripunctata
(5–6 mm)

Plate 9
18-spot Ladybird
Myrrha octodecimguttata
(4–6 mm)

1	2
3	4
5	6
7	8
9	10

Plate 1
Larch Ladybird
Aphidecta obliterata
(4–5 mm)

Plate 2
Pine Ladybird
Exochomus quadripustulatus
(3–5 mm)

Plate 3
Striped Ladybird
Myzia oblongoguttata
(6–8 mm)

Plate 4
Adonis Ladybird
Hippodamia variegata
(4–5 mm)

Plate 5
11-spot Ladybird
Coccinella undecimpunctata
(4–5 mm)

Plate 6
14-spot Ladybird
Propylea quattuordecimpunctata
mating pair (4 mm)

Plate 7
22-spot Ladybird
Psyllobora vigintiduopunctata
(3–4 mm)

Plate 8
24-spot Ladybird
Subcoccinella vigintiquattuorpunctata
(3–4 mm)

Plate 9
Water Ladybird
Anisosticta novemdecimpunctata
(4 mm) [SF]

Plate 10
Rhyzobius litura
(2–2.5 mm)

THICK-LEGGED FLOWER BEETLES – Family Oedemeridae

UK: 10 species
New Forest: 6 species [60%]

Includes the bright green **Swollen-thighed Beetle *Oedemera nobilis*** (8–11 mm, widespread), often seen on flowers in grassland from April to August feeding on pollen of flowers, including bramble, hawthorn, hogweed and ox-eye daisy; the male has thickened hindlegs. The larvae live in hollow plant stems.

OIL BEETLES – Family Meloidae

UK: 10 species, 5 species now extinct
New Forest: at least 4 species, including 3 probably extinct [40%]

Oil beetles are large flightless beetles with short wingcases, which appear to be suffering declines in population. ***Meloe proscarabaeus*** (11–35 mm, very rare) has been recorded from the New Forest, but not seen in recent years. It is, however, found in the surrounding areas, including the Isle of Wight and Hengistbury Head, also Martin Down. This parasitic species has a complex life cycle. The plump female is considerably larger than the male and lays numerous eggs in a burrow near bee colonies. The larvae are known as tringulins, which climb up to reach flowers; the hook-like forelegs attach them to bees. The aim is to be carried by a ground nesting female solitary bee to her nest burrow, where the larva becomes more maggot-like and feeds on the bee's egg and pollen store. It pupates in the burrow and overwinters, hatching the following year into an adult beetle. Adults feed on leaves of buttercup and lesser celandine, amongst others, mainly between late April to July. In defence, adults release a pungent oily liquid. Other species are found in the Forest including an old record from Bank for ***Meloe brevicollis*** (8–20 mm) from 1921. This species was rediscovered in south Devon in 2007. The blister beetle ***Sitaris muralis*** (8–14 mm, very rare) develops in the nests of the bee *Anthophora* and are found in old walls; until this species was rediscovered in Brockenhurst village in August 2010, it was only known from old Forest records, the last in 1947. This is the only record in Britain since 1969, except for two possible sightings in Kent in 2000 and 2001. The bright green **Spanish Fly *Lytta vesicatoria*** (9–21 mm, no longer in the Forest, probably only on the Isle of Wight), is the source of the aphrodisiac cantharidin (Spanish Fly) and was listed as a rare Hampshire species from Ringwood in the Victoria County History (1900). It is a rare migrant to Britain, occasionally breeding; it still occurs and appears to be resident in parts of the Isle of Wight.

Oil beetle larvae (triungulins) attached to a mining bee *Andrena* species [CT]

1a	1b
2a	3a
2b	3b
2c	4

Plates 1a & 1b
Swollen-thighed Beetle
a) male
b) female

Plates 2a–2c
Meloe proscarabaeus
b) at burrow
c) rolling over in efforts to enter burrow

Plates 3a and 3b
Sitaris muralis
a) on old brick wall
b) curls up in defence

Plate 4
Spanish Fly

DARKLING BEETLES – Family Tenebrionidae

UK: 47 species
New Forest: at least 19 species [40%], presumably under recorded

Most likely to be seen is ***Nalassus laevioctostriatus*** (7–11 mm, common). The broad-bodied ***Prionychus ater*** (12–15 mm, local) is a nocturnal species in Denny Wood and elsewhere on black wood mould. ***Pseudocistela ceramboides*** (10–12 mm, local) may be seen on decayed oaks and beech, or at hawthorn flowers. ***Diaperis boleti*** (6–8 mm, rare) develops deep inside large brackets of fungi *Piptoporus betulinus* on birch. ***Opatrum sabulosum*** (7–9 mm, rare) is mainly coastal.

CARDINAL BEETLES – Family Pyrochroidae

UK: 3 species
New Forest: 2 species [67%]

Brightly coloured beetles with comb-like antennae. The **Black-headed Cardinal *Pyrochroa coccinea*** (12–18 mm, local) is easily recognised by its black head and legs and bright red body and is rather conspicuous on flowers or vegetation in woodland rides and hedgerows in the Forest and surrounds between May to July. The **Red-headed Cardinal *Pyrochroa serraticornis*** (10–18 mm, rare, although widespread in surrounds) also has the head red. The larvae of both species feed on other insects beneath the bark of freshly dead broadleaved trees.

FALSE DARKLING BEETLES – Family Melandryidae

UK: 17 species
New Forest: 12 species [71%]

Includes the **Bearded False Darkling Beetle *Melandrya barbata*** (9–12 mm, very rare) found in decaying wood of oak and beech. This species has its stronghold in the Forest but is rarely recorded (for example Whitley Wood, 1990), whereas ***Melandrya caraboides*** (10–15 mm, local) is occasionally seen on logs in localities such as Denny Wood and New Copse Inclosure. Larvae feed on white-rotted heartwood of a wider range of broadleaved trees, particularly ash and beech. ***Phloiotrya vaudoueri*** (6–12 mm, local) is likely to be encountered on pine logs in New Copse Inclosure amongst other localities.

Fresh pine logs, habitat for various nocturnal beetles

1	2
3 / 4 / 5	
6	7
8	9

Plate 1 ***Nalassus laevioctostriatus*** **mating pair**

Plate 2 ***Prionychus ater***

Plate 3 ***Pseudocistela ceramboides***

Plate 4 ***Diaperis boleti*** [TB]

Plate 5 ***Opatrum sabulosum***

Plate 6 **Black-headed Cardinal**

Plate 7 **Red-headed Cardinal**

Plate 8 ***Melandrya caraboides***

Plate 9 ***Phloiotrya vaudoueri***

LONGHORN BEETLES – Family Cerambycidae

UK: 60 species
New Forest: at least 41 species [68%]
The UK total omits a few long extinct species [Duff, 2007]

Named after the long antennae, longhorns have slender bodies and long legs, and are amongst our most attractive insects. They fly well, many at dusk, and some are attracted to lights. If handled, some longhorns stridulate loudly and the larger species have a strong grip. The larvae mostly feed in dead wood and may take several years to mature. Adults vary in size and sometimes in colour or markings. Longhorns are likely to be noticed by the casual observer, as some of the larger, colourful species are readily seen in the daytime, feeding on pollen (whilst other species hardly feed at all), resting or flying around log piles. The Forest is one of the best places in Britain for longhorns and they are best looked for along woodland rides, on or near log piles, in places like Pignal and adjoining Parkhill, also New Copse and Wootton Inclosures, but also readily seen in other woodlands. Old beech stumps such as in Denny Wood can produce a number of longhorns. At night, some species are attracted to lights, or may be found on logs. Following a survey by members, the Southampton Natural History Society Annual Report for 2007 records 25 longhorn species, mainly in the Forest surrounds. Duff (2007) is a useful illustrated guide to species. A selection of species most likely to be seen in the Forest is included below.

Tanner Beetle *Prionus coriarius* (body length: 18–45 mm)

CURRENT STATUS IN THE NEW FOREST: Local
IDENTIFICATION: A large robust black species, broader than other longhorns.
HABITAT: Broadleaved or mixed woodlands and gardens. Adults usually found between July to September, flying around lights or wood. The larvae feed in roots of dead or moribund trees of various species, sometimes conifers. The New Forest is well known for this species which has been recorded from Brockenhurst, Brockishill, Deerleep and Parkhill Inclosures, Ashurst Wood, Bishops Dyke, Ladycross and Roydon Woods amongst others and is probably quite widespread, being attracted to lights. Also occasionally reported from the Forest surrounds. A very local species in southern England and Wales.

Black-spotted Longhorn Beetle *Rhagium mordax*
(body length: 13–23 mm)

CURRENT STATUS IN THE NEW FOREST: Widespread
IDENTIFICATION: Black, finely mottled with light brown; antennae rather short. Wingcases with large black marks, edged with buff.
HABITAT: Adults are found in woodlands, most often between April to June, either visiting flowers or around dead wood and logs; oak is often preferred for the larvae. A walk through Inclosures or open Forest during May should result in specimens seen on hawthorn blossom, on or under bark. Widespread throughout the Forest, the Isle of Wight and much of Britain. Also recorded from Ireland.

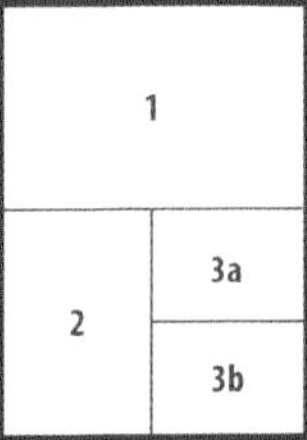

1	
2	3a
	3b

Plate 1
Golden-haired Longhorn Beetle female, which has attracted two males

Plate 2
Tanner Beetle [GP]

Plates 3a & 3b
Black-spotted Longhorn Beetle
b) burrow [CT]

1a | 1b
2 | 3 | 4

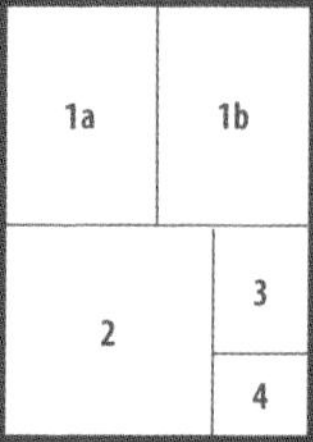

Plates 1a & 1b
Two-banded Longhorn Beetle
a) mating pair
b) aberration, with bands merged

Plate 2
Variable Longhorn Beetle

Plate 3
Common Grammoptera

Plate 4
Burnt-tip Grammoptera

Two-banded Longhorn Beetle *Rhagium bifasciatum*

(body length: 12–22 mm)

CURRENT STATUS IN THE NEW FOREST: Widespread

IDENTIFICATION: Similar to *R. mordax*, but dark brown with a pair of conspicuous oblique buff-coloured bands on the wingcases; the antennae are also longer than in *R. mordax.*

HABITAT: Adults are found in woodlands, most often between April to June, around dead wood, logs and posts; Scots pine is often preferred for the larvae, but the dead wood of various deciduous and coniferous trees are used. Widespread throughout the Forest, and much of Britain, although very local in central England and East Anglia. Recorded from the Isle of Wight, also from Ireland.

Variable Longhorn Beetle *Stenocorus meridianus*

(body length: 15–27 mm)

CURRENT STATUS IN THE NEW FOREST: Widespread

IDENTIFICATION: Black, sometimes brown, reddish or yellowish in part. The pronotum has a distinct central groove.

HABITAT: Adults are usually found in or around broadleaved woodlands between May to August, when they visit flowers. The larvae live underground in dead roots of various broadleaved trees. Occasional in the Forest but widespread, recorded from Brinken Wood, Crockford Bridge, Denny Wood, Roydon Woods and Wootton Coppice Inclosure amongst others. Widespread in southern England (including the Isle of Wight) and Wales, becoming very local further north; absent in Scotland.

Common Grammoptera *Grammoptera ruficornis*

(body length: 3–7 mm)

CURRENT STATUS IN THE NEW FOREST: Common

IDENTIFICATION: A small, mainly black species.

HABITAT: Adults are usually found in woodlands between April to July, visiting flowers, particularly hawthorn. The larvae feed on fungus-infected small branches of various broadleaved trees. One of the commonest longhorns in the Forest, recorded from Brinken, Denny, Eyeworth, Parkhill and Roydon Woods, also Holmsley, Pondhead and Sloden Inclosures, Warwick Slade and many others. Widespread in the Forest surrounds, including the Isle of Wight, throughout England and Wales, local in southern Scotland. Also recorded from Ireland.

Burnt-tip Grammoptera *Grammoptera ustulata*

(body length: 5–9 mm)

CURRENT STATUS IN THE NEW FOREST: Local

IDENTIFICATION: A small species, covered in a fine, short golden pubescence, except for a black tip to the wingcases.

HABITAT: Adults are found in pasture woodlands between April to August, visiting flowers, including hawthorn. Best looked for in the Forest in June, recorded from Brinken, Denny and Matley Woods, Mark Ash, Sway and others. A very local species in England and Wales, also recorded from Ireland.

1	
2a	3
2b	4

Plate 1
Four-banded Longhorn Beetle mating pair [GP]

Plates 2a & 2b
Golden-haired Longhorn Beetle
a) egglaying female
b) red form

Plate 3
Large Black Longhorn Beetle

Plate 4
Tawny Longhorn Beetle mating pair

Four-banded Longhorn Beetle *Leptura quadrifasciata*

(body length: 10–20 mm)
CURRENT STATUS IN THE NEW FOREST: Local
IDENTIFICATION: Black, with four attractive wavy yellow bands on the wingcases.
HABITAT: Adults are found in woodlands between May to September, visiting flowers. Associated with dead wood of various broadleaved trees, particularly birch. In the Forest, recorded from Denny and Wootton Coppice Inclosures, but likely to be much more widespread, as the species is distributed throughout Britain. In the Forest surrounds, reported from Lower Test, but it appears to be absent from the Isle of Wight. Also recorded from Ireland.

Golden-haired Longhorn Beetle *Leptura aurulenta*

(body length: 12–25 mm)
CURRENT STATUS IN THE NEW FOREST: Local
IDENTIFICATION: Black, with four attractive wavy yellow (sometimes reddish) bands on the wingcases, but unlike the similar *L. quadrifasciata*, there are golden yellow hairs on the front and back of the pronotum; also the legs are reddish black.
HABITAT: Adults are found in broadleaved and pasture woodlands between June to August, visiting flowers, but most likely to be observed on or near log piles, particularly oak, where one can watch females ovipositing. In the Forest recorded from Denny and Mallard Woods, also Churchplace, Hawkhill, Lodgehill, New Copse, Parkhill and Pignal Inclosures, Clay Hill Heath and Parc Pale. Local in southern parts of Cornwall/south Devon and Hampshire/West Sussex. Not recorded in the Isle of Wight, nor Forest surrounds.

Large Black Longhorn Beetle *Stictoleptura scutellata*

(body length: 12–20 mm)
CURRENT STATUS IN THE NEW FOREST: Widespread
IDENTIFICATION: Almost all-black, sometimes with a yellow mark between the wingcases.
HABITAT: Adults are found in broadleaved and pasture woodlands between June to August, visiting flowering hawthorn, but also observed on or near log piles, particularly beech. In the Forest well distributed and occasionally recorded from Denny, Eyeworth, Roydon and Whitley Woods, Balmer Lawn, Beaulieu Heath, Knightwood Oak, Lyndhurst area, also Lodgehill, New Copse, Parkhill and Vinney Ridge Inclosures. Local in central and south-east England and south-east Wales.

Tawny Longhorn Beetle *Paracorymbia fulva* (body length: 9–14 mm)

CURRENT STATUS IN THE NEW FOREST: Very rare
IDENTIFICATION: Black except for black-tipped yellowish-brown wingcases.
HABITAT: Adults are found in broadleaved woodlands from June to August, visiting flowers. In the Forest recorded from Mallard Wood in 1969 and Fordingbridge in 2009. Also recorded just outside the Forest at Lower Test Reserve, this very local species is found in few locations in central and southern England, the mating pair photographed at Stockbridge Down.

Six-spotted Longhorn Beetle *Anoplodera sexguttata*
(body length: 7–12 mm)
CURRENT STATUS IN THE NEW FOREST: Local
IDENTIFICATION: Attractive black species with three yellow spots on each wingcase, the spots sometimes fused.
HABITAT: Adults are found in broadleaved woodlands between May to July, visiting flowers; they may only appear for a few days in the season, but can be numerous. Larvae feed in dead wood of deciduous trees, particularly beech and oak. In the Forest recorded from Brinken, Denny, Hollands, Mallard and Whitley Woods, Balmer Lawn, Crockford Bridge, Matley Bog, also Furzy Lawn, Pondhead, Poundhill and Vinney Ridge Inclosures. Could be regarded as common as well over 100 may be found in some sites, except it appears to be absent in some well known Inclosures, although because of its short appearance in the adult stage, it may be overlooked. The New Forest is a stronghold for this species, which is very local in eastern and southern England.

Tobacco-coloured Longhorn Beetle *Alosterna tabacicolor*
(body length: 6–10 mm)
CURRENT STATUS IN THE NEW FOREST: Widespread
IDENTIFICATION: A small, narrow species. Head, thorax, tarsi and much of antennae black; tip of antennae, most of femora and tibiae and wingcases brownish yellow.
HABITAT: Adults are found in woodlands between April to August, visiting flowers. Feed in damp rotten wood and branches of various broadleaved and coniferous trees. In the Forest, recorded from Bramshaw, Crockford, Denny and Eyeworth Woods, Exbury Gardens, Holmsley Bog, also Parkhill, Pondhead and Sloden Inclosures, amongst others. Widespread in southern England (but apparently not recorded in the Isle of Wight) and Wales, local in northern England and southern Scotland. Also recorded from Ireland.

Fairy-ring Longhorn Beetle *Pseudovadonia livida*
(body length: 5–9 mm)
CURRENT STATUS IN THE NEW FOREST: Local
IDENTIFICATION: Small, broad black species with yellowish brown wingcases.
HABITAT: Adults are found in grassland between May to September, visiting flowers. Larvae feed in soil infested by the fairy-ring fungus. In the Forest, recorded from Keyhaven Marshes but this species is likely to be much more widespread. There are several records in the Forest surrounds, including Barton-on-Sea, Lower Test, the Southampton area and Southbourne. A local species in central and southern England, mainly coastal in south-west England. Also recorded from Ireland.

Black-and-yellow Longhorn Beetle *Rutpela maculata*
(body length: 13–20 mm)
CURRENT STATUS IN THE NEW FOREST: Common
IDENTIFICATION: Large and elongate, rather variable but usually the bright yellow wingcases have four black bands, some broken.
HABITAT: Adults are found in woodlands between May to September, visiting flowers, particularly bramble. Larvae feed in damp rotting wood of various broadleaved trees, particularly birch, or pine. In the Forest and surrounds, widespread and probably the commonest longhorn, found in most Inclosures and other woods. This species is widespread throughout England and Wales, local in south-west Scotland. Also recorded from Ireland.

1	4a
2	4b
3	

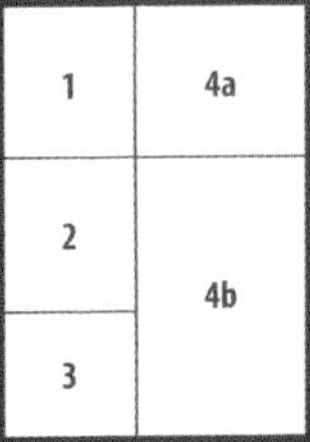

Plate 1
Six-spotted Longhorn Beetle

Plate 2
Tobacco-coloured Longhorn Beetle

Plate 3
Fairy-ring Longhorn Beetle

Plates 4a & 4b
Black-and-yellow Longhorn Beetle
b) extreme colour form

Black-striped Longhorn Beetle *Stenurella melanura*
(body length: 6–10 mm)
CURRENT STATUS IN THE NEW FOREST: Common
IDENTIFICATION: Small and slender, black with brownish yellow, black-tipped wingcases.
HABITAT: Adults are found in woodlands between May to September, visiting flowers, particularly bramble. Larvae feed in moist, decaying wood close to the ground, or bases of tree stumps. In and around the Forest, widespread and rivals *Ruptela maculata* for status of commonest longhorn; found in most Inclosures and other woods. This species is widespread in southern England, local in central to northern England and Wales. Also recorded from Ireland.

Pine-stump Borer *Asemum striatum* (body length: 8–23 mm)
CURRENT STATUS IN THE NEW FOREST: Local
IDENTIFICATION: Large, robust dark brown species with short antennae.
HABITAT: The mainly nocturnal adults are found in coniferous woodlands mainly in May to September and are associated with dead wood of various conifers. They sometimes fly in warm sunshine. In the Forest, recorded recently from Millyford Bridge, Rakes Brakes Bottom and Tantany Wood and likely to be much more widespread, with numerous pre-1960 records in the literature. Also occasional in the Forest surrounds, including the Isle of Wight. Native in northern Scotland, but now spread into conifer plantations throughout Britain. Also recorded from Ireland.

Dusky Longhorn Beetle *Arhopalus rusticus* (body length: 10–30 mm)
CURRENT STATUS IN THE NEW FOREST: Local
IDENTIFICATION: Large, rather plain dark brown species.
HABITAT: The mainly nocturnal adults are found in coniferous woodlands mainly in July and August and are associated with dead wood of various conifers. In the Forest, recorded from Bramshaw Wood, Exbury Gardens, New Copse and Wootton Coppice Inclosures, also occasional in the Forest surrounds and the Isle of Wight, but likely to be much more widespread. Native in central Scotland, local in coniferous plantations in mainly south-east England and Wales. This species is attracted to light.

Musk Beetle *Aromia moschata* (body length: 13–35 mm)
CURRENT STATUS IN THE NEW FOREST: Local
IDENTIFICATION: Large, stunning metallic green or sometimes bluish species.
HABITAT: Adults are found in wet areas between May to September, visiting flowers such as hogweed and meadowsweet. Larvae live in young, healthy wood of willows and sallows. In the Forest recorded from Ferny Crofts, Holmsley, Warwick Slade, also Wootton Coppice Inclosure. Seldom found in the Forest surrounds, this is a local species in England, Wales and south-west Scotland. Also recorded from Ireland.

1	3
2	
4	

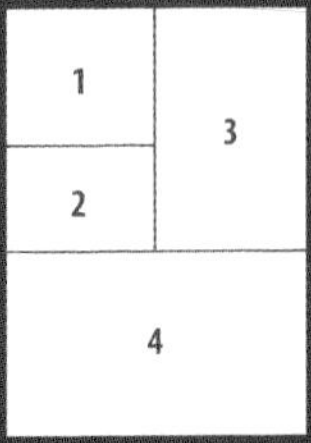

Plate 1
Black-striped Longhorn Beetle

Plate 2
Pine-stump Borer [TP]

Plate 3
Dusky Longhorn Beetle

Plate 4
Musk Beetle

Tanbark Borer *Phymatodes testaceus* (body length: 6–18 mm)
CURRENT STATUS IN THE NEW FOREST: Local
IDENTIFICATION: A broad species often black or slightly bluish black with a reddish pronotum, but can be rather variable.
HABITAT: Adults are found in woodlands between May to July and at night can be attracted to lights or seen on log piles. Associated with dead wood of various trees, including oak and pine. In the Forest, recorded from New Copse and Park Ground Inclosures, Ladycross and Millyford Bridge. This species is widespread in the Forest surrounds and with a scattered distribution throughout much of England and Wales, although is very local towards southern Scotland.

Wasp Beetle *Clytus arietis* (body length: 6–15 mm)
CURRENT STATUS IN THE NEW FOREST: Widespread
IDENTIFICATION: An attractive black and yellow patterned species with a superficial resemblance to a wasp.
HABITAT: Adults are found in woodlands between May to July, visiting flowers, or resting on or near log piles. Associated with dead wood of various trees. In the Forest, recorded from well known beetle sites such as Bramshaw, Brinken and Denny Woods, New Copse, Parkhill and Sloden Inclosures, also Warwick Slade. This species is widespread in the Forest surrounds, including Southampton area and the Isle of White and distributed throughout England and Wales, although local in Scotland. Also recorded from Ireland.

Rufous-shouldered Longhorn Beetle *Anaglyptus mysticus*
(body length: 8–15 mm)
CURRENT STATUS IN THE NEW FOREST: Widespread
IDENTIFICATION: Mostly black with beautiful markings on the wingcases, the upper half reddish; the tip has a grey pubescence.
HABITAT: Adults are found in woodlands between April to June, visiting flowers such as hawthorn. Associated with compact dead wood of various broadleaved trees. In the Forest, recorded from Ashurst, Brinken, Denny, Gibbet, Mallard, Matley, Pinnick and Whitley Woods, Balmer Lawn, Bramshaw, Warwick Slade and Pignal Inclosure, amongst others. However, it appears to be absent from the Forest surrounds. Widespread in England (except north) and Wales.

White-clouded Longhorn Beetle *Mesosa nebulosa*
(body length: 9–16 mm)
CURRENT STATUS IN THE NEW FOREST: Rare
IDENTIFICATION: Robust and stocky, attractively marked with yellowish-brown, white and blackish markings. The wingcases have irregular deep punctures.
HABITAT: Adults are found in woodlands between April to August and are seldom seen, possibly remaining high up much of the time. Larvae feed in rotten branches of various broadleaved trees, particularly oak. In the Forest, recorded from Bramshaw, Denny and Mallard Woods, also Holmsley, New Copse (photographed at night on a log) and Pondhead Inclosures. Could easily be overlooked and may be fairly widespread, they have been found on flowers or beaten from vegetation in the daytime. Not recorded from the Forest's immediate surrounds. This is a local species in southern England and south Wales.

1a	2
	3
1b	
	4

Plates 1a & 1b
Tanbark Borer
a) female, black form
b) female, brown form

Plate 2
Wasp Beetle

Plate 3
Rufous-shouldered Longhorn Beetle

Plate 4
White-clouded Longhorn Beetle

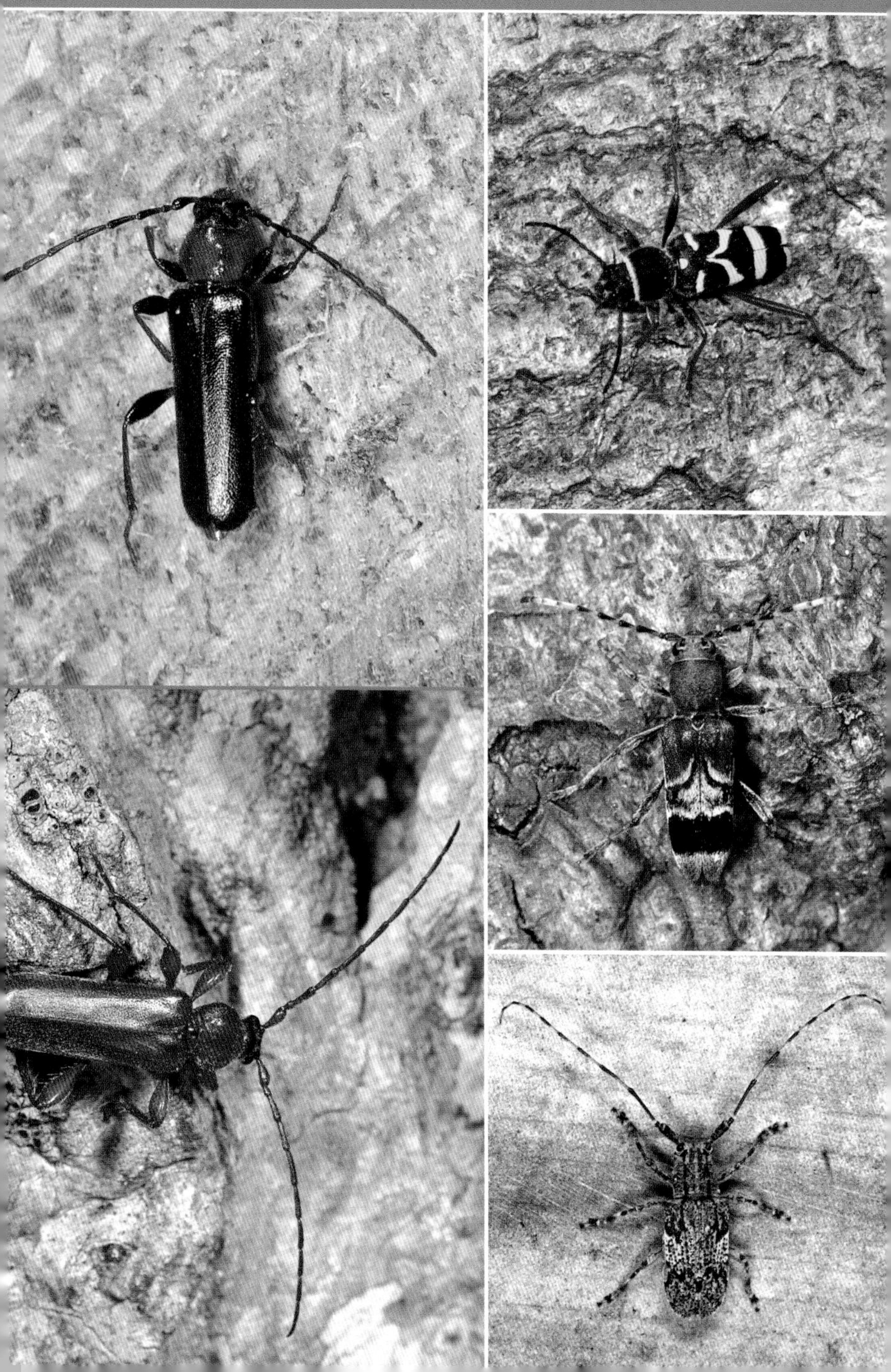

Greater Thorn-tipped Longhorn Beetle *Pogonocherus hispidulus*
(body length: 5–8 mm)
CURRENT STATUS IN THE NEW FOREST: Widespread
IDENTIFICATION: Small, broad species rather like a bird dropping with brown and white wingcases.
HABITAT: Adults are found in woodlands between April to June, sometimes also in autumn. Larvae feed in dead twigs of various broadleaved trees. In the Forest, recorded from Bramshaw, Mark Ash and Matley Woods, also Burley Old, Holmhill and Holmsley Inclosures, amongst others. Recorded from the Forest surrounds, including the Isle of Wight. Fairly widespread in Britain, except for north-west Scotland. Also recorded from Ireland.

Lesser Thorn-tipped Longhorn Beetle *Pogonocherus hispidus*
(body length: 4–6 mm)
CURRENT STATUS IN THE NEW FOREST: Widespread
IDENTIFICATION: Possibly a little smaller than *P. hispidulus*, very similar, but always distinguishable from it by the black area between the wingcases (checked with a 10x lens).
HABITAT: Adults are found in woodlands and hedgerows between April to June, sometimes also in autumn. Larvae feed in dead twigs of various broadleaved trees and shrubs, often apple, holly, ivy and pear. In the Forest, recorded from Bramshaw, Mark Ash and Pinnick Woods, Crockford Bridge, Half Moon Common, Highland Water and Warwick Slade, also Holmhill, Holmsley and Sloden Inclosures, amongst others. Recorded from the Forest surrounds, including the Isle of Wight. Fairly widespread throughout England and Wales. Also recorded from Ireland.

Black-clouded Longhorn Beetle *Leiopus nebulosus*
(body length: 6–10 mm)
CURRENT STATUS IN THE NEW FOREST: Widespread
IDENTIFICATION: A small, broad, brown species with brownish grey pubescence, some black and whitish areas.
HABITAT: Adults are found in woodlands between April to August. Larvae feed under the bark and in outer sapwood in dead branches of various broadleaved and occasionally coniferous trees. In the Forest, recorded from Bramshaw, Denny, Mallard, Mark Ash, Pinnick and Roydon Woods, also Churchplace, Deerleep, Parkhill and Sloden Inclosures, amongst others. Widely recorded from the Forest surrounds, including Hamble, Southampton area and the Isle of Wight. Widespread throughout England and Wales, becoming local in the north and Scotland. Also recorded from Ireland.

Plum Longhorn Beetle *Tetrops praeustus* (body length: 3–6 mm)
CURRENT STATUS IN THE NEW FOREST: Widespread
IDENTIFICATION: Small, with the eyes divided into two sections. Black with yellowish legs and wingcases.
HABITAT: Adults are found in woodlands between April to July. Larvae feed in dead or dying branches of various broadleaved trees and shrubs, often members of the rose family. In the Forest, recorded from Bramshaw, Eyeworth, Mark Ash, Pinnick and Whitley Woods, Crockford Bridge and Matley Bog, also Holmsley and Pignal Inclosures, amongst others, also the Forest surrounds, Bournemouth area, Southampton area and Isle of Wight. Widespread in England and Wales, except the far west. Also recorded from Ireland.

1	2
3	4
5	

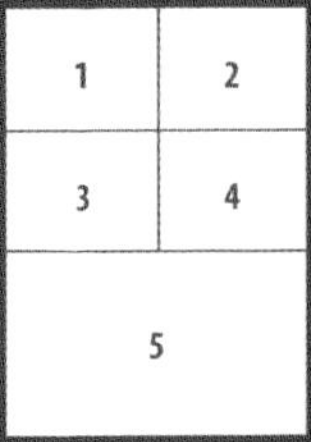

Plate 1
Greater Thorn-tipped Longhorn Beetle, cleaning antennae

Plate 2
Lesser Thorn-tipped Longhorn Beetle

Plate 3
Black-clouded Longhorn Beetle [TP]

Plate 4
Plum Longhorn Beetle

Plate 5
Golden-bloomed Grey Longhorn Beetle *Agapanthia villosoviridescens* (10–22 mm), one to look out for outside the Forest i.e., Martin Down [MPi]

LEAF BEETLES – Family Chrysomelidae

UK: 269 species
New Forest: at least 185 species [69%]

A large family of mainly smooth and shiny rounded leaf-eating beetles, some with stunning colours. Most likely to be seen in the Forest are various ***Donacia* species** (c.5–13 mm, mainly widespread) on water reeds or other aquatic vegetation, the **Green Dock Beetle *Gastrophysa viridula*** (4–8 mm, common) in damp areas in May to August where dock is present; the similar metallic green **Mint Leaf Beetle *Chrysolina herbacea*** (7–11 mm, widespread) on water mint, often found by Forest streams from May to September where the green glint catches the eye, which may be present with ***Chrysolina polita*** (c.6–9 mm, local), which has reddish or chestnut wingcases. ***Chrysolina banksi*** (6–12 mm, local) is metallic bronze, found on roadside verges and waste ground on black horehound, particularly plentiful in the Forest surrounds on the coast. ***Chrysolina oricalcia*** (6–8 mm, local) is found on various umbellifers. The striped **Rosemary Beetle *Chrysolina americana*** (6–8 mm, rare, local in surrounds) is usually found in parks and gardens feeding on rosemary and lavenders and appears to be spreading, particularly in the Forest surrounds, including the Isle of Wight and Southampton area. Not recorded from the Forest, but worth looking for, is the stunning ***Chrysolina violacea*** (c.10 mm, not in the Forest) photographed at Martin Down and probably under recorded. **Cereal Leaf Beetle *Oulema melanopus*** (4–5 mm, widespread) occurs in grassy areas, the larvae known to damage cereal crops, whilst the vivid red **Lily beetle *Lilioceris lilii*** (6–8 mm, widespread), is often a garden pest. The **Asparagus Beetle *Crioceris asparagi*** (5–6 mm, local) is one of our most colourful species, always associated with asparagus. Well represented, but needing to be carefully searched for, are the meadow loving, well camouflaged tortoise beetles. The **Green Tortoise Beetle *Cassida viridis*** (7–10 mm, local) is sometimes found with *Chrysolina herbacea* between June to September, there are several tortoise beetles recorded in the Forest on various plants, including the stunning mainly coastal ***Cassida nobilis*** (4–6 mm, rare). ***Cassida murraea*** (6–9 mm, local) have black spots on a green background in less mature specimens, developing to reddish-orange. They feed on common fleabane and marsh thistle in damp habitats. The **Bloody-nosed Beetle *Timarcha tenebricosa*** (10–20 mm, rare) is Britain's largest leaf beetle, a flightless dark bluish black species which feeds on bedstraw and defends itself when disturbed by exuding a red fluid from its mouth. It has a conspicuous walk and although uncommon within the Forest boundary (most likely at Badminston Common), it is common in the surrounds, including Barton-on-Sea, Hengistbury Head and the Isle of Wight. The **Small Bloody-nosed Beetle *Timarcha goettingensis*** (8–11 mm, rare) is also occasionally recorded in the Forest, for example near Lyndhurst, but more widespread in the Forest surrounds. The attractive bright red ***Chrysomela populi*** (10–12 mm, widespread) is found in May to August. The small, sometimes brightly coloured flea beetles such as the small ***Aphthona* species**, are also common; they are good jumpers. ***Cryptocephalus fulvus*** (2–3 mm, widespread) is often found on sheep's sorrel. ***Galeruca tanaceti*** (6–11 mm, local) may occasionally be seen on a range of plants in open habitats, including at Hurst Spit and the **Heather Beetle *Lochmaea suturalis*** (4–6 mm, common) is sometimes abundant on heather. ***Gonioctena viminalis*** (5–7 mm, widespread) is usually found on willows and poplars.

Leaf beetle Plates are continued overleaf.

1	2	3
4		5
6	7	8
9	10	11
12	13	14

Plate 1
***Donacia crassipes* (9–13 mm)**

Plate 2
***Donacia marginata* pair (8–11 mm)** [GP]

Plate 3
***Donacia simplex* (7–8 mm)**

Plate 4
***Donacia versicolorea* (6–10 mm)**

Plate 5
***Donacia vulgaris* (6–8 mm)**

Plate 6
Green Dock Beetle mating pair

Plate 7
Mint Leaf Beetle mating pair

Plate 8
***Chrysolina polita* mating pair**

Plate 9
Chrysolina banksi

Plate 10
Chrysolina oricalcia [GP]

Plate 11
Rosemary Beetle

Plate 12
Chrysolina violacea

Plate 13
***Chrysolina hyperici* (5–7 mm)**

Plate 14
***Chrysolina brunsvicensis* (5–6 mm)**

Plate 1
Cereal Leaf Beetle [GP]

Plate 2
Lily Beetle feeding [GP]

Plate 3
Asparagus Beetle

Plate 4
Green Tortoise Beetle

Plate 5
Cassida nobilis [CT]
normally found inland, often on chalk, is difficult to distinguish from the similar *C. vittata*, associated with coastal habitats, including saltmarsh

Plates 6a–6c
Cassida murraea
a) green form
b) red form
c) larva

Plate 7
Cassida flaveola
(4–6 mm) [CT]

Plate 8
Cassida rubiginosa
(6–8 mm)

Plate 9
Cassida vibex
(6–7 mm)

1	
2	3
4	5
6	7

Plate 1
Bloody-nosed Beetle

Plate 2
Small Bloody-nosed Beetle

Plate 3
Chrysomela populi [GP]

Plate 4
Cryptocephalus fulvus

Plate 5
Galeruca tanaceti [SF]

Plate 6
Heather Beetle

Plate 7
Gonioctena viminalis

WEEVILS

Family Curculionidae

UK: 475 species
New Forest: estimated 305 species [65%]

Another large family of mainly small, vegetarian beetles with a characteristic beak or rostrum, taken to an extreme in some species, such as the **Acorn Weevil *Curculio glandium*** (4–8 mm, widespread), often found in the Forest on oaks between April to July. The related **Nut Weevil *Curculio nucum*** (6–9 mm, common) prefers hazel. The Forest is a good hunting ground for rare ***Bagous*** species (c.3 mm): ***B. czwalinai*** has only been associated with sphagnum bogs in the Forest, in places like Crockford, ***B. frit*** in wet heathland or ponds and ***B. brevis*** in several ponds, including Balmer Lawn, where it is associated with submerged lesser spearwort. Other common Forest species include ***Cionus scrophulariae*** (4–5 mm), the **Vine Weevil *Otiorhynchus sulcatus*** (7–10 mm) known as a pest to gardeners and **Pine Weevil *Hylobius abietis*** (8–14 mm), associated with coniferous woodlands. The larvae live in dead stumps and adults often seen on log piles. A small selection of other local Forest species is shown. The **Hazel Leaf-roller Weevil *Apoderus coryli*** (6–8 mm, local) [Family Attelabidae] is found in May to July on hazel and is easily recognised by its black head and narrow neck.

Family Anthribidae

UK: 9 species
New Forest: at least 2 species [22%]

Although apparently not recorded in the Forest, one of the most stunning British weevils is the **Cramp-ball Fungus Weevil *Platyrhinus resinosus*** (8–13 mm), which breeds in fungi on dead trees, particularly ash, and has been recorded in Dorset and may have been overlooked in the area.

Various other beetles

A small selection of other species associated with logs or bark is shown: ***Pediacus dermestoides*** [Cucujidae] (4 mm, local) under bark of deciduous timber, ***Glischrochilus quadriguttatus*** [Nitidulidae] (5–8 mm, local) feeds on fermenting sap of broadleaved trees and conifers. The **Powderpost Beetle *Lyctus brunneus*** [Bostrichidae] (2.5–4 mm, rare), ***Platypus cylindrus*** [Platypodidae] (5–5.5 mm, local), ***Triplax russica*** [Erotylidae] (5–7 mm, local), ***Tomoxia bucephala*** [Mordellidae] (5–8.5 mm, rare) and ***Lymexylon navale*** [Lymexylidae] (7–13 mm, rare) are illustrated, along with the ladybird lookalike ***Endomychus coccineus*** [Endomychidae] (4–6 mm, local), which lives on or near fungoid growth under bark of dead timber. The **Pill Beetle *Byrrhus pilula*** [Byrrhidae] (7.5–11 mm, common) can be found walking around, particularly in spring, as well as under stones or around heather, moss and leaf litter, including sandy areas. When disturbed they feign death by tucking antennae and legs underneath the body, to resemble a large seed.

1	2	3
4	5	6
7	8	9
10	11	12
13	14	15
16	17	18

Plate 1
Acorn Weevil

Plate 2
Nut Weevil

Plate 3
***Neliocarus sus* (4–6 mm**

Plate 4
Green Nettle Weevil
Phyllobius pomaceus
(7–10 mm)

Plate 5
Vine Weevil

Plate 6
Pine Weevil

Plate 7
Liparus coronatus
(8–12 mm) [in Forest surrounds, including Martin Down]

Plate 8
Hazel Leaf-roller Weevil
[SF]

Plate 9
Cramp-ball Fungus Weevil [CT]

Plate 10
Pediacus dermestoides

Plate 11
Glischrochilus quadriguttatus

Plate 12
Powderpost Beetle

Plate 13
Platypus cylindrus

Plate 14
Triplax russica

Plate 15
Tomoxia bucephala

Plate 16
Lymexylon navale

Plate 17
Endomychus coccineus

Plate 18
Pill Beetle

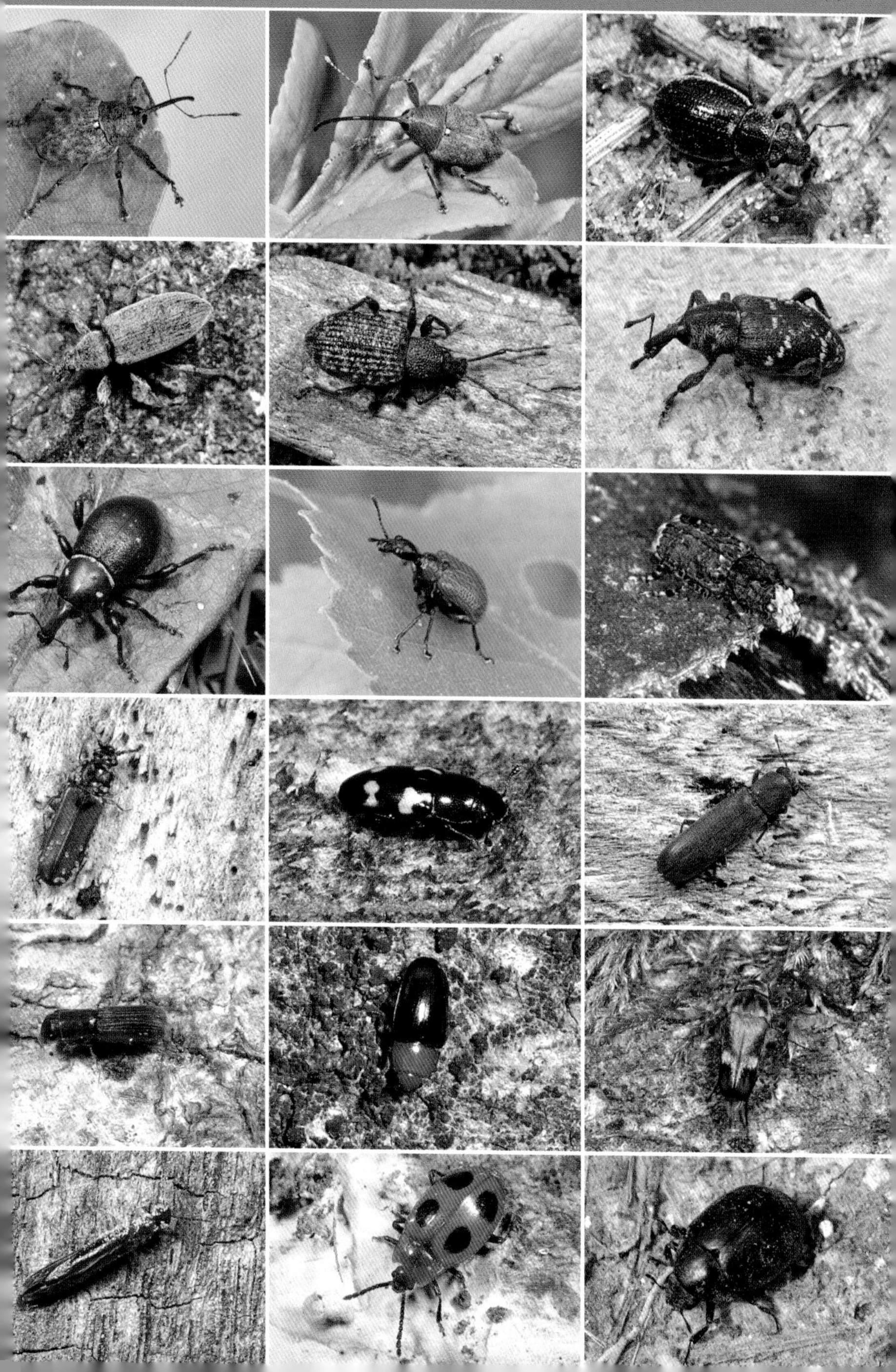

STYLOPS [also known as TWISTED-WINGED PARASITES] – Order STREPSIPTERA

UK: c. 20 species
New Forest: estimated 12 species [60%]

A group of small internal parasites of aculeate Hymenoptera (mainly bees and wasps) or Homoptera (planthoppers). Male adults do not live long, but may be encountered in flight; they have conspicuous large hindwings, but tiny drum-stick forewings. In contast, females are grub-like, remaining in the host. There is an incomplete life cycle: egg, larva and adult. Larvae rest on flowers visited by the host. An estimated number of species is given for the New Forest, based on the rich host fauna.

SCORPIONFLIES – Order MECOPTERA

UK: 4 species
New Forest: at least 2 species [50%]

Easy to recognise by their long, download pointing beak and, in some species, the male has the genital area swollen and held over its body like a scorpion's tail, hence the common name. They are unable to sting, but if handled will pretend to sting. There are three look-alike winged ***Panorpa*** species (10–15 mm), also the under-recorded wingless snow-flea, active in winter where it becomes conspicuous on lying snow on moors and heathland. There is a complete life cycle: egg, larva, pupa and adult. The winged scorpion flies are common in rough grassland and woodland margins, where they feed on small invertebrates; two species are common in the Forest: ***Panorpa communis*** and ***Panorpa germanica***. A third scorpion fly ***Panorpa cognata*** has been recorded in the immediate Forest surrounds.

CADDISFLIES – Order TRICHOPTERA

UK: 198 species
New Forest: estimated 99 species [50%]

Trichoptera means 'hairy winged' and are a large group of freshwater insects, often drab and rather moth-like (forewing length 3–28 mm), with wings held over the back. Antennae are long. Many are nocturnal, but some day fliers are often seen swarming around lakes, ponds or streams with aquatic or marginal vegetation. There is a complete life cycle: egg, larva, pupa and adult. Nearly all species have aquatic larvae, which have jaws for biting and chewing, most living in transportable cases. Adult caddisflies are usually on or near waterside vegetation, and are attracted to lights, in some cases well away from water. Whilst some species only live a few days and rarely feed, others including ***Glyphotaelius*** exploit temporary pools, ditches and marshes that dry up over summer, living as adults from spring until autumn, feeding on nectar of umbellifers and other flowers. Several common Forest species are illustrated.

1	2a	2b
3	4	
5	6a	
	6b	
7	8	

Plate 1
A stylopid female parasite on the mining bee *Andrena scotica* [CT]

Plates 2a & 2b
Panorpa germanica
a) male [SF]
b) female

Plate 3
Brown Sedge
Anabolia nervosa
(forewing length 11–15 mm)

Plate 4
Brown Silverhorn
Athripsodes albifrons
(forewing length 8–9 mm)

Plate 5
Limnephilus sparsus
(forewing length c.13 mm)

Plates 6a & 6b
Mottled Sedge
Glyphotaelius pellucidus
(forewing length 13–17 mm)
a) male
b) female

Plate 7
Caperer
Halesus radiatus
(forewing length c.18 mm)

Plate 8
Silver or Grey Sedge
Odontocerum albicorne
(forewing length 13–17 mm)

BUTTERFLIES and MOTHS – Order LEPIDOPTERA

UK: 2,560 species (in Hampshire 2051 species [80%])
New Forest: at least 1,508 species [59%], but a conservative estimate for the poorly recorded micro moths results in c. 1,700 species overall [66%]

This group of insects range from 2–135 mm in wingspan in Britain and have two pairs of wings in adults, usually covered in scales. The adult mouthparts are adapted into a slender proboscis (tongue) for feeding on nectar, coiled up under the head when not in use. One of the commonest questions asked is 'What is the difference between butterflies and moths.' Many moths are nocturnal, but there are some very colourful day-flying species, and others may be disturbed during the day. The antennae of butterflies are narrow-stemmed, with a club at the tip. Moth antennae are much more variable, usually hairline or feathery. Burnet moths do, however, have thickened, rather clubbed antennae. When resting, butterflies hold their wings together above the body, whereas most moths tend to hold their wings flat. The life cycle is complete metomorphosis, involving egg, larva (caterpillar), pupa (chrysalis) and adult.

Butterfly Conservation, Hampshire and Isle of Wight Branch is very active in recording species and produce informative annual reports of sightings. David Green's report on New Forest Lepidoptera (2000) excludes coastal sites, but refers to 1,488 species recorded in the New Forest, including 72 Red List and 192 Nationally Scarce species.

BUTTERFLIES

UK: 60 species, including 4 extinct (in Hampshire 51 species, including 5 extinct)
New Forest: 48 species [80%], including 7 extinct

The beautiful, sun-loving, day flying butterflies have always fascinated people. The woodland butterfly fauna took the brunt of a decline from abundance compared with Victorian times, with some species either becoming extinct, or reduced to small populations, although other species have successfully increased their presence in the New Forest. All the heathland butterflies occur in relatively low numbers, except the heather specialist, the Silver-studded Blue. This is not surprising, as heavy grazing pressure reduces the availability of larval foodplants, whilst trampling presumably also affects numbers of developing larvae. In the New Forest, there are a number of sites, particularly in the southern half, where one can expect to see at least 20 species of butterflies each year, going about their business of nectaring, looking for a mate and egg-laying. Since 2000, 31 species have been seen in Pignal and adjoining Parkhill Inclosure, and 30 species in New Copse Inclosure. Other sites approaching this number are Badminston Common and surrounds (near Fawley), Churchplace Inclosure, Hawkhill Inclosure, Keyhaven and immediate surrounds, Roydon Woods and Wootton Coppice Inclosure, although for much of the time the density of butterflies at these sites is low. Just outside the New Forest, coastal areas such as Barton-on-Sea and Barton Common combined are productive, whilst Southampton is one of the best cities for butterflies in the United Kingdom. The butterfly enthusiast can also reach other exciting habitats in Hampshire such as Bentley Wood, Magdalen Hill Down, Martin Down, Noar Hill, Shipton Bellinger and Stockbridge Down within an hour's drive, but some species found in these localities are only briefly mentioned in this book.

The measurements given below are the usual range, occasionally dwarf specimens are seen. Status of butterflies in the New Forest for 2009 is given for **OF** – open forest (anywhere except formal Inclosures) and **In** – Inclosures. The flight periods are a guide only, in warm years, butterflies may be earlier than normal and have an additional brood.

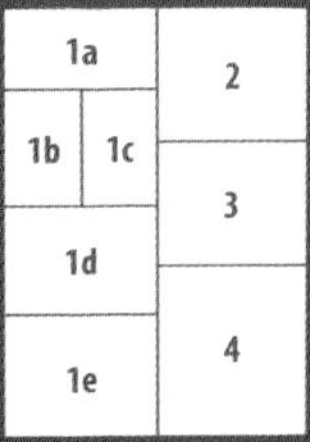

1a	2
1b 1c	3
1d	
1e	4

Butterflies

Plates 1a–1e
Purple Emperor life history
[all photos, NH]
a) egg
b) caterpillar [also known as larva]
c) chrysalis [also known as pupa]
d) adult male
e) adult female

Moths

Plate 2
Six-spot Burnet moths

Plate 3
Eyed Hawkmoth

Plate 4
Dark Crimson Underwing feeding on sap run with Copper Underwing [GP]

SKIPPERS – Family Hesperiidae

Small Skipper *Thymelicus sylvestris* (wingspan: 27–34 mm)

CURRENT STATUS IN THE NEW FOREST: OF Local, **In** Widespread

IDENTIFICATION: Attractive small golden coloured skipper, only the male has conspicuous black scent scales on the forewings. The antennal tip is orange underneath (black in the similar Essex Skipper).

HABITAT: Common and widespread in New Forest Inclosures, less likely to be seen so frequently in open forest sites, but still regular in some areas, also surrounds, including coastal sites. Found on the Isle of Wight, this is a common species throughout most of England and Wales. Adults are usually found in mid or late June to early August, occasionally into September, in rough grassland along woodland rides, wasteland, roadside verges and beside hedgerows, also in gardens. Yorkshire-fog is the main larval foodplant; other tall grasses may also be used.

Essex Skipper *Thymelicus lineola* (wingspan: 26–30 mm)

CURRENT STATUS IN THE NEW FOREST: OF Local, **In** Rare

IDENTIFICATION: Easily confused with the Small Skipper, but with a rather greyer underside and the antennal tip is black underneath and obviously clubbed whereas the Small Skipper is more tapered and orange underneath (Plate 2c). The black scent scales on forewings of males are also shorter than in the Small Skipper.

HABITAT: Considered rare in Inclosures and presumed extinct in open forest in the 1990s [Oates *et al.*, *Butterflies of Hampshire* (2000), they are, however, reliably found in small numbers in widespread locations such as Badminston (can be common), Brockenhurst, Hawkhill Inclosure, Shirley Holms and near Exbury. In the Forest surrounds examples of records include Barton, the Southampton area and the Isle of Wight. This is a widespread species throughout much of the southern half of England and was first recorded from Wales in 2000. Adults are usually found in late June to late August (occasionally in September) in tall grassland. The overlap with the Small Skipper may cause confusion, as these fast flying insects need to be carefully examined. Habitat includes woodland rides, wasteland, roadside verges and gardens, including coastal areas. Feeds on cock's-foot or creeping soft-grass, amongst other grasses.

Large Skipper *Ochlodes faunus* (wingspan: 29–36 mm)

CURRENT STATUS IN THE NEW FOREST: OF Widespread, **In** Common

IDENTIFICATION: Attractive orange and brown skipper, the male with conspicuous black scent scales on the forewings.

HABITAT: Common and widespread both in New Forest Inclosures and open forest sites, particularly plentiful at sites such as Hawkhill, New Copse, Pignal and Wootton Coppice Inclosures. Found on the Isle of Wight, this is a common species throughout most of England, Wales and south-west Scotland. Adults are usually found in early June to late August (occasionally in May and September) in tall grassland along woodland rides, wasteland, roadside verges and beside hedgerows, also in gardens. Cock's-foot and false brome are the main larval foodplants, other grasses may also be used, including purple moor-grass on heaths. Adults are often seen nectaring on bramble and thistle, also bell heather on heathland, they also pollinate the rare wild gladioli.

1a	2a	2b
1b	2c	2d
	3a	3b
1c	3c	3d

Plates 1a–1c
Small Skipper
a) male
b) female
c) female underside [GP]

Plates 2a–2d
Essex Skipper
a) male [GP]
b) female [GP]
c) male, close-up of antennae [GP]
d) female underside [GP]

Plates 3a–3d
Large Skipper
a) male
b) female
c) underside [GP]
d) mating pair

Dingy Skipper *Erynnis tages* (wingspan: 27–34 mm)
CURRENT STATUS IN THE NEW FOREST: **OF** Rare, **In** Very rare
IDENTIFICATION: Dark brown skipper, with grey patches, wings edged with white spots, which could be mistaken for a day-flying moth.
HABITAT: Rare, most likely to be seen at Badminston, but occasionally observed in Calshot, Crockford, New Copse Inclosure and Roydon Woods, amongst others. This species is often associated with chalk grassland in Hampshire (including the Isle of Wight), but is the most widespread of British skippers, although in England commoner in the south and the Midlands, also found in Wales, Scotland and Ireland, although colonies are sporadic. Adults are usually found in mid May to late June (occasionally in April and even July to August if there is a second brood) in dry meadows and occasionally heathland, along railway embankments and woodland clearings. The larval foodplant is usually common bird's-foot-trefoil. The quick-flying adults are often seen basking on low vegetation, or on bare ground.

Grizzled Skipper *Pyrgus malvae* (wingspan: 23–29 mm)
CURRENT STATUS IN THE NEW FOREST: **OF** Rare, **In** Very rare
IDENTIFICATION: Dark brown (or more rarely black) and white mottled skipper, which could be mistaken for a day-flying moth.
HABITAT: Rare and in low numbers, perhaps most likely to be seen around Crockford Bottom and surrounds, but worth looking for in Perrywood Haseley, Pignal Inclosures and Roydon Woods, amongst others. Also found on the Isle of Wight. This species is fond of sunny, sheltered areas, and is generally distributed across England and Wales, commonest in central and southern England, although greatly declined over recent decades. Adults are usually found in early May to late June (occasionally in April and even July to August if there is a second brood, although this is rare) in scrub (including heathland), near hedgerows, along railway embankments and woodland rides. In Hampshire, larger colonies are spread over chalk grasslands. The larval foodplant is often wild strawberry or tormentil. The quick-flying adults will often bask with wings open on low vegetation, stones, or even bare earth.

WHITES – Family Pieridae

Clouded Yellow *Colias croceus* (wingspan: 52–58 mm)
CURRENT STATUS IN THE NEW FOREST: **OF** Vagrant, **In** Vagrant (common in some years)
IDENTIFICATION: Beautiful vivid yellow, tinged with green on the underside. The upperside has a broad black border, plain in the male, but with yellow spots in the female. The female form *helice* is not uncommon (up to a tenth of all females) and this has the ground colour creamy white.
HABITAT: This is a migrant from southern Europe and north Africa, which can be seen flying over much of the New Forest in open areas especially flowery grasslands when there is a major influx, but normally one would have to look for them on the undercliffs at Barton-on-Sea, or Southbourne Undercliff in Dorset, where there is evidence of breeding. A regular immigrant, numbers across England, Wales, Scotland and Ireland vary from year to year, in some years numbers are very disappointing. However, from 1992 to 2009 there have been eight good years in Britain for Clouded Yellows, rather more than the previous norm of one per decade. Adult flight periods are unpredictable, although they are usually seen between May to October (but sometimes as early as February). In Hampshire, larger colonies are likely on coastal areas or chalk downland (including the Isle of Wight), with up to three generations a year. The larval foodplants are common and hairy bird's-foot-trefoil, also red and white clover. The quick-flying adults seldom settle, then only with wings closed, so photographers need patience.

1a		1b
2a	2b	2c
3a		3b
3c	3d	3e

Plates 1a & 1b
Dingy Skipper
a) [GP]
b) underside

Plates 2a–2c
Grizzled Skipper
a) male
b) female [GP]
c) underside

Plates 3a–3e
Clouded Yellow
a) male [GH]
b) male underside
c) female underside [GP]
d) female underside, form *helice* [GP]
e) female egglaying

Brimstone *Gonepteryx rhamni* (wingspan: 60–74 mm)
CURRENT STATUS IN THE NEW FOREST: **OF** Widespread, **In** Common
IDENTIFICATION: Unmistakable sulphur yellow male (the female is greenish-white) with hooked wing-tips.
HABITAT: A familiar sight in spring, flying over the New Forest and surrounds, when they emerge from hibernation. Also found on the Isle of Wight, this species is widespread in England, Wales and Ireland, but local in the north and rare in Scotland, in sunny woodland rides, gardens and hedgerows. Adults are seen from March to May then June until the end of September. The larval foodplants are purging buckthorn and alder buckthorn. The adults rest with wings closed.

Large White *Pieris brassicae* (wingspan: 53–70 mm)
CURRENT STATUS IN THE NEW FOREST: **OF** Widespread, **In** Widespread
IDENTIFICATION: Usually larger than our other white butterflies and easily recognised by the bold black patch from the wing tip to outer edge of wing (black goes down side of wing as well as along the top). In addition, the female has two rounded black spots on the forewing.
HABITAT: A familiar sight in the New Forest and surrounds, often bolstered by migrants from continental Europe. Commonest on the coast where they may be seen in hundreds on the undercliffs, including Barton-on-Sea and Hordle. Widespread in gardens and around allotments and brassica crops in Britain and Ireland, from April to October, in two to three generations. A well known garden species, they are attracted to the larval foodplants: cabbages and relatives, as well as nasturtiums, where they are sometimes regarded as a pest.

Small White *Pieris rapae* (wingspan: 38–57 mm)
CURRENT STATUS IN THE NEW FOREST: **OF** Widespread, **In** Widespread
IDENTIFICATION: Usually smaller than the Large White, with a smaller, often fainter grey to black patch on the wing tip only along the top edge.
HABITAT: A familiar site in the New Forest and surrounds, again numbers often bolstered by migrants and commonest on the coast, often flying with the Large White. Widespread in Britain and Ireland, in all habitats, from late March to October, occasionally later. A well known garden species, like the Large White, attracted to cabbages and relatives, where they are sometimes regarded as a pest.

Green-veined White *Pieris napi* (wingspan: 40–52 mm)
CURRENT STATUS IN THE NEW FOREST: **OF** Widespread, **In** Widespread
IDENTIFICATION: May be confused with the Small White, however easily recognised by the bold veins, (less obvious in summer brood) particularly on the underside.
HABITAT: Regarded as rare in the New Forest up to the 1990s, but quite widespread, although often in smaller numbers than the Small and Large White. Widespread in Britain and Ireland, from April to September, in two main broods, sometimes with a later third generation. A well known species in damp meadows, woodland rides, hedgerows, ditches and gardens, larvae feed on wild crucifers, such as cuckooflower, garlic mustard, hedge mustard, horse-radish and watercress.

1a	1b	1c	1d
2a	2b	4a	
2c	2d	4b	
3a	3b		
3c	3d	4c	

Plates 1a–1d
Brimstone
a) male underside
b) female underside
c) mating pair caught by Crab Spider [GH]
d) egg [GP]

Plates 2a–2d
Large White
a) male
b) female
c) female underside [GP]
d) larvae

Plate 3a–3d
Small White
a) male [GP]
b) female
c) male underside [GP]
d) larva

Plates 4a–4c
Green-veined White
a) male [GP]
b) female
c) mating pair [GP]

Orange-Tip *Anthocharis cardamines* (wingspan: 40–52 mm)
CURRENT STATUS IN THE NEW FOREST: **OF** Local / Rare, **In** Rare
IDENTIFICATION: The male is the arguably our most attractive springtime butterfly, the only one with orange-tipped forewings; these are absent in the female, which is sometimes mistaken for one of our other Whites, but easily recognised at rest.
HABITAT: Regarded as rare in both New Forest Inclosures and open forest sites in the 1990s, it is, however, occasional in both, in low numbers (for example Pignal and New Copse Inclosures), but generally more numerous in areas surrounding the forest, such as Keyhaven. Also present on the Isle of Wight. A welcome spring sight, this species is widespread in England, Wales and Ireland, but local further north, particularly in Scotland. Found in a variety of habitats, such as damp meadows, ditches, roadside verges, woodland rides and glades, gardens and hedgerows. Generally absent from heathlands. Adults are found in mid April to mid June, but may occasionally be observed outside these times, with a rare second brood in July or August. The larval foodplants include garlic mustard and cuckooflower. The larvae are cannibalistic when young, so the female usually rejects a plant already bearing an egg.

HAIRSTREAKS, COPPERS and BLUES – Family Lycaenidae

Green Hairstreak *Callophrys rubi* (wingspan: 27–34 mm)
CURRENT STATUS IN THE NEW FOREST: **OF** Widespread, **In** Rare
IDENTIFICATION: Chocolate brown butterfly, with metallic green underside, usually with white spots, although sometimes incomplete or absent.
HABITAT: Often unnoticed, small colonies can be observed in Inclosures such as Wootton Coppice, heathlands and elsewhere including Badminston, Roydon Woods and Setley, also coastal sites, such as Barton and Keyhaven, wherever the main foodplant, gorse, occurs; they also widely use birds-foot-trefoil. Found throughout the British Isles (including the Isle of Wight) and Ireland. Adults are found fluttering around shrubs in April to early July, although they are commonest in May in the New Forest, often appearing later than surrounding areas.

Purple Hairstreak *Neozephyrus quercus* (wingspan: 31–40 mm)
CURRENT STATUS IN THE NEW FOREST: **OF** Widespread, **In** Widespread
IDENTIFICATION: Males have a purple sheen, which is restricted to the base of the forewings in females, otherwise purplish black. The underside is silvery-grey.
HABITAT: Colonies can be observed along woodland rides in most Inclosures and elsewhere in open forest sites and New Forest surrounds, including gardens, with adults seen in July to mid September. Also found on the Isle of Wight. This is our commonest hairstreak, found across southern England and Wales, more scattered further north and in Ireland. Although they sometimes fly low (particularly when newly-hatched) or rest on vegetation such as bracken, one often first notices them flitting high around tall oak trees, particularly early evening. The adults feed mainly on honeydew. Pupae have been found in the nests of red ants *Myrmica ruginodis*.

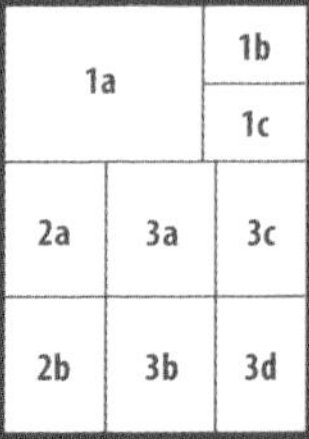

1a		1b
		1c
2a	3a	3c
2b	3b	3d

Plates 1a–1c
Orange-tip
a) male [GP]
b) female
c) male underside

Plates 2a & 2b
Green Hairstreak
a) underside
b) underside, lacking white marks

Plates 3a–3d
Purple Hairstreak
a) male [NH]
b) female [TM]
c) male underside [GP]
d) larva

White-letter Hairstreak *Satyrium w-album* (wingspan: 25–35 mm)
CURRENT STATUS IN THE NEW FOREST: **OF** Very rare, **In** Extinct
IDENTIFICATION: Dark brown with the underside with a conspicuous white 'W' shaped lines on the hindwings, also orange lunules.
HABITAT: Since the 1940s, regarded as rare in open forest sites, but extinct in New Forest Inclosures, this small butterfly can be overlooked and should be searched for wherever elms occur, including roadside and woodland edges and parks. Colonies are sometimes very small. Close to the New Forest, Bransgore and Mudeford Woods in Dorset hold populations, as well as the Southampton area in Hampshire, including Peartree Green. They are possibly still present around Ashurst. Adults are seen in late June to August, peaking in mid July. This is an uncommon hairstreak, although found in England as far north as Lancashire and County Durham. It is also local in Wales. Rare on the Isle of Wight. The adults fly around the larval foodplant, elm trees, particularly wych elm and hybrids, basking (always with wings shut) or sipping honeydew, although they are sometimes seen nectaring on brambles.

Small Copper *Lycaena phlaeas* (wingspan: 26–36 mm)
CURRENT STATUS IN THE NEW FOREST: **OF** Widespread, **In** Local
IDENTIFICATION: Delightful little species with conspicuous shining coppery forewings.
HABITAT: Occasional in some New Forest Inclosures, such as Wootton Coppice and Hawkhill, widespread in open forest sites, including heathland in small numbers, but only likely to be seen in double figures in coastal grassland such as Barton, Hordle and Keyhaven, and towards Boscombe and beyond. However, some acid grassland with sheep's sorrel can have very good numbers. Also found on the Isle of Wight. Adults are seen in various habitats ranging from woodland rides, waste ground, roadside verges and gardens in late April to October, in three generations (but can occur earlier and later than this, particularly in coastal areas). Found throughout the British Isles and Ireland, aberrations frequently occur, with ab. *caeruleo-punctata* (blue spots on the upper hindwing) commonest. Highly territorial, adults are often seen nectaring on flowers such as ragwort and daisies, where they rise to see off any approaching intruders, including large butterflies. They also bask on low-growing vegetation or soil. Larval foodplants are common sorrel and sheep's sorrel.

Small Blue *Cupido minimus* (wingspan: 18–27 mm)
CURRENT STATUS IN THE NEW FOREST: **OF** Vagrant?, **In** Absent
IDENTIFICATION: Our smallest butterfly, this species is dark brown, with a dusting of silvery blue in fresh males. The underside is silvery grey with tiny black dots with very thin white surround.
HABITAT: A great rarity in the New Forest, the author found one at Hurst Castle in 2009, possibly blown across in winds from the nearby Isle of Wight. Two were also recorded at Acres Down in 2009, the only records in the Forest since 1998, where several were found in Pig Bush. Also found at Fletchwood Meadows in 1996, indicating they are likely to be breeding in the area. They are said to occur sporadically on shingle along the New Forest shore and on imported rubble, where the foodplant, kidney vetch grows. The strongholds of this species are, however, well away from the New Forest, on chalk grasslands, such as Martin Down. Adults are found in mid May to September, in two broods, in isolated colonies throughout the British Isles and Ireland, commonest in southern England.

1		2a
		2b
		2c
3a	3b	3c

Plate 1
White-letter Hairstreak female underside [GP]

Plates 2a–2c
Small Copper
a) male [GP]
b) female, blue-spotted aberrant form *caeruleo-punctata* [GP]
c) male underside [GP]

Plates 3a–3c
Small Blue
a) male [GP]
b) underside [GP]
c) mating pair

Silver-studded Blue *Plebejus argus* (wingspan: 28–32 mm)
CURRENT STATUS IN THE NEW FOREST: **OF** Common, **In** Rare
IDENTIFICATION: Upperside bright blue with black borders in the male, dark brown, with a variable number of orange spots around the edges in the female. The underside greyish with bluish at base, edges with shiny bluish in centre of spots and orange lunules.
HABITAT: Heathlands of Hampshire and Dorset may account for 40% of the UK numbers of this species. This species is widespread throughout practically all suitable New Forest heathlands, particularly those with abundant cross-leaved heath and sheltered hollows. They are occasionally seen in Inclosures, such as Hawkhill (mostly coniferous plantation), but normally present in numbers on the surrounding heaths, in this example, Beaulieu Heath. The requirements for the species include not only heathers in the pioneer or early stages (overgrown areas are not suitable), but the correct species of black ants *Lasius* species, which attend the larvae and are attracted to pupae. Adults deliberately lay eggs near the ants nests and are found in June to about the end of August, sometimes in colonies of hundreds of individuals with staggered emergence dates, which sit and bask on low vegetation, particularly in early morning when they congregate, and are often seen paired later in the day. The larvae live by day in the ants nest, emerging at dusk to feed, under protection of ants. When the pupa hatches, up to eight ants accompany the adult until its wings have inflated and hardened (see front cover photo), attracted by drops of liquid on the furry body. Distributed in scattered colonies in central and southern England, and Wales, but often rare outside of southern English heathlands. Absent from the Isle of Wight. Foodplants include ling and cross-leaved heath and possibly bell heather.

Brown Argus *Aricia agestis* (wingspan: 25–31 mm)
CURRENT STATUS IN THE NEW FOREST: **OF** Rare, **In** Very rare
IDENTIFICATION: Chocolate brown with orange spots around the edges of the wings, may be confused with the female Common Blue (which also has varying blue near wing-bases). Underside greyish brown with orange marginal spots and a number of white-ringed black spots, none on the forewing nearer than halfway in to the body (unlike the Common Blue).
HABITAT: Always very local, this species has been considered to be a vagrant in the New Forest since the 1960s, but found breeding in grasslands at Badminston, Efford and Shirley Holms in 2009, perhaps little changed from the Victoria County History' record (1900): 'also occurs in some parts of the Forest'. It is also found just outside the New Forest at Testwood Lakes, near Totton and small colonies may well occur elsewhere, but they are rarely likely to be seen in Inclosures. Elsewhere in Hampshire, chalk downloads are the preferred sites, where the main foodplant, common rock-rose grows; common stork's-bill and dove's-foot crane's-bill may also be used. Distribution is scattered, mainly in southern England, where this species is commonest on chalk in Dorset and the Isle of Wight. Adults fly from early May to early October, in two broods, occasionally emerging in April in favourable years. The larvae are attended by ants.

1a	1d	
1b		
1c	1e	
2a	2b	2c

Plates 1a–1e
Silver-Studded Blue
a) male
b) female
c) male underside
d) mating pair
e) group [GP]

Plates 2a–2c
Brown Argus
a) male
b) female [GP]
c) male underside

Common Blue ***Polyommatus icarus*** (wingspan: 29–36 mm)
CURRENT STATUS IN THE NEW FOREST: OF Widespread, **In** Local
IDENTIFICATION: Male with violet-blue upperside, female rich brown with orange and black spots around the edges of the wings. The female may be confused with the Brown Argus, but the Common Blue female has a varying amount of blue near the wing-bases. The underside is grey or brown with orange marginal spots and a number of white-ringed black spots.
HABITAT: Considered local in open forest and rare in Inclosures in the New Forest in the 1990s, it is, however, rather widespread in small colonies in grassland throughout the area, although double figures are mainly to be encountered in coastal areas such as Barton, Keyhaven and Milford-on-Sea, with occasional sightings in Inclosures. The largest local population is at Efford, but they are present in much stronger numbers on chalk downland, where the main foodplants, common bird's-foot-trefoil and white clover grow. Found on the Isle of Wight and widespread throughout the UK and Ireland, adults of our commonest Blue butterfly fly from early May to October, in two broods, occasionally outside these months in favourable years. The larvae may have occasional contact with ants.

Holly Blue ***Celastrina argiolus*** (wingspan: 26–34 mm)
CURRENT STATUS IN THE NEW FOREST: OF Widespread, **In** Local
IDENTIFICATION: The male has a shiny blue upperside with narrow black margins, much broader in the female. The distinctive underside is silvery blue with only small black spots.
HABITAT: Occasional in many Inclosures between mid April to October in two broods, but perhaps more often noticed in open forest in the New Forest and surrounds, including churchyards, parks and gardens, often associated with the main larval foodplants, holly and common ivy. This butterfly flies much higher than other Blues and is found on the Isle of Wight. Widespread in Britain, but mainly southern, less frequent in the midlands and north. Found in Wales and Ireland, but a rare vagrant in Scotland. Rarely seen in numbers, there is an account in the 1890s of hundreds on holly on the borders of Holmsley Inclosure, also 'phenomenal numbers' in August at Brook.

Duke of Burgundy ***Hamearis lucina*** (wingspan: 29–32 mm)
CURRENT STATUS IN THE NEW FOREST: OF Rare, **In** Extinct
IDENTIFICATION: Easily recognisable by its orange spots on a dark brown background.
HABITAT: Whilst widespread in open parts of the New Forest pre-1900, following a decline was thought to be extinct by the 1990s, the few records including one at New Copse Inclosure in 1981. However, a small colony still exists on private land near Exbury. The Victoria County History record (1900) records: 'In the New Forest it is local, but common in one or two enclosures in the extreme east and also in Stubby Copse, New Copse, and elsewhere in the south-east.' Found mainly in sheltered and traditionally coppiced woodlands where the larval foodplant, primrose, grows in late April to early June. In downland, they feed on cowslips. Occurs in small colonies, mainly in southern and south-eastern England, with scattered populations further north to Cumbria and Yorkshire. One of the most popular sites in Hampshire for them is the chalk pits at Noar Hill. Males defend their territories, which are usually warm, sheltered spots.

1a	2a	2b
1b		2c
1c	3a	
1d	3b	3c

Plates 1a–1d
Common Blue
a) male
b) female (many specimens have less blue)
c) male underside [GP]
d) female underside [GP]

Plates 2a–2c
Holly Blue
a) male [GP]
b) female [GP]
c) female underside [GP]

Plates 3a–3c
Duke of Burgundy
a) male
b) female [GP]
c) female underside

NYMPHALIDS, FRITILLARIES and BROWNS – Family Nymphalidae

1a	2a
1b	2b
1c	2c

Plates 1a–1c
White Admiral
a) male
b) female [GP]
c) male underside [GP]

Plates 2a–2c
Purple Emperor
a) male
b) female [JA]
c) male underside, on dung

White Admiral ***Limenitis camilla*** (wingspan: 56–66 mm)

CURRENT STATUS IN THE NEW FOREST: **OF** Local / Rare, **In** Widespread

IDENTIFICATION: Sooty brown with white band and markings on the upperside; tawny orange with grey and white markings on the underside.

HABITAT: Classic butterfly of mainly deciduous woodland rides and glades, typically where the foodplant honeysuckle occurs, along with a good supply of bramble flowers. In the 1990s considered local in Inclosures and rare in open forest areas of the New Forest. Can be seen in most major Inclosures, including Brockishill, Costicles, Great Linford, Lodgehill, New Copse, Pignal and Pondhead, the highest numbers perhaps in Churchplace and Wootton Coppice. Also still likely to be encountered in low numbers in woodlands or margins not Inclosed, such as at Badminston and Roydon Woods, also road verges in open forest areas. The Victoria County History' (1900) records 'no-where so abundant as in the New Forest, where it may in some seasons be seen in thousands.' Also established on the Isle of Wight, found locally in central and southern England, also some eastern parts of Wales from late June to August, with a rare second brood in late September to early October. Whilst adults enjoy basking on oak leaves and drinking aphid honeydew from the canopy, they periodically glide low down to nectar on bramble blossoms or occasionally take in the dissolved salts in dung. However, they can fly fast, but the gliding readily identifies this butterfly from some distance away.

Purple Emperor ***Apatura iris*** (wingspan: 70–92 mm)

CURRENT STATUS IN THE NEW FOREST: **OF** Extinct, **In** Very rare

IDENTIFICATION: One of our most beautiful butterflies. Males flash every shade of purple in the sun, on the upperside, but at certain angles look like the brown females, with whitish markings; the underside is paler brown, with darker areas, white markings and a large black ring, with brown border on the forewings.

HABITAT: Found mainly in woodland rides and glades, where the foodplant sallow grows. For much of their time they are rather elusive, staying high up in the canopy, perhaps on oaks. Since the 1960s considered a vagrant in the New Forest, but occasional annual sightings, for example in Costicles and possibly Wootton Coppice Inclosures in 2008 and 2009, implies they may still be resident, in small numbers in the few areas where sallows are still present. The hope is they are at least attempting to recolonise the area. Herbert Goss (in The Victoria County History, 1900) records 'not abundant in the New Forest, although a considerable number of larvae are taken in some seasons.... Sometimes it is found on dead jays, or other birds in a state of decomposition, nailed to the trees near a keeper's lodge or woodman's cottage.' Goss then goes on to state that he has 'taken specimens near Lyndhurst in Pond Head and Jones's Enclosures, in Rhamnor Enclosure, between Lyndhurst and Brockenhurst, also in Little Holme Hill Enclosure, and about Denny, Stubby Copse, and elsewhere in the southern and eastern parts of the Forest.' Absent from the Isle of Wight, this uncommon butterfly is found in small colonies scattered in central southern England from late June or early July to August. Many enthusiasts in Hampshire and elsewhere, travel to well known areas for them, such as Bentley Wood on the Hampshire / Wiltshire border, where sightings are often made even in, or by the car park. Whilst high up, adults enjoy basking on oak leaves and drinking aphid honeydew or sap. In sunny weather the butterfly is attracted to cars, or descends to the ground, usually in the mornings, to dung, rotting flesh and puddles, where they probe with their yellow probosces, occasionally for an hour, but sometimes only fleetingly. A challenge to photograph, standing over the butterfly may produce a picture with all purple wings, but often images only show the purple sheen on one side.

Red Admiral *Vanessa atalanta* (wingspan: 64–78 mm)
CURRENT STATUS IN THE NEW FOREST: **OF** Widespread, **In** Widespread
IDENTIFICATION: A familiar black and scarlet butterfly.
HABITAT: Reported as rare in the 1990s in Inclosures, but they are occasional in practically all Inclosures, but more often noticed in open forest in the New Forest and surrounds, including coastal areas, parks and particularly gardens, often on buddleja, sedum and other nectar plants. They are also fond of dung, puddles, sap, rotting fruit (in autumn) and ivy flowers. Found most often in March to November, usually specimens that have successfully hibernated or survived the winter are noticed in spring, and numbers build up in summer and autumn, supplemented by immigrants. The foodplant is tall common nettle in dappled shade at ride edges. Found over much of the United Kingdom, including the Isle of Wight. Fast flying, when near the canopy, can sometimes be confused for the more elusive, Purple Emperor.

Painted Lady *Vanessa cardui* (wingspan: 58–74 mm)
CURRENT STATUS IN THE NEW FOREST: **OF** Vagrant, **In** Vagrant (numbers vary)
IDENTIFICATION: Attractive rosy-orange upperside, the black wing tips marked with white.
HABITAT: Occurs anywhere where flowers provide nectar. The Victoria County History (1900) surprisingly records 'not met with it in the New Forest.' Yet nowadays this can be a common sight throughout the New Forest, although in poor years, one may only see a few of these butterflies on the coast. Found most often in April to October, but rarely survive our winters. One of the world's most successful butterflies in terms of distribution, this can be a common immigrant from North Africa, Arabia and continental Europe, as in 2009 when huge numbers invaded our shores, outnumbered other butterflies many times over, laid eggs on thistles (sometimes common nettle) and spread over much of the United Kingdom; returning to the Mediterranean and North Africa late in the year. However, in a normal year the species is less common than the Red Admiral, but a more frequent visitor than the Clouded Yellow.

Small Tortoiseshell *Aglais urticae* (wingspan: 45–62 mm)
CURRENT STATUS IN THE NEW FOREST: **OF** Local / Widespread, **In** Local
IDENTIFICATION: Rich orange ground colour, with blue marginal spots on the upperside. The black and whitish underside is quite a contrast.
HABITAT: Occurs anywhere where flowers provide nectar, but particularly in sunny and sheltered conditions where the foodplant nettles, grow. A very welcome sight in gardens, fairly widespread in the New Forest and surrounds, including the Isle of Wight (and throughout the United Kingdom), although numbers have declined since the 1990s and now vary from year to year, possibly due to attacks by the immigrant parasitic fly, *Sturmia bella*. Found most often in March to October, numbers are supplemented by immigrants from continental Europe. Adults hibernate in hollow trees and buildings.

1a	1b
2a	2b
3a	3b

Plates 1a & 1b
Red Admiral
b) underside

Plates 2a & 2b
Painted Lady
a) [GP]
b) underside [GP]

Plates 3a & 3b
Small Tortoiseshell
a) [GP]
b) underside [GP]

Peacock *Aglais io* (wingspan: 63–75 mm)
CURRENT STATUS IN THE NEW FOREST: **OF** Widespread, **In** Widespread
IDENTIFICATION: Easily recognised by the bold eye-spots on the upperside. The underside is black.
HABITAT: Favours woodland clearings and wood edges, but found practically anywhere where the foodplant, common nettle, grows. Frequent in gardens, widespread throughout the New Forest and surrounds, including the Isle of Wight (and throughout much of the United Kingdom, but less common in Scotland). Found most often in March to September, hibernating as adults. Batches of the black, spiky larvae, are a common sight on nettles. If an adult is disturbed, the wings are flashed open, in an effort to startle a possible predator; in addition, wings are rubbed together to produce a warning sound.

Comma *Polygonia c-album* (wingspan: 50–64 mm)
CURRENT STATUS IN THE NEW FOREST: **OF** Widespread, **In** Widespread
IDENTIFICATION: Easily recognised by its ragged wing margins and the white comma on the underside.
HABITAT: Found in woodland, hedgerows and gardens, in the vicinity of its foodplants, common nettle, elm and currant. Frequent in gardens, particularly on buddleja, in other areas prefers bramble. Widespread throughout the New Forest and surrounds, including the Isle of Wight (and in southern England and Wales, gradually progressing further north, including Scotland). This is a significant change in distribution, as it was absent from the New Forest until well into Victorian times. Found most often in March to September, main peaks are perhaps in early April and July to mid-September. In early summer larvae develop into either normal (dark) specimens which hibernate or golden form *hutchinsoni* adults, which breed again later in summer.

Small Pearl-bordered Fritillary *Boloria selene* (wingspan: 35–44 mm)
CURRENT STATUS IN THE NEW FOREST: **OF** Rare, **In** Rare
IDENTIFICATION: Orange with black spots, careful examination is needed to distinguish them from the Pearl-bordered Fritillary, when checking the underside, note that the Pearl-bordered only has two whitish blotches in the middle of the hindwing, compared to several in the Small Pearl-bordered.
HABITAT: Found in open woodland or edges, often damp, with plenty of grass and nectar sources. In Victorian times the record for Hampshire states 'prefers the heaths, where it is often abundant'. However, it is now regarded as rare in the New Forest and surrounds, because populations are small and limited to only a few sites. They are most likely to be observed in Roydon Woods, also Holmsley and Wootton Coppice Inclosures. Also found on the Isle of Wight, this is a declining species throughout its range, mainly in the west of the British Isles, including Scotland, but also found in southern countries of England. Found in late May to early July, the larvae feeding on dog-violet. Adults nectar on thistle, cross-leaved heath, buttercup and other flowers, close to the breeding area. Obtaining good photographs requires patience, as they often settle in areas with a lot of vegetation, obscuring the butterflies; in addition they rarely stay still. In the early morning, they are more likely to bask.

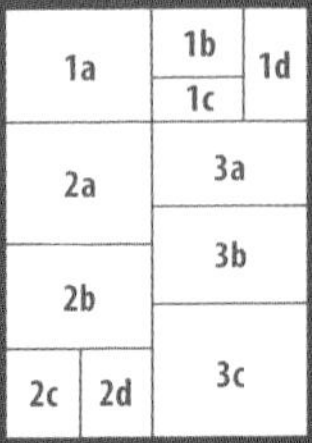

1a	1b / 1c	1d
2a	3a	
2b	3b	
2c, 2d	3c	

Plates 1a–1d
Peacock
b) underside
c) larva
d) larval group

Plates 2a–2d
Comma
a) male, form *hutchinsoni* [GP]
b) female, form *hutchinsoni* [GP]
c) male underside
d) female, form *hutchinsoni* underside [GP]

Plates 3a–3c
Small Pearl-bordered Fritillary
a) male [GP]
b) female [GP]
c) male underside [GP]

Pearl-bordered Fritillary *Boloria euphrosyne* (wingspan: 38–47 mm)
CURRENT STATUS IN THE NEW FOREST: **OF** Rare, **In** Local
IDENTIFICATION: Orange with black spots, sometimes confused with the Small Pearl-bordered Fritillary, particularly where they overlap.
HABITAT: Found in open deciduous woodland and clearings, particularly those with early stages of coppice woodland and young plantations. In Victorian times the record for Hampshire states 'common….especially in the woods of the New Forest'. However, nowadays regarded as rare / locally common in the New Forest and surrounds, as this butterfly is limited to only a few sites in Inclosures. However, this species can reach good numbers in Pignal and adjoining Ramnor and Parkhill, also New Copse and Wootton Coppice Inclosures, occasionally straying to surrounding open forest areas when dispersing. There are occasionally sightings in other lesser known sites. A small colony is present in Parkhurst Forest, Isle of Wight. A declining species, found in isolated, scattered colonies in southern and western England, Wales, Scotland and part of western Ireland, in early May to mid June, the larvae feeding on common dog-violet. Whilst spines in full grown larvae are normally yellow, they are sometimes black. Adults often bask on bracken, or the ground, nectar on bugle, buttercup, bluebell and other flowers, staying close to the breeding area initially and later dispersing along the rides. As with the Small Pearl-bordered Fritillary, obtaining good photographs requires patience, as they often settle in areas with a lot of spring vegetation and, once warmed up, seldom stay still.

Dark Green Fritillary *Argynnis aglaja* (wingspan: 56–68 mm)
CURRENT STATUS IN THE NEW FOREST: **OF** Rare, **In** Rare
IDENTIFICATION: Large orange species with black spots; underside with basal half of the hindwing containing the silver spots, mainly green.
HABITAT: Found in woodland clearings and heathlands, also chalk downland. The Victoria County History (1900) records 'It still occurs in the New Forest, chiefly on thistle-heads about Holmsley and Wooton, and between Holmsley and Christchurch. I have not seen any specimens about Lyndhurst or Brockenhurst for many years past.' Still rare in the New Forest and surrounds, as it is limited to only a few sites, including Hawkhill Inclosure and surrounding Beaulieu Heath, spreading along streams to Crockford Bottom and surrounds, also still present in Wootton Coppice and Little Wootton Inclosures. Records are possible from other areas if they disperse, as they are quick fliers. Fairly widely distributed on the Isle of Wight, they are reasonably widely distributed in Great Britain and Ireland, particularly around the coast. The larval foodplant is various violets. Adults fly from mid June to mid August, often nectaring on thistles in the New Forest.

Sign at Frohawk Ride, Parkhill Inclosure

1a	2a
1b	2b
1c	2c
1d	

Plates 1a–1d
Pearl-bordered Fritillary
a) male
b) female
c) male underside
d) larva

Plates 2a–2c
Dark Green Fritillary
a) male [GP]
b) female
c) female underside

Silver-washed Fritillary *Argynnis paphia* (wingspan: 69–80 mm)
CURRENT STATUS IN THE NEW FOREST: **OF** Local, **In** Widespread
IDENTIFICATION: Large tawny species with black spots and bars in the male; underside greenish with silver streaks. In the female form *valezina*, the tawny ground colour is replaced by bronze-green, paler towards the tip.
HABITAT: Found in deciduous woodland clearings and rides. The Victoria County History (1900) records 'especially characteristic of the New Forest, where it occurs in most seasons in great profusion in the enclosed woods, and also in the open forest whenever the bramble is in flower, from the end of June to the end of July.' Widespread and plentiful at many Inclosures in the New Forest on bramble and thistle flowers, and occasional in open Forest such as Roydon Woods where the butterfly may be seen nectaring in nearby gardens after dispersal during August. Found in the Isle of Wight, distributed in England south of Cumbria, Wales and Ireland, breeding mainly on dog-violets. The female form *valezina* occurs regularly in Hampshire, including the New Forest, and some other areas in central southern England, but rarely elsewhere. The form possibly applies to about 10% of females in some colonies. At localities such as Churchplace, New Copse and Wootton Coppice Inclosures, it is not uncommon to see butterflies congregating in sheltered spots, and also observe mating pairs.

Glanville Fritillary *Melitaea cinxia* (wingspan: 38–52 mm)
CURRENT STATUS IN THE NEW FOREST: **OF** Rare, **In** Absent
IDENTIFICATION: Orange or sandy brown, with a network of dark brown lines.
HABITAT: At the edge of its range in the United Kingdom, always associated with the undercliffs on the Isle of Wight, but it occasionally finds it way to the nearby south coast. It is also found on Guernsey and Alderney in the Channel Islands. A small colony has been found at Hurst Castle since 2006 and in windy conditions takes shelter by the castle walls. Likely to have flown or blown across from the nearby Isle of Wight, visitors by boat and foot are amazed by the sight of these small Fritillaries, nectaring on thrift, trefoils and other flowers in mid May to June. Previously found at nearby Hordle Undercliffs from 1991 until 2007 and may recolonise from Hurst in future. A male was found at Barton-on-Sea in 2009. In inland New Forest, Watson and Reeves introduced a colony to Sway in 1945, which survived 22 years, but other reintroduction attempts have not been successful. There are historic records of occasional finds along the south coast, including a likely sighting at Hurst spit in 1971. The main foodplant is ribwort plantain.

The meadow surrounding Hurst Castle is home to the Glanville Fritillary

1a		1b / 1c
1d	1e	1f
2a	2b	2e
2c	2d	

Plates 1a–1f
Silver-washed Fritillary
a) male
b) female
c) female form *valezina* [GP]
d) male underside
e) female, form *valezina* underside
f) mating pair

Plates 2a–2e
Glanville Fritillary
a) male
b) female [GP]
c) male underside
d) larva
e) mating pair, Hurst lighthouse in background [GP]

Speckled Wood ***Parage aegeria*** (wingspan: 46–56 mm)
CURRENT STATUS IN THE NEW FOREST: **OF** Widespread, **In** Widespread
IDENTIFICATION: Cream spots on a dark brown background, with a mottled brown underside.
HABITAT: Frequent in woodland and hedgerows, also in churchyards and sometimes in gardens. Widespread throughout the New Forest, but found in larger numbers in the Inclosures, often sighted in March to October. Widespread on the Isle of Wight, throughout the British Isles and Ireland; absent in parts of Scotland. The larval foodplants are grasses such as wood meadow-grass and rough meadow-grass, amongst others. The butterflies enjoy sun and shade, males fly to investigate every passing insect for the possibility of intruders. If it happens to be another male, an aerial battle takes place. After a minute or so, the intruder flies away, leaving the original occupant to return to his territory.

Wall ***Lasiommata megera*** (wingspan: 45–53 mm)
CURRENT STATUS IN THE NEW FOREST: **OF** Rare, **In** presumed extinct
IDENTIFICATION: Golden upperwings, with conspicuous eye-spots, and a zig-zag pattern on the underside, readily distinguish this species.
HABITAT: Since the mid 1990s the species has become almost completely a coastal species in Hampshire, although it still holds out well inland at Shipton Bellinger. Preferring warm grassland areas, with plenty of paths and bare ground, it now occurs along the coast from Normandy Marshes to Keyhaven and slightly inland to Efford / Pennington. Appears to have died out in Inclosures such as Hawkhill, but worth still searching for, particularly as the species has been recorded in inland New Forest at Shirley Holms since 2009, also found just outside the Forest at Barton-on-Sea in 2009. Still present on the Isle of Wight. A declining species, previously widespread and common in much of the British Isles and Ireland, but now mainly coastal. Found in May to September, in some years a small third brood lasts into October. The larval foodplants are grasses. The butterflies enjoy sun and bask on bare ground, or patrol paths, males flying up and down in search for a female, only occasionally nectaring.

Marbled White ***Melanargia galathea*** (wingspan: 50–60 mm)
CURRENT STATUS IN THE NEW FOREST: **OF** Local, **In** Local
IDENTIFICATION: Easily recognised by its black and white or cream coloration.
HABITAT: In the New Forest there is a history of the butterfly appearing and disappearing. By 2009, there are several widespread colonies in Inclosures, including Churchplace, Hawkhill, Parkhill and Wootton Coppice, and it also occurs in several open forest areas inland and near the coast at places like Efford. The species prefers open, grassy areas, including meadows and woodland rides, also chalk downland, where the larvae eat various grasses. Sometimes seen on roadside verges in the New Forest. Widespread and sometimes in large colonies, mainly in the southern half of England and Wales, extending as far north as Yorkshire. Present on the Isle of Wight. Found from mid June to August, when groups of these butterflies cluster around nectar plants, such as scabious, knapweeds and thistles. When basking they are easiest to photograph.

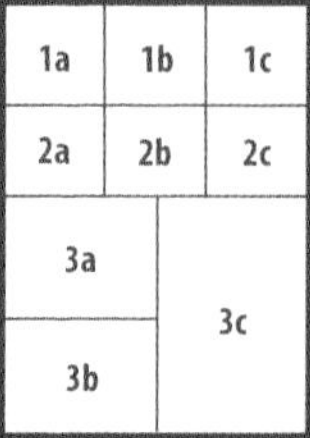

1a	1b	1c
2a	2b	2c
3a		3c
3b		

Plates 1a–1c
Speckled Wood
a) male [GP]
b) female [GP]
c) female underside

Plates 2a–2c
Wall
a) male
b) female [GP]
c) male underside

Plates 3a–3c
Marbled White
a) male [GP]
b) female [GP]
c) mating pair [GP]

Grayling *Hipparchia semele* (wingspan: 51–62 mm)
CURRENT STATUS IN THE NEW FOREST: **OF** Widespread, **In** Local
IDENTIFICATION: Orange and brown uppersides, mottled grey underside.
HABITAT: Dry New Forest heathlands are one of the strongholds for this species. Seldom seen in Inclosures, except Fawley and Hawkhill, they are widespread in open forest with scattered populations of good numbers in areas such as Badminston and Beaulieu Heath, but rather smaller colonies in many other areas. Usually absent in neglected heathlands, they prefer heavily grazed areas with patches of bare ground, using clumps of bristle bent for egg-laying. Occasionally found on the coast, such as Barton-on-Sea and Needs Ore Point. Still present in the Isle of Wight. One of our best camouflaged butterflies, best photographed at rest or when nectaring on heather or bramble; rarely seen with the wings open and even when resting on twigs, bare earth or low vegetation, when landing they quickly tuck the forewings down so the eyespots are hidden. If disturbed, the forewing is raised in a startle display, revealing the eyespots, which may startle possible predators. Widespread, but mainly coastal in the United Kingdom, although there are some significant inland populations. Found from mid July to mid September.

Gatekeeper *Pyronia tithonus* (wingspan: 37–48 mm)
CURRENT STATUS IN THE NEW FOREST: **OF** Common, **In** Widespread
IDENTIFICATION: Very orange upperside, eye spot with two pupils.
HABITAT: Widespread and often common throughout the New Forest Inclosures and open forest areas, the larvae eat various grasses, and adults are often seen nectaring in a variety of habitats, particularly woodland edges and hedgerows, including gardens. Widespread throughout southern England and Wales, mainly coastal in Ireland. Found in July to August, sometimes well into September.

Meadow Brown *Maniola jurtina* (wingspan: 40–60 mm)
CURRENT STATUS IN THE NEW FOREST: **OF** Widespread, **In** Widespread
IDENTIFICATION: Male dark brown, female with orange patches.
HABITAT: Widespread and often common throughout the New Forest Inclosures and open forest areas wherever rough ground is found. The larvae eat various grasses and adults can be seen in a variety of habitats, particularly woodland rides, meadows and grasslands, roadside verges also gardens, inland and coastal. One of the UK's commonest butterflies, widespread throughout Britain and Ireland. Found in June to August, sometimes into October.

Ringlet *Aphantopus hyperantus* (wingspan: 42–52 mm)
CURRENT STATUS IN THE NEW FOREST: **OF** Local, **In** Local
IDENTIFICATION: Dark brown upperside usually with indistinct eye-spots, could possibly be confused with the Meadow Brown, but the underside has conspicuous yellow-ringed eye-spots.
HABITAT: Prefers damp woodlands and lush grassland. Found in low numbers in some New Forest Inclosures, but common along many rides, including at Busketts Lawn, Churchplace, Costicles, Lodgehill, Parkhill and Wootton Coppice. Whilst presumed extinct in open forest areas since 1960, it is still to be seen in low numbers in several locations. Sparsely distributed in the Isle of Wight. The larvae eat various tall, lush grasses. Found throughout much of Britain and Ireland, in late June to early August, in some specimens, the eyespots are practically absent.

1a		1b
2a	2b	2c
3a	3b	4a
3c	3d	4b

Plates 1a & 1b
Grayling
a) underside, eyespot visible
b) underside

Plates 2a–2c
Gatekeeper
a) male [GP]
b) female [GP]
c) mating pair [GP]

Plates 3a–3d
Meadow Brown
a) male
b) female [GP]
c) male underside
d) female underside

Plates 4a & 4b
Ringlet
b) underside [GP]

Small Heath *Coenonympha pamphilus* (wingspan: 30–40 mm)
CURRENT STATUS IN THE NEW FOREST: **OF** Widespread, **In** Local
IDENTIFICATION: Small, almost plain pale orange butterfly.
HABITAT: Regarded as rare in New Forest Inclosures and local in open forest areas in the 1990s, this species is, in fact, very widespread and occasionally common on the heathlands, good examples being Crockford and Beaulieu Heath. It is occasionally met with in Inclosures such as Pignal and adjoining Parkhill, but these do not often meet its need for dry grassland habitat. In Hampshire, it is also found on chalk grassland. It is present on coastal sites, including Keyhaven, and across the sea on the Isle of Wight. Widespread throughout much of Britain and Ireland, the larvae feeding on small, fine-leaved grasses, such as fescues. Found in mid May to September, in two broods.

EXTINCTIONS Other species have long been extinct in the New Forest. Below are some quotes from Herbert Goss in the Victoria County History of Hampshire and the Isle of Wight (1900).

Wood White *Leptidea sinapis* 'was formerly very abundant in the enclosed woods in the New Forest, but suddenly disappeared as a common insect about 1883, though a few specimens may still be found in the spring about New Copse, Wood Fidley, and elsewhere in the south-eastern parts of the Forest.' They were collected in numbers in Stubby Copse and died out about 1888. Regarded as extinct in the New Forest since 1923, and in Hampshire since 1940–1945. However, the species held on in the Forest at Whiteparish Common on the Wiltshire border, until 1957.

Black-veined White *Aporia crataegi* 'formerly abundant, though local, in the Forest. In 1866, 1868, 1869, and 1870 it occurred in thousands about Butt's Lawn, Holme Hill and Puck Pits; between Boldrewood and Burley (in Oakleigh Enclosure); and in Warwickslade and Rhinefield; also more sparingly on the eastern side of the Forest, about Little Holme Hill and Denny. I caught a few specimens as late as 1878, and it is believed the last stragglers were taken by my old friend, the late J. Jenner Weir, about 1883, between Vinney Ridge and Holmsley. It's disappearance cannot, I think, be attributed to over-collecting.' The last reliable UK record is from Kent, in 1922 and attempts at reintroducing this species have failed.

Brown Hairstreak *Thecla betulae* 'In the New Forest it is common in the larval state in many localities where the blackthorn is abundant, but I have never met there with the insect in the perfect state.' Known from Balmer Lawn, Linford Bottom and Roe Wood, also Redlynch and Whiteparish, the species is thought to have died out during the early 1970s, with the few remaining thickets of blackthorn unsuitable for the butterfly. Now rare in Hampshire, but regularly recorded at Noar Hill and Shipton Bellinger.

Silver-spotted Skipper *Hesperia comma* 'reported from the New Forest, but I have never seen it there'. There are possible later records, Pitman worked the northern Forest and in 1963 reported it as 'not uncommon on the heaths' in 1928–1931 at a time when there were large populations in the Redlynch area, near Fordingbridge. However, it is long extinct. Now rare in Hampshire, but reliable at Broughton Down and Stockbridge Down.

1a		1b
2		3
4a	4b	4c
5a	5b	5c

Plates 1a & 1b
Small Heath
a) male underside
b) female underside [GP]

Plate 2
Wood White
mating pair [PCr]

Plate 3
Black-veined White

Plates 4a–4c
Brown Hairstreak
a) female [MP]
b) female underside [GP]
c) male underside

Plates 5a–5b
Silver-Spotted Skipper
a) male
b) female [GP]
c) female underside [GP]

More recent extinctions in the New Forest are three members of the Family Nymphalidae.

High Brown Fritillary *Argynnis adippe* – Victoria County History (1900) records: 'It is far more common in the New Forest than *A. aglaia* [Dark Green Fritillary], but never occurs in such profusion as *A. paphia* [Silver-washed Fritillary]. I have taken it near Bournemouth and in all the woods about Lyndhurst and Brockenhurst, and also about Boldrewood and Burley, but it generally prefers the open heaths, especially where thistles are abundant.' The last open Forest records appear to be from near Burley and Thorney Hill in 1983, a specimen also noted from Burley Inclosure in 1982. Habitat changes appear to have resulted in the extinction of the species in the New Forest, whereas it was only in the late 1960s and early 1970s that it was considered not uncommon at Wootton Coppice Inclosure, where it was last recorded in 1981. There is a possible sighting in 1992 from Matley Passage, but the few 'possible' sightings in the New Forest from 2000–2008 are almost certainly of the similar Dark Green Fritillary, which are able to disperse widely.

Marsh Fritillary *Euphydryas aurinia* – always rare in the New Forest, small colonies were known in the 1920s. There is a late record of a mating pair for a small reintroduced colony at Roydon Woods in 1993, on the foodplant devil's-bit scabious, but the only recent record is from just outside the Forest, in Barton-on-Sea, 3 June 2006. Also recorded from Parkhill Inclosure in 1982.

Large Tortoiseshell *Aglais polychloros* – Victoria County History (1900) records: 'very common in the New Forest in some seasons, not only in the villages, where its larvae feed upon sallow, and apple, plum, and other orchard trees, but also in the Forest woods, especially about the keepers' and woodmen's cottages.' How times change. Regarded as extinct in the New Forest by 1956 (and by about 1980 in the United Kingdom as a whole), a report in 2009 implies they are overwintering and possibly breeding at Woodhouse Copse on the Isle of Wight, as they have been noted and photographed a few years in succession. This species could be confused by recorders with the brighter and often smaller, Small Tortoiseshell, but in the same year, there were definite sightings at New Copse Inclosure on 16 March 2009, Normandy, near Lymington on 14 March 2009 and further outside the Forest at Lords Hill, Southampton on 8 August 2009. The species was also seen in Churchplace Inclosure, 10 May 2008. This follows on from sightings near Boscombe and Lymington in 2006 and New Milton, 30 July 2007. Is this species starting to make a comeback near the south coast and, in particular, the New Forest, or are the specimens seen rare immigrants?

Isolated records, in some cases possibly immigrants, are listed below.

Lulworth Skipper *Thymelicus acteon* – established along the Holmsley branch line in the New Forest in the early 1920s, where it flourished for several years. Possibility of introduction by an entomologist, but origin unknown.

Chequered Skipper *Carterocephalus palaemon* – there is an 1857 report from Lyndhurst and others, possibly suspect, as the records may have been releases.

Adonis Blue *Lysandra bellargus* – recorded from near Matley pre-1969, if correct, possibly a vagrant or attempted introduction. Associated with chalk downland, this species is fairly common on the Isle of Wight.

1a		1b
2a	2b	2c
3a	3b	4
5a	5b	5c

Plates 1a & 1b
High Brown Fritillary
a) [DG]
b) underside [MPi]

Plates 2a–2c
Marsh Fritillary
a) male [GP]
b) male underside
c) mating pair

Plates 3a & 3b
Large Tortoiseshell
a) [PR]
b) underside [PR]

Plate 4
Lulworth Skipper male

Plates 5a & 5b
Adonis Blue
a) male
b) female [GP]
c) male underside

Chalkhill Blue *Lysandra coridon* – the male is our only blue with a pale silvery-blue upperside, with dark borders and chequered fringes; the female is brown. Confined to unimproved chalk grasslands, this is a rare vagrant in either Inclosures or open forest in the New Forest and surrounds, with occasional annual records of strays, usually males, although not seen every year. It appears they have traveled miles from their nearest colonies, possibly in some cases flying or blown across in winds, from the Isle of Wight. The species is known to have been introduced along the railway line in Woodfidley in the 1920s, the population persisting for several years. The larvae feed on horseshoe vetch.

Mazarine Blue *Polyommatus semiargus* – a very rare immigrant, said to occur in the Ringwood area prior to 1836 and several specimens labelled from Brockenhurst were in the pre-1839 collection of W. Bentley.

Camberwell Beauty *Nymphalis antiopa* – Victoria County History records: 'Mr. Fletcher....saw a specimen by the roadside between Beaulieu and Brockenhurst in the New Forest.' There is also a record from Lyndhurst, August 1995, also Ringwood and other areas just outside the New Forest, part of a large immigration. There is a record from Ventnor, Isle of Wight, 9 March 2009.

Queen of Spain Fritillary *Issoria lathonia* – one seen at Denny Bog on 20 June 1928. A very rare immigrant, one recorded outside the New Forest from Hengistbury Head on 1 August 1988.

Cardinal *Argynnis pandora* – one claimed in the New Forest in the 1950s.

Niobe Fritillary *Fabriciana niobe* – mentioned from the New Forest as being taken in 1869 by Mr Gerrard of Lyndhurst, a misidentification? (Green, 2000).

Monarch *Danaus plexippus* – a very rare immigrant, recorded from Hurst Castle, Keyhaven, Needs Ore Point, Pennington and other places near the New Forest in October 1995. Another was seen at Lymington on 23 July 1996 and Needs Ore in 2007; also occasionally observed on the Isle of Wight.

Scarce Swallowtail *Iphicles podalirius* – a pair caught in the New Forest in the early 1820s, which may include one traced in a collection from Lyndhurst. Unlikely that a pair would be found and the record is considered highly suspect, although cannot be ruled out, as possible migrants from continental Europe have appeared on the southern UK coastline.

Swallowtail *Papilio machaon gorganus* – the continental race of the Swallowtail, recorded at Pennington Marshes on 17 September 1985 by Richard Coomber. Otherwise there are just a few pre-1960 records.

Other very rare immigrant butterflies reported since 1980 within 15 miles of the New Forest are: **Bath White *Pontia daplidice***, **Pale Clouded Yellow *Colias hyale***, **Geranium Bronze *Cacyreus marshalli***, **Long-tailed Blue *Lampides boeticus*** (one at Bartley in the Forest, in 1995) and the **Short-tailed Blue *Everes argiades***.

Attempted but failed introductions:

Black Hairstreak *Satyrium pruni* – reintroduction attempt made in the New Forest in 1922, using stock from Monks Wood; further attempt in 1969.

European Map *Araschnia levana* – introduction attempt made in the New Forest in 1922.

Heath Fritillary *Melitaea athalia* – several attempts made at reintroduction in the New Forest in the 1950s, mainly by C.B. Antram; also noted at Roydon Woods in 1986 and Holmsley in 1990.

1a	2a	6a
1b	2b	6b
1c	3	7a
1c	4	7b
1d	5	8

Plates 1a–1d
Chalkhill Blue
a) male
b) female
c) male underside [GP]
d) female underside [GP]

Plates 2a & 2b
Queen of Spain Fritillary
a) [NH]
b) underside [NH]

Plate 3
Monarch female

Plate 4
Swallowtail [RC]

Plate 5
Bath White

Sometimes aberrations are seen, a few examples are shown in plates 6–8

Plates 6a & 6b
Small Copper
a) male ab. *radiata* [GH]
b) ab. *auronitens-subradiata*

Plates 7a & 7b
Pearl-bordered Fritillary
a) ab. *tatrica*
b) ab. *transversa* [GP]

Plate 8
Small Pearl-bordered Fritillary
ab. *chlorographa*

MOTHS

UK: c.2,500 species i.e. c.900 macro moths plus 1,600 micro moths, (in Hampshire c.2,000 species [80%], i.e. 750 larger macro moths and 1,250 smaller micro moths)
New Forest: c.1,460 species [58%] (650 macro moths [72%], 810 micro moths [51%], including extinctions). NB – the micro moths have been partly neglected by specialists and under recorded, it is estimated that at least 80% of the Hampshire micros should be found in the New Forest, increasing the number of micros to 1,000 and the moths overall to 66% of the UK fauna.

The mainly nocturnal moths are one of the most popular insect groups in Britain, particularly the larger, macro moths. The New Forest has always been one of the premier sites in the country for moths, with more than its fair share of specialities. It has always been a stronghold for two nationally rare crimson underwings and the Clifden Nonpareil (a blue underwing) also appears to be breeding in the area, once again.

There are several individuals regularly moth trapping in their gardens, which result in a wide range of species, as well as in the Forest, where over 100 species a night would not be unusual on a warm still night. Why are moths attracted to light? The main theory is that they use the moon to navigate at night and are confused by bright lights. Gardens are also often useful places to find caterpillars. Woodlands are excellent spots to run moth traps, but permission is needed from the Forestry Commission at Lyndhurst to run traps in the Forest, or to sugar trees in a long narrow strip. There is no shortage of suitable habitats, with rarities associated with woodland, including the colourful Scarce Merveille du Jour and the Triangle, and open heathland where the Shoulder-striped Clover flies. The distribution of moths is probably much more extensive than recorded, as it is mainly the familiar sites that have been worked, leaving many areas without records. Although a rich fauna, the percentage of moths associated with the Forest looks a little low, compared with the number of species in Hampshire. There have been some extinctions, notably the New Forest Burnet in 1927 and, more recently, the Speckled Footman, last seen in 1960.

Photographs of a wide selection of moths are provided in this book, including selected caterpillars (larvae). Although not all species are included, notes are provided on many species, including rarities, or those most likely to be encountered by the public.

Dew Moth with Hurst Castle in background

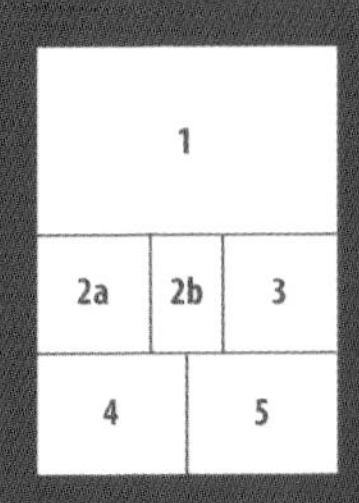

Plate 1
Black Arches
male (right) and female

Plates 2a & 2b
Argent & Sable
a) female egglaying [RC
b) egg [RC]

Plate 3
Scarlet Tiger larva [PCr]

Plate 4
Winter Moth female

Plate 5
Green Long-horn
Adela reaumurella
[a micro moth] [PCr]

SWIFT MOTHS – Family Hepialidae

UK: 5 species
New Forest: 5 species [100%].

Ghost Moth *Hepialus humuli* (wingspan: 44–48 mm)

CURRENT STATUS IN THE NEW FOREST: Widespread
IDENTIFICATION: Attractive white forewings in male, sometimes with buff coloration, compared with yellowish-orange forewings in the female. The hindwings are grey.
HABITAT: Grassy areas, waste ground, where the larvae feed on roots of grasses and many other plants. Widespread in the Forest and surrounds, including the Isle of Wight, both sexes may be attracted to light from June to early August, or may be observed on fences or shop windows. Widespread and common throughout much of Britain.

The **Orange Swift *Hepialus sylvina*** (32–48 mm), **Gold Swift *Hepialus hecta*** (26–32 mm), **Common Swift *Hepialus lupulinus*** (25–40 mm) and **Map-winged Swift *Hepialus fusconebulosa*** (32–50 mm), are common in the Forest.

LEOPARD and GOAT MOTHS – Family Cossidae

UK: 3 species
New Forest: 2 species [67%]

Leopard Moth *Zeuzera pyrina* (wingspan: 45–78 mm)

CURRENT STATUS IN THE NEW FOREST: Widespread
IDENTIFICATION: Whitish, with six black spots on the thorax, and blackish spotting on the wings.
HABITAT: Open deciduous woodland, gardens, parks, scrub and orchards where the larvae feed in stems and branches of a variety of trees and shrubs, including fruit trees, sallow, lilac and honeysuckle. Widespread in the Forest and surrounds, including the Isle of Wight, males are attracted to light from late June to early August and may be spotted on tree trunks or fences in the daytime. Widespread in Britain as far north as Yorkshire.

Goat Moth *Cossus cossus* (wingspan: 68–96 mm)

CURRENT STATUS IN THE NEW FOREST: Widespread
IDENTIFICATION: Large, wings greyish brown with crosslines.
HABITAT: Deciduous woodland edges, gardens, marshes and parks where the larvae burrow into the trunk of a variety of trees and shrubs, including ash, birch, oak, willow and fruit trees, producing large exit holes; the life cycle may be around five years. Recorded in a few scattered parts of the Forest, including Beaulieu, Brockenhurst, Burley, Denny Wood, Ladycross and Perrywood Ivy Inclosures, Mark Ash, Queen's Bower and Roydon Woods, also occasionally in the Forest surrounds, including the Isle of Wight. Probably overlooked in many areas and likely to be widespread. Occasionally attracted to light from June to July, but the large reddish larvae (sometimes smelling goat-like) are more likely to be seen wandering around between August to October before pupating in the soil. Locally widespread in southern Britain, less common further north.

1a		1b
2	3a	3b
4a	4b	5
6	7a	7b
		7c

Plates 1a & 1b
Ghost Moth
a) male [RC]
b) female [DG]

Plate 2
Orange Swift [RC]

Plates 3a & 3b
Gold Swift
a) male [GP]
b) female [RC]

Plates 4a & 4b
Common Swift
a) male [RC]
b) female [RC]

Plate 5
Map-winged Swift [RC]

Plate 6
Leopard Moth [CT]

Plates 7a–7c
Goat Moth
a) with pupal case [CT]
b) Goat Moth tree, showing exit holes of larvae
c) larva

FORESTER and BURNET MOTHS – Family Zygaenidae

UK: 10 species
New Forest: 6 species [60%], including 2 extinct

The Zygaenidae are attractive day-flying moths with club-shaped antennae, but only occasional in inland parts of the Forest, as they are more likely to be numerous in grassland and chalk downs. Nevertheless, the attractive **Six-spot Burnet *Zygaena filipendulae*** (25–40 mm, local) and **Narrow-bordered Five-spot Burnet *Zygaena lonicerae*** (30–46 mm, local) are likely to be encountered in some meadows and grassy areas from late June, including Keyhaven and surrounds. However, they are commoner in the Forest surrounds, including Barton common, Milford-on-Sea and the Southampton area. The **Five-spot Burnet *Zygaena trifolii decreta*** (32–40 mm, rare) is uncommon in the Forest. All three species mentioned are found in the Isle of Wight. The **Cistus Forester *Adscita geryon*** (20–25 mm, very rare) was found in the northern part of the Forest in 2004.

EXTINCTIONS: The **Forester *Adscita statices*** (24–29 mm) was last seen in 1950 in the Bishops Dyke to Woodfidley area, hence it is presumed extinct in the Forest, although found elsewhere in Hampshire. The **New Forest Burnet Moth *Zygaena viciae ytenensis*** (22–32 mm) was last recorded in Woodfidley in 1927 and the demise of this subspecies in its last known English site was possibly contributed to by over-collecting, in addition to conifer planting and forest fires. Subspecies *argyllensis* is found in Scotland.

FESTOON and TRIANGLE – Family Limacodidae

UK: 2 species
New Forest: 2 species [100%]

Festoon *Apoda limacodes* (wingspan: 28–32 mm)

CURRENT STATUS IN THE NEW FOREST: Widespread
IDENTIFICATION: Orange-brown, with curved cross-lines; the male rests with abdomen upturned.
HABITAT: Deciduous woodlands, where the larvae feed on oak and beech. Recorded in several parts of the Forest, including Denny, Roydon and Stubbs Woods, Knightwood and Sloden Inclosures, Brockenhurst, also the Forest surrounds, including the Isle of Wight. Attracted to light in June and July, also occasionally noticed flying around the top of oak trees in sunshine. Locally distributed in southern England.

Triangle *Heterogenea asella* (wingspan: 16–22 mm)

CURRENT STATUS IN THE NEW FOREST: Rare
IDENTIFICATION: Rather small, brown species with triangular forewing and tent-like resting position.
HABITAT: Deciduous woodlands, where the larvae feed on oak, beech and occasionally poplar, horse chestnut and small-leaved lime. Appears to be in decline, the Forest is one of the strongholds for the species, where it has been recorded from Ashurst, Mallard Wood and New Copse Inclosure, amongst others. Occasionally attracted to light from mid June to July, also noticed flying around the top of oak trees in sunshine. A scarce species found in parts of southern England.

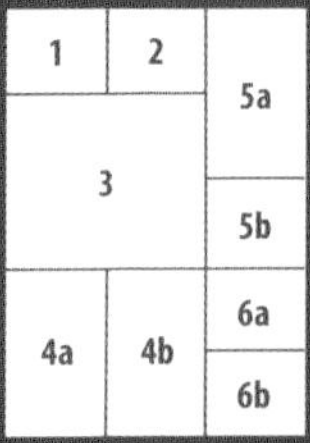

1	2	5a
3		5b
4a	4b	6a
		6b

Plate 1
Forester [DG]

Plate 2
New Forest Burnet, extinct in the Forest, photographed in Europe [DG]

Plate 3
Six-spot Burnet

Plates 4a & 4b
Narrow-bordered Five-spot Burnet
b) larva [GP]

Plates 5a & 5b
Festoon
a) pair [DG]
b) larva [DG]

Plates 6a & 6b
Triangle
a) male [SR]
b) female [SR]

CLEARWING MOTHS – Family Sesiidae

UK: 16 species
New Forest: 10 species [63%]

The Sesiidae fly in sunny weather and the maggot-like larvae are found in stems, branches, trunks and roots of trees and shrubs, or in roots of low-growing plants. Several of these attractive wasp-like species with partly transparent wings are occasionally recorded in the Forest in gardens, allotments and woodlands. Most likely to be seen are the **Currant Clearwing *Synanthedon tipuliformis*** (18–22 mm), **Orange-tailed Clearwing *Synanthedon andrenaeformis*** (19–25 mm), **Red-belted Clearwing *Synanthedon myopaeformis*** (18–26 mm) and **Six-belted Clearwing *Bembecia ichneumoniformis*** (17–22 mm). These species are also occasional in the Forest surrounds. Other species more rarely recorded from the Forest are the **Yellow-legged Clearwing *Synanthedon vespiformis*** (19–27 mm), **White-barred Clearwing *Synanthedon spheciformis*** (28–32 mm), **Sallow Clearwing *Synanthedon flaviventris*** (18–22 mm), **Red-tipped Clearwing *Synanthedon formicaeformis*** (18–26 mm) and **Large Red-belted Clearwing *Synanthedon culiciformis*** (23–29 mm), also the larger **Lunar Hornet Moth *Sesia bembeciformis*** (32–44 mm, very rare), the latter most likely from the Lyndhurst area in July, on sallow trunks. Moth hunters may use pheromone baits to try to attract these seldom seen insects, which has increased the number of records in recent years. It is also possible they will just fly close by in the daytime.

EGGAR MOTHS – Family Lasiocampidae

UK: 12 species
New Forest: 10 species [83%]

Lackey *Malacosoma neustria* (wingspan: 30–41 mm)

CURRENT STATUS IN THE NEW FOREST: Widespread
IDENTIFICATION: Yellowish to reddish brown, forewings with two cross-lines.
HABITAT: Gardens, hedgerows, parks and woodlands, where the conspicuously coloured gregarious larvae are often seen on hawthorn and wild cherry. Widespread in the Forest and surrounds, including the Isle of Wight. Adults are found in July to August. Widespread in much of Britain, scarcer in northern parts up to Cumbria and Yorkshire.

Oak Eggar *Lasiocampa quercus* (wingspan: 58–90 mm)

CURRENT STATUS IN THE NEW FOREST: Common
IDENTIFICATION: Male dark brown with white central spot and yellow band, same in female except larger with buff or light brown ground colour.
HABITAT: A heathland species, the adults may be seen in July to August flying in the sunshine, but females are also attracted to lights at night (they are also found on the coast). The large larvae are often seen in late summer on heather or bilberry. Widespread in the Forest and surrounds, including the Isle of Wight, throughout southern England as far north as County Durham and Lancashire.

1	2a	2b
	3	4
5	6	7
8a	8c	9a
8b	8d	9b

Plate 1
Lunar Hornet Moth [RA]

Plates 2a & 2b
Currant Clearwing
a) male [RC]
b) female [GP]

Plate 3
Yellow-legged Clearwing [TB]

Plate 4
Orange-tailed Clearwing [RC]

Plate 5
Red-belted Clearwing [TB]

Plate 6
Red-tipped Clearwing [DG]

Plate 7
Six-belted Clearwing female

Plates 8a–8d
Lackey
a) male [RC]
b) male [RC]
c) larval web
d) larva [GP]

Plates 9a & 9b
Oak Eggar
a) female [GP]
b) larva [GP]

Fox Moth ***Macrothylacia rubi*** (wingspan: 48–72 mm)
CURRENT STATUS IN THE NEW FOREST: Common
IDENTIFICATION: Plain mid to dark brown, with pale cross-bands, but lacking a central spot.
HABITAT: A heathland and coastal species, the fast-flying males may be seen in May to June flying in the sunshine, although both sexes are attracted to lights. The large larvae are often seen by walkers in late summer on heather, bramble, bilberry and others. Widespread in the Forest and immediate surrounds, including the Isle of Wight and throughout Britain.

Drinker ***Euthrix potatoria*** (wingspan: 50–70 mm)
CURRENT STATUS IN THE NEW FOREST: Common
IDENTIFICATION: Male reddish brown, with yellowish patches, the cross-line on the forewing runs to the wing tip. Two central spots are present. The larger female varies in colour from buff or yellow to dark brown.
HABITAT: Damp areas including marshes and riversides, adults are found in July to August. The large, hairy grass or reed-feeding larvae are often seen by walkers. Widespread in the Forest and immediate surrounds, including the Isle of Wight and throughout Britain.

Of the remaining species of eggar moths recorded in the Forest, the attractive **December Moth** ***Poecilocampa populi*** (18–22 mm, widespread) is late out, adults flying in late October to January. Arguably the **Lappet** ***Gastropacha quercifolia*** (28–42 mm, widespread) is the most stunning species in the family, with its elaborately scalloped wings, unusual resting posture and snout. The **Grass Eggar** ***Lasiocampa trifolii*** (46–76 mm) has not been recorded in the Forest since 1923, and the Isle of Wight since 1954; it is still found further afield in south Hayling Island. Other species recorded in the Forest are the **Pale Eggar** ***Trichiura crataegi*** (33–40 mm, rare), **Small Eggar** ***Eriogaster lanestris*** [not recorded in the Forest since 1931] (36–47 mm) and the **Pine-tree Lappet** ***Dendrolimus pini*** (45–70 mm, very rare)

EMPEROR MOTHS – Family Saturniidae [well known as Silk Moths]

UK: 1 species
New Forest: 1 species [100%]

Emperor Moth ***Saturnia pavonia*** (wingspan: 55–85 mm)
CURRENT STATUS IN THE NEW FOREST: Widespread
IDENTIFICATION: One of our largest, most attractive moths, with conspicuous eye-spots.
HABITAT: A typical heathland species, less frequent in marshy areas or elsewhere, adults may be seen in April to June flying in the sunshine, although both sexes are attracted to lights. The large green and black banded (but somewhat variable) larvae are sometimes seen by walkers in summer on ling and in marshes on meadowsweet or sallow; also feeds on bramble and others, overwintering as a pupa in a pear-shaped cocoon. Widespread in the Forest and immediate surrounds, also recorded from the Isle of Wight, and throughout Britain in suitable habitat.

Family Endromidae

UK: 1 species
New Forest: 1 species [100%] – if record genuine, long extinct

The **Kentish Glory** ***Endromis versicolora*** (55–89 mm) is associated with the Forest by two specimens, labelled "New Forest, 1917". The species is not figured in this book.

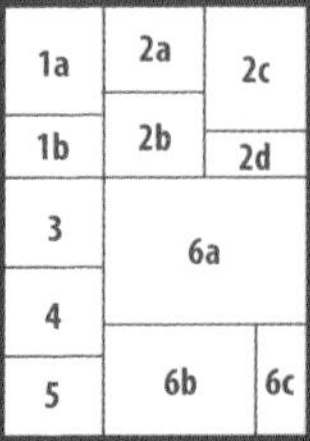

1a	2a	2c
1b	2b	2d
3	6a	
4		
5	6b	6c

Plates 1a & 1b
Fox Moth
a) [RC]
b) larva

Plates 2a–2d
Drinker
a) male [GP]
b) female
c) larva
d) larva moulting

Plate 3
December Moth

Plate 4
Pine-tree Lappet [RC]

Plate 5
Lappet [RC]

Plates 6a–6c
Emperor Moth
a) male [KT]
b) female [RC]
c) larva

HOOK-TIPS – Family Drepanidae

UK: 7 species
New Forest: 5 species [71%]

The Drepanidae are easily recognised by the hook-like tips on the forewings, except for the **Chinese Character *Cilix glaucata*** (22–27 mm, widespread), which resembles a bird dropping. The true hook-tips are often attracted to light, although some species fly high around oaks by day, such as the **Oak Hook-tip *Watsonalla binaria*** (28–35 mm, common), whose larvae feed on oak in parks and woods. The other hook-tips recorded in the Forest are the **Scalloped Hook-tip *Falcaria lacertinaria*** (34–38 mm, widespread), **Barred Hook-tip *Watsonalla cultraria*** (24–33 mm, widespread) and **Pebble Hook-tip *Drepana falcataria*** (36–40 mm, common).

Family Thyatiridae

UK: 9 species
New Forest: 9 species [100%]

The Thyatiridae include some mainly common species with interesting patterns on the wings, such as the **Peach Blossom *Thyatira batis*** (39–44 mm, widespread), whose larvae feed on bramble in woodlands. A selection of other Forest species is shown.

GEOMETRIDS – Family Geometridae

UK: 305 species
New Forest: 242 species [79%]

Only a selection of the more interesting species in each subfamily is discussed, along with figures of a representative range of species.

Subfamily Archiearinae (Orange Underwings)

UK: 2 species
New Forest: 2 species [100%]

Orange Underwing *Archiearis parthenias* (Wingspan: 35–39 mm)
CURRENT STATUS IN THE NEW FOREST: Local
IDENTIFICATION: Forewings brown with white central cross-band; hind wings dark, with orange band.
HABITAT: Deciduous woodlands and other areas with the foodplant, birch. Widely recorded in the Forest, also north-east Isle of Wight. Found flying high around birch trees from March to April. Local throughout Britain.

Light Orange Underwing *Archiearis notha* (Wingspan: 33–36 mm)
CURRENT STATUS IN THE NEW FOREST: Rare
IDENTIFICATION: Forewings brown, lacking white central cross-band in the similar Orange Underwing; hind wings dark, with orange band, lacking a central projection present in the Orange Underwing.
HABITAT: Found flying high in sunshine in woodlands around aspen trees (foodplant) from late March to mid April, possibly into early May. Can be dislodged in dull weather by shaking the trees. In the Forest recorded from few localities, such as Brockenhurst, Clumber and Ladycross Inclosures, but may be overlooked and needs careful examination to confirm its identity. Very local in the southern half of England, absent from the extreme south-west.

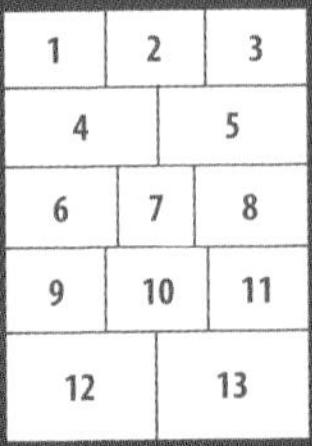

1	2	3
4		5
6	7	8
9	10	11
12		13

Plate 1
Scalloped Hook-tip

Plate 2
Oak Hook-tip

Plate 3
Barred Hook-tip [RC]

Plate 4
Pebble Hook-tip

Plate 5
Chinese Character [RC]

Plate 6
Peach Blossom [RC]

Plate 7
Buff Arches
Habrosyne pyritoides
(40–44 mm) [GP]

Plate 8
Figure of Eighty
Tethea ocularis
(36–44 mm) [RC]

Plate 9
Oak Lutestring
Cymatophorima diluta
(33–36 mm)

Plate 10
Yellow Horned
Achlya flavicornis
(39–44 mm) [RC]

Plate 11
Frosted Green
Polyploca ridens
(36–40 mm) [RC]

Plate 12
Orange Underwing mating pair [DG]

Plate 13
Light Orange Underwing [KT]

Subfamily Alsophilinae (March Moth)

UK: 1 species
New Forest: 1 species [100%]

The **March Moth *Alsophila aescularia*** (34–38 mm, common), is an early species (February to April), with a wingless female found on tree trunks.

Subfamily Geometrinae (Emeralds)

UK: 11 species
New Forest: 8 species [73%]

An attractive group of emerald green moths (particularly when freshly emerged), including the **Small Grass Emerald *Chlorissa viridata*** (24–27 mm, rare), found in June to early July in damper parts of Beaulieu Heath and Denny Bog amongst others; may be disturbed from the foodplant, heather, in the daytime. The **Large Emerald *Geometra papilionaria*** (50–64 mm, common) inhabits woodland and heath; the larvae mainly feed on birch. The **Blotched Emerald *Comibaena bajularia*** (29–33 mm, common) is found in old oak woodland.

Subfamily Sterrhinae (Mochas and waves)

UK: 38 species
New Forest: 29 species [81%]

An interesting group of small woodland and garden moths. The **Dingy Mocha *Cyclophora pendularia*** (26–29 mm, rare) is associated with sallow in boggy areas, but is seldom recorded compared with the **Mocha *Cyclophora annularia*** (22–26 mm, local) which has larger eye spots than its relatives. Some species have bars to break up the wing pattern and provide better camouflage, such as the **Maidens Blush *Cyclophora punctaria*** (25–32 mm, common), and the appropriately named **Blood-vein *Timandra comae*** (30–34 mm, common). The stunning **Purple-bordered Gold *Idaea muricata*** (18–20 mm, widespread) may be disturbed by day in boggy heathland in June and July. The **Portland Ribbon Wave *Idaea degeneraria*** (26–31 mm, rare), by contrast, is a rarity (a possible immigrant), only occasionally recorded from the Forest and Isle of Wight. Its relatives are much commoner and some species of waves are amongst the most commonly seen moths attracted to lights in shop windows.

Subfamily Larentiinae (Carpets, pugs and allies)

UK: 165 species
New Forest: 132 species [80%]

Carpets and pugs (see pages 208–211) are a large subfamily, easily recognised by the shape and resting posture. Well represented in the Forest and surrounds, the carpets include the familiar and variable **Garden Carpet *Xanthorhoe fluctuata*** (27–31 mm, common). The **Yellow Shell *Camptogramma bilineata*** (28–32 mm, common) is particularly variable and often disturbed in the daytime. The conspicuous **Argent & Sable *Rheumaptera hastata*** (34–38 mm, very rare) was formerly common in several places in the Forest up to the late 1960s, but populations have declined. **Winter Moth *Operophtera brumata*** (28–33 mm, common) males are often seen on fences in October to January, but the wingless female needs to be carefully searched for at the base of tree trunks. The **Lime-speck Pug *Eupithecia centaureata*** (20–24 mm, common) is just one of many pugs, another widespread species is the **Treble Bar *Aplocera plagiata*** (37–43 mm, common), easily disturbed by day. The almost completely black (but for white wing tips) **Chimney Sweeper *Odezia atrata*** (27–30 mm, very rare) was found at Rush Bush in 2007, after not being recorded in the Forest since 1970.

1	2	3
	4	5
6	7	8
9	10	11
12	13	14
15	16	17

Plate 1
March Moth [RC]

Plate 2
Large Emerald

Plate 3
Blotched Emerald [RC]

Plate 4
Common Emerald
Hemithea aestivaria
(29–34 mm) [RC]

Plate 5
Small Grass Emerald [KT

Plate 6
Dingy Mocha [KT]

Plate 7
Mocha [RC]

Plate 8
Birch Mocha
Cyclophora albipunctata
(25–29 mm) [GP]

Plate 9
Maidens Blush

Plate 10
ClayTriple-lines
Cyclophora linearia
(26–33 mm) [RC]

Plate 11
Blood-vein

Plate 12
Mullein Wave
Scopula marginepunctat
(25–28 mm) [RC]

Plate 13
Rosy Wave
Scopula emutaria
(23–26 mm) [DG]

Plate 14
Cream Wave
Scopula floslactata
(29–33 mm) [RC]

Plate 15
Purple-bordered Gold [C

Plate 16
Treble Brown Spot
Idaea trigeminata
(23–25 mm) [RC]

Plate 17
Portland Ribbon Wave [

1	2
3	4
5	6
7	8
9	10
11	12

Plate 1
Red Twin-spot Carpet
Xanthorhoe spadicearia
(24–27 mm) [RC]

Plate 2
Dark-barred Twin-spot Carpet
Xanthorhoe ferrugata
(24–27 mm)

Plate 3
Silver-ground Carpet
Xanthorhoe montanata
(29–33 mm) [RC]

Plate 4
Garden Carpet

Plate 5
Shaded Broad-bar
Scotopteryx chenopodiata
(34–38 mm) [RC]

Plate 6
July Belle
Scotopteryx luridata
(32–38 mm)

Plate 7
Common Carpet [RC]

Plate 8
Yellow Shell [RC]

Plate 9
The Streamer
Anticlea derivata
(30–34 mm)

Plate 10
Water Carpet
Lampropteryx suffumata
(32–38 mm) [RC]

Plate 11
Devon Carpet
Lampropteryx otregiata
(27–30 mm) [RC]

Plate 12
Purple Bar
Cosmorhoe ocellata
(28–30 mm) [RC]

1		2
3	4	5
6		7
8		9
10		11
12		13

Plate 1
Phoenix *Eulithis prunata*
(37–42 mm) [RC]

Plate 2
Small Phoenix
Ecliptopera silaceata
(29–34 mm) [RC]

Plate 3
Red-green Carpet
Chloroclysta siterata
(30–36 mm) [RC]

Plate 4
Barred Yellow
Cidaria fulvata
(25–30 mm) [RC]

Plate 5
Blue-bordered Carpet
Plemyria rubiginata
(22–28 mm) [RC]

Plate 6
Pine Carpet *Thera firmata*
(30–34 mm) [RC]

Plate 7
Spruce Carpet
Thera britannica
(30–36 mm) [RC]

Plate 9
Broken Barred Carpet
Electrophaes corylata
(27–31 mm) [RC]

Plate 9
Beech-green Carpet
Colostygia olivata
(26–35 mm) [RC]

Plate 10
Green Carpet
Colostygia pectinataria
(25–29 mm)

Plate 11
July Highflyer
Hydriomena furcata
(26–39 mm) [RC]

Plate 12
Fern *Horisme tersata*
(31–36 mm) [RC]

Plate 13
Pretty Chalk Carpet
Melanthia procellata
(35–43 mm) [RC]

1	2
3	4
5	6
7	8
9	10
11	12
13	14

Plate 1
Argent & Sable [RC]

Plate 2
Sharp-angled Carpet
Euphyia unangulata
(27–30 mm) [RC]

Plate 3
November Moth
Epirrita dilutata
(38–44 mm) [RC]

Plate 4
Winter Moth

Plate 5
Barred Rivulet
Perizoma bifaciata
(20–26 mm) [RC]

Plate 6
Sandy Carpet
Perizoma flavofasciata
(26–32 mm) [RC]

Plate 7
Foxglove Pug
Eupithecia pulchellata
(18–22 mm) [RC]

Plate 8
Marbled Pug
Eupithecia irriguata
(20–22 mm) [RC]

Plate 9
Netted Pug
Eupithecia venosata
(21–24 mm) [RC]

Plate 10
Lime-speck Pug [RC]

Plate 11
Freyer's Pug
Eupithecia intricata
(20–24 mm) [RC]

Plate 12
Wormwood Pug
Eupithecia absinthiata
(21–23 mm) [RC]

Plate 13
Currant Pug
Eupithecia assimilata
(17–22 mm) [RC]

Plate 14
Common Pug
Eupithecia vulgata
(18–21 mm) [RC]

1	2
3	4
5	6
7	8
9 10	11
12	13

Plate 1
Grey Pug
Eupithecia subfuscata
(17–21 mm) [RC]

Plate 2
Plain Pug
Eupithecia simpliciata
(21–23 mm) [RC]

Plate 3
Narrow-winged Pug
Eupithecia nanata
(17–20 mm) [RC]

Plate 4
Brindled Pug
Eupithecia abbreviata
(19–22 mm) [RC]

Plate 5
V Pug *Chloroclystis v-ata*
(14–19 mm) [RC]

Plate 6
Green Pug
Pasiphila rectangulata
(17–21 mm) [RC]

Plate 7
Double-striped Pug
Gymnoscelis rufifasciata
(15–19 mm) [RC]

Plate 8
Dentated Pug
Anticollix sparsata
(20–24 mm) [RC]

Plate 9
Treble Bar [RC]

Plate 10
Purple Treble-bar
Aplocera praeformata
(39–49 mm) [RC]

Plate 11
Chimney Sweeper [RC]

Plate 12
Small Yellow Wave
Hydrelia flammeolaria
(20–22 mm) [RC]

Plate 13
Small Seraphim
Pterapherapteryx sexalata
(22–26 mm) [RC]

Subfamily Ennominae (Thorns, beauties, umbers and allies)

UK: 88 species
New Forest: 70 species [80%]

These include some of the most attractive, larger geometrids, again well represented in the Forest and surrounds. The attractive **Magpie *Abraxas grossulariata*** (42–48 mm, widespread) may be seen fluttering around gardens, particularly if foodplants such as currant and gooseberry are present. The **Brimstone Moth *Opisthograptis luteolata*** (33–46 mm, common) is a conspicuous yellow species in hedgerows and gardens, as is the even more spectacular pale lemon **Swallow-tailed Moth *Ourapteryx sambucaria*** (50–62 mm, common), whose larvae feed on ivy. Still on the theme of yellow, the unmistakable **Speckled Yellow *Pseudopanthera macularia*** (28–30 mm, common) flies in sunny weather and is found in most woodland rides in Inclosures from mid May to June, where the main foodplant wood sage grows. The open heathland has characteristic scarcer species, the rather drab **Horse Chestnut *Pachycnemia hippocastanaria*** (28–32 mm, widespread) found in the Forest in April to May and July to August, the **Bordered Grey *Selidosema brunnearia scandinaviaria*** (37–43 mm, local), less frequent, but may be disturbed from heather by day in July to August; for example in 2008 it was recorded from Brockenhurst, Hatchet Pond and Ocknell Plain. Where there are isolated pines or birches, the **Ringed Carpet *Cleora cinctaria*** (36–42 mm, local) may sometimes be found resting on tree trunks during late April to May. A common heathland speciality in May and June, is the sun-loving **Common Heath *Ematurga atomaria*** (22–34 mm, common), whereas the **Latticed Heath *Chiasmia clathrata*** (26–32 mm, rare), is only occasionally seen in the Forest, where clover is common. The thorns are attractive moths, some species resting like butterflies with the held closed or partly closed. The **Dusky Thorn *Ennomos fuscantaria*** (38–42 mm, common) is a good example, whose larvae feed on ash. There are very contrasting colour forms in the **Peppered Moth *Biston betularia*** (45–62 mm, common) which may be found from May to August; the black form *carbonaria* more often seen in industrial areas. Another very variable, often seen species is the **Mottled Umber *Erannis defoliaria*** (male 40–45 mm, common), found in October to January; the female has minute wing stumps and is unable to fly. Typical finds in woodlands include the **Scalloped Oak *Crocallis elinguaria*** (40–46 mm, common) and **Great Oak Beauty *Hypomecis roboraria*** (60–68 mm, local), the latter one of several well camouflaged species of similar appearance, commonly attracted to light. Moving on to coastal localities, the **Yellow Belle *Semiaspilates ochrearia*** (28–36 mm, local) is found on shingle around Hurst Castle between May to June and August to September, where is flies in the daytime as well as at night. The **Speckled Beauty *Fagivorina arenaria*** (35–39 mm) is included as a reminder of an extinct species lost from the Forest (and UK) in 1898, and the **Black-veined Moth *Siona lineata*** (38–48 mm) as a great rarity to look out for; nowadays, only breeding at a few sites on the Kent coast, but has been recorded on parts of the south coast in the past, including Dorset.

1	2	3
4	5	6
7	8	9
10	11	12a
13	14	12b

Plate 1
Magpie Moth

Plate 2
Clouded Border
Lomaspilis marginata
(24–28 mm) [RC]

Plate 3
Scorched Carpet
Ligdia adustata
(25–30 mm) [RC]

Plate 4
Peacock Moth
Macaria notata
(28–32 mm) [KT]

Plate 5
Sharp-angled Peacock
Macaria alternata
(27–32 mm)

Plate 6
Tawny-barred Angle
Macaria liturata
(28–34 mm) [RC]

Plate 7
Latticed Heath [RC]

Plate 8
Little Thorn
Cepphis advenaria
(27–30 mm) [RC]

Plate 9
Brown Silver Line
Petrophora chlorosata
(31–37 mm)

Plate 10
Scorched Wing
Plagodis dolabraria
(34–38 mm) [RC]

Plate 11
Horse Chestnut [RC]

Plates 12a & 12b
Brimstone Moth
b) larva [DG]

Plate 13
Bordered Beauty
Epione repandaria
(28–31 mm) [RC]

Plate 14
Speckled Yellow

Plate 1
Lilac Beauty
Apeira syringaria
(38–42 mm) [RC]

Plate 2
August Thorn
Ennomos quercinaria
(42–50 mm) [RC]

Plate 3
Canary-shouldered Thorn *Ennomos alniaria*
(38–42 mm)

Plate 4
Dusky Thorn

Plate 5
September Thorn
Ennomos erosaria
(38–42 mm)

Plate 6
Early Thorn
Selenia dentaria
(40–51 mm)

Plate 7
Purple Thorn
Selenia lunularia
(44–52 mm) [DG]

Plate 8
Scalloped Hazel
Odontopera bidentata
(46–50 mm) [RC]

Plate 9
Scalloped Oak

Plate 10
Swallow-tailed Moth [R

Plate 11
Feathered Thorn
Colotois pennaria
(46–50 mm) [RC]

Plates 12a & 12b
Orange Moth
Angerona prunaria
(42–56 mm)
a) male [DG]
b) male, form *corylaria* [DG]

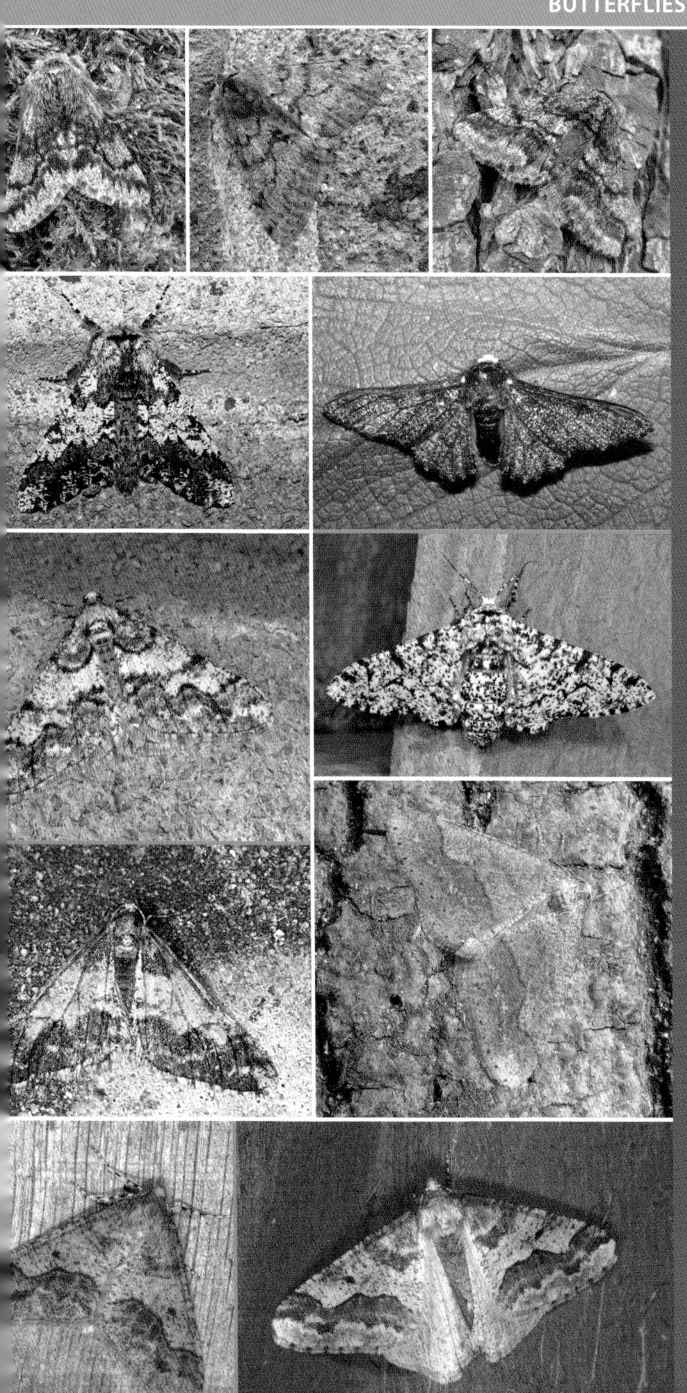

1	2	3
4	5a	
6a	5b	
6b	7	
8a	8b	

Plate 1
Small Brindled Beauty
Apocheima hispidaria
(35–37 mm) [RC]

Plate 2
Pale Brindled Beauty
Phigalia pilosaria
(45–50 mm) [RC]

Plate 3
Brindled Beauty
Lycia hirtaria
(42–52 mm) [RC]

Plate 4
Oak Beauty
Biston strataria
(51–56 mm) [RC]

Plates 5a & 5b
Peppered Moth
a) form *carbonaria* [RC]

Plates 6a & 6b
Spring Usher
Agriopis leucophaearia
(31–37 mm) [RC]

Plate 7
Dotted Border male
Agriopis marginaria
(36–42 mm) [RC]

Plates 8a & 8b
Mottled Umber

1	2
3	4
5	6
7a	7b
8	9
10a	10b

Plate 1
Waved Umber
Menophra abruptaria
(36–42 mm)

Plate 2
Willow Beauty
Peribatodes rhomboidaria
(40–48 mm) [RC]

Plate 3
Bordered Grey
Selidosema brunnearia
(37–43 mm) [RC]

Plate 4
Ringed Carpet [RC]

Plate 5
Satin Beauty ***Deileptenia ribeata***
(42–48 mm) [RC]

Plate 6
Mottled Beauty
Alcis repandata
(43–56 mm) [RC]

Plates 7a & 7b
Great Oak Beauty
a) [RC]
b) larva [DG]

Plate 8
Pale Oak Beauty
Hypomecis punctinalis
(46–55 mm) [RC]

Plate 9
Speckled Beauty [DG]

Plates 10a & 10b
Brussels Lace
Cleorodes lichenaria
(31–38 mm)
a) [RC]
b) larva [DG]

1		2
3a	3b	4
5		6
7		8
9		10
11	12a	12b

Plate 1
Engrailed
Ectropis bistortata
(38–45 mm) [RC]

Plate 2
Square Spot
Paradarisa consonaria
(40–45 mm) [RC]

Plates 3a & 3b
Common Heath
a) male
b) female

Plate 4
Bordered White
Bupalus piniaria
(34–40 mm) [RC]

Plate 5
Common White Wave
Cabera pusaria
(32–35 mm) [RC]

Plate 6
White-pinion Spotted
Lomographa bimaculata
(27–31 mm) [RC]

Plate 7
Clouded Silver
Lomographa temerata
(27–34 mm) [RC]

Plate 8
Early Moth
Theria primaria
(32–37 mm)

Plate 9
Light Emerald
Campaea margaritata
(42–54 mm)

Plate 10
Barred Red
Hylaea fasciaria
(32–44 mm)

Plate 11
Black-veined Moth [PCr]

Plates 12a & 12b
Yellow Belle
a) male
b) female

HAWKMOTHS – Family Sphingidae

UK: 18 species
New Forest: 14 species [78%]

The fast flying, medium to large hawkmoths (including the largest species in Britain) are colourful, robust moths often attracted to lights. Rearers are keen to keep the spectacular larvae, with their characteristic horn, all of which can be found by searching foodplants in the day. The pupae overwinter.

Convolvulus Hawkmoth *Agrius convolvuli* (Wingspan: 94–120 mm)
CURRENT STATUS IN THE NEW FOREST: Occasional immigrant
IDENTIFICATION: Large, grey with various streaks, hindwings with pink areas. The abdomen is banded black and pink.
HABITAT: Mainly suitable coastal habitats and gardens, but sometimes spreads well inland, hence recorded in scattered parts of the Forest and surrounds, including the Isle of Wight. In some years there are only a few records in Hampshire, during major influxes, hundreds (such as in 2003), particularly on or near the coast. This species is attracted to light in June to December, although mainly likely to be seen in September to October. May also appear in gardens from dusk nectaring on *Nicotiana* and *Petunia*. This species has been recorded in much of Britain, although the larvae are seldom found on bindweed, morning glory or related plants.

Privet Hawkmoth *Sphinx ligustri* (Wingspan: 100–120 mm)
CURRENT STATUS IN THE NEW FOREST: Widespread
IDENTIFICATION: Dark brown, with paler areas on the forewings; abdomen and hindwings pink and black banded.
HABITAT: Open woodlands, hedgerows and gardens, recorded in much of the Forest and surrounds, including the Isle of Wight. Attracted to light from June to July, this species is widely recorded in the southern half of Britain. The attractive larvae – apple green with mauve stripes, are sometimes noticed on privet, lilac, holly and ash, it is worth examining these closely if there are signs of stripped branches.

Pine Hawkmoth *Hyloicus pinastri* (Wingspan: 72–80 mm)
CURRENT STATUS IN THE NEW FOREST: Widespread
IDENTIFICATION: Grey or brownish-grey, with black streaks on the forewings; abdomen banded black and white.
HABITAT: Coniferous woodlands and nearby habitat, such as heathland, recorded in much of the Forest and surrounds, including the Isle of Wight. Attracted to light from May to early August, this species is widespread in southern and eastern England. The adult feeds on flowers after dark, particularly honeysuckle. The larvae feed on Scots pine and Norway spruce.

Lime Hawkmoth *Mimas tiliae* (Wingspan: 70–80 mm)
CURRENT STATUS IN THE NEW FOREST: Widespread
IDENTIFICATION: Shades of green, with dark olive-green central blotches.
HABITAT: Deciduous woodlands and gardens, with scattered records in the Forest, but more widespread in the surrounds (particularly in more built up areas, such as Southampton area), including the Isle of Wight. Attracted to light from May to early July; flies earlier than many species. This species is generally distributed in the southern half of England and north to Yorkshire. The larvae feed on lime, elm, alder and birch; newly emerged adults are sometimes seen on lime trunks and pupae can be dug up from the base surrounds.

1	3a
2	3b
4	

Plate 1
Convolvulus Hawkmoth

Plate 2
Privet Hawkmoth [RC]

Plates 3a & 3b
Pine Hawkmoth
b) larva walking to find a suitable site in the ground to pupate

Plate 4
Lime Hawkmoth [RC]

Eyed Hawkmoth *Smerinthus ocellata* (wingspan: 75–95 mm)
CURRENT STATUS IN THE NEW FOREST: Widespread
IDENTIFICATION: The forewings are pinkish brown to dark brown or black; the hindwings reveal large eyespots on a pink background.
HABITAT: Deciduous woodlands, scrub, gardens and parks, recorded in much of the Forest and surrounds, including the Isle of Wight. Attracted to light from early May to mid July, occasionally with a later second generation. This species is widely distributed in England and Wales, local in Ireland. The larvae mainly feed on willow, aspen, sallow and apple. If disturbed by potential predators, the species has an effective startle display, flashing open its hindwings and rocking from side to side.

Poplar Hawkmoth *Laothoe populi* (wingspan: 72–92 mm)
CURRENT STATUS IN THE NEW FOREST: Common
IDENTIFICATION: Grey, with chestnut brown patch on the hindwings. At rest, the hindwings project well in front of the forewings.
HABITAT: Deciduous woodlands, gardens, heathland, moors and parks, recorded in much of the Forest and surrounds, including the Isle of Wight. Attracted to light from May to early August, occasionally with a later second generation. This species is widely distributed throughout Britain. The larvae feed on poplar, aspen, sallow and willow.

Narrow-bordered Bee Hawkmoth *Hemaris tityus* (wingspan: 41–46 mm)
CURRENT STATUS IN THE NEW FOREST: Very rare
IDENTIFICATION: Small bee-like species, with transparent wings, except for a narrow outer, brown margin.
HABITAT: Woodland, marshland and wetter parts of moorland, also chalk downland. Except for a single record at Longdown in 2010, there have been no records in the Forest and immediate surrounds, post 1980. Before that, they were not uncommon in Holmsley Bog, amongst others, but there is a chance it has been overlooked in some areas. Now rare in Hampshire, but holding on and usually recorded each year at Martin Down. Also recorded at Purewell, Christchurch in 2000. Usually found from mid May to June on sunny days, often in late morning or early afternoon; the adults do not stop, but hover to feed on flowers, including bird's foot trefoil and bugle. This declining species has been recorded throughout much of Britain, but is uncommon and now has a restricted range. The larvae feed on devil's-bit scabious, small scabious and field scabious.

Broad-bordered Bee Hawkmoth *Hemaris fuciformis*
(wingspan: 46–52 mm)
CURRENT STATUS IN THE NEW FOREST: Rare
IDENTIFICATION: Small bee-like species, with transparent wings, except for an outer, brown margin, wider than in the Narrow-bordered Bee Hawkmoth. When fresh, beautiful olive-grey on upper part of body and part of forewings.
HABITAT: Woodland rides and clearings, recorded in parts of the Forest and immediate surrounds, until the species declined. Although there were only a few records from 1980 to 2000, this species appears to be recovering. It is worth looking for on sunny days in May to mid July, hovering around flowers such as bugle at New Copse, Parkhill, Pignal and Wootton Inclosures, also Roydon Woods; it is most likely to be seen about mid May. This species is rather local in the southern half of England and Wales. The larvae feed on honeysuckle in bright, exposed places.

1a	3
1b	4a
2	4b

Plates 1a & 1b
Eyed Hawkmoth
a) starting to show eyespots on hindwings

Plate 2
Poplar Hawkmoth

Plate 3
Narrow-bordered Bee Hawkmoth [RC]

Plates 4a & 4b
Broad-bordered Bee Hawkmoth
a) [RC]
b) larva [DG]

Hummingbird Hawkmoth *Macroglossum stellatarum*
(wingspan: 50–58 mm)
CURRENT STATUS IN THE NEW FOREST: Widespread immigrant
IDENTIFICATION: Small bee-like species, grey with various darker markings, hindwings orange. Named after its resemblance to a Hummingbird.
HABITAT: Locations with plenty of flowers including buddleja, honeysuckle, lilac, petunia and red valerian, often seen in gardens. Recorded in a few parts of the Forest and more often in the surrounds, including the Isle of Wight. In some years there are few records in Hampshire, in a good year for migrants, hundreds. This species is a rapid flier, found in April to December, but mainly August to September, hovering over flowers in sunny weather, but in drab weather may settle for a while. This immigrant has been recorded in much of Britain, the larvae feeding on hedge bedstraw, lady's bedstraw and wild madder. Occasionally adults overwinter.

Striped Hawkmoth *Hyles livornica* (wingspan: 78–90 mm)
CURRENT STATUS IN THE NEW FOREST: Rare immigrant
IDENTIFICATION: Forewings dull olive green with broad pale bands, and white veins, giving a striped appearance. Hindwings with pink areas.
HABITAT: Most likely in gardens, visiting flowers including red valerian and petunia at night. Recorded in Brockenhurst and a few other areas, including the Isle of Wight. Attracted to light from April to October. Scattered reports in Britain, the larvae feed on hedge bedstraw and snapdragon.

Elephant Hawkmoth *Deilephila elpenor* (wingspan: 62–72 mm)
CURRENT STATUS IN THE NEW FOREST: Common
IDENTIFICATION: Pink and olive green forewings and body; hindwings pink and black.
HABITAT: Deciduous woodlands, gardens, grassland, parks and sand dunes, widely recorded in much of the Forest and surrounds, including the Isle of Wight. Attracted to light in May to early August, may also be seen nectaring at night on honeysuckle and rhododendron. This species is widely recorded in Britain, up to southern Scotland. Also found in Ireland. The large brown or green larvae with huge eye-spots surprise gardeners, both resembling an elephant's trunk when extended; when ready to pupate they wander. They feed on willowherb, bedstraw, fuchsia and others.

Small Elephant Hawkmoth *Deilephila porcellus* (wingspan: 47–56 mm)
CURRENT STATUS IN THE NEW FOREST: Widespread
IDENTIFICATION: A smaller, similar version of the Elephant Hawkmoth, pink and yellowish brown.
HABITAT: Chalk downland, heathland, coastal shingle and sandhills, fairly widely distributed in the Forest and surrounds, including the Isle of Wight, but recorded nowhere near as frequently as the Elephant Hawkmoth. Attracted to light in May to July, may also be seen nectaring at night on honeysuckle and rhododendron. This species is widely distributed throughout Britain. The larvae mainly feed on bedstraw and look like a small version of Elephant Hawkmoth larvae.

The **Death's Head Hawkmoth *Acherontia atropos*** (102–135 mm, very rare) is the largest British species, an immigrant. The adult has a short proboscis, adapted for stealing honey from nesting bees, but it is the larvae which are more likely to be seen on potato or deadly nightshade. An adult was found at Southbourne in September 2008 and one in the Isle of Wight in 2010. There are also old records in the Forest for the rare migrant **Silver-striped Hawkmoth *Hippotion celerio*** (72–80 mm, very rare), which was recorded in the Isle of Wight in the mid 1990s and Fordingbridge in 1996. Other species may occur in the surrounds, particularly coastal areas.

1a	3a	3b
1b	3c	
2	4a	4b
5a	5b	6

Plates 1a & 1b
Hummingbird Hawkmoth
a) [GP]

Plate 2
Striped Hawkmoth [RC]

Plates 3a–3c
Elephant Hawkmoth
a) [GP]
b) larva, showing eyespots
c) larva

Plates 4a & 4b
Small Elephant Hawkmoth
a) [KT]
b) larva

Plates 5a & 5b
Death's-head Hawkmoth
b) larva [PE]

Plate 6
Silver-striped Hawkmoth
[KT]

PROMINENTS and ALLIES – Family Notodontidae

UK: 27 species
New Forest: 23 species [85%]

The **Puss Moth *Cerura vinula*** (62–80 mm, common) is found from May to July with a stunning larva, worth looking for on sallow, poplar and aspen. Possibly an even more stunning larva is that of the **Lobster Moth *Stauropus fagi*** (55–70 mm, common) widespread in beech woodlands, although also feeds on birch, hazel and oak. The appropriately named **Chocolate-tip *Clostera curtula*** (36–38 mm, widespread) and **Small Chocolate-tip *Clostera pigra*** (24–28 mm, local) are reasonably widespread in the Forest, the latter mainly from boggy areas where creeping willow occurs. An attempt to introduce the **Scarce Chocolate-tip *Clostera anachoreta*** (36–38 mm, extinct) to Denny Wood and Ladycross was made in 1980. Other species recorded from the Forest are the **Buff-tip *Phalera bucephala*** (55–68 mm, common), **Alder Kitten *Furcula bicuspis*** (40–48 mm, albeit with doubt over old records, rare), **Sallow Kitten *Furcula furcula*** (35–42 mm, widespread), **Poplar Kitten *Furcula bifida*** (44–48 mm, rare), **Iron Prominent *Notodonta dromedarius*** (42–50 mm, common), **Pebble Prominent *Notodonta ziczac*** (42–52 mm, common), **Great Prominent *Peridea anceps*** (52–72 mm, common), **Lesser Swallow Prominent *Pheosia gnoma*** (46–58 mm, widespread), **Swallow Prominent *Pheosia tremula*** (50–64 mm, widespread), **Coxcomb Prominent *Ptilodon capucina*** (40–50 mm, common), **Maple Prominent *Ptilodon cucullina*** (37–46 mm, rare), **Scarce Prominent *Odontosia carmelita*** (44–52 mm, local), **Pale Prominent *Pterostoma palpina*** (42–60 mm, common), **White Prominent *Leucodonta bicoloria*** (38–42 mm, records from Brockenhurst in the 1950s doubtful), **Plumed Prominent *Ptilophora plumigera*** (33–44 mm, rare), **Marbled Brown *Drymonia dodonaea*** (39–44 mm, widespread), **Lunar Marbled Brown *Drymonia ruficornis*** (38–46 mm, widespread) and **Figure of Eight *Diloba caeruleocephala*** (34–40 mm, local).

TUSSOCK MOTHS – Family Lymantriidae

UK: 11 species
New Forest: 8 species [73%]

Another family widespread throughout much of the Forest (see Plates on page 227 overleaf), with well known, colourful larvae. The **Vapourer *Orgyia antiqua*** (35–38 mm, widespread) has a wingless female, which is searched for by the day and night flying orange-brown males, which rarely settle and are sometimes mistaken for butterflies. Some members of this family are regularly attracted to lights. The stunning **Pale Tussock *Calliteara pudibunda*** (50–70 mm, common) larva may be seen quickly walking on the ground prior to finding a spot to spin its cocoon; if disturbed, it curls up into a ball. Similarly, but this time with adults, the **Brown-tail *Euproctis chrysorrhoea*** (36–42 mm, common) raises or curls its abdomen into view if disturbed, in the hope this startles possible predators. The larval hairs can cause severe irritation to the human skin, best look but do not touch. Webs containing a number of the larvae are commonly seen on bramble, blackthorn, hawthorn, sallow and other shrubs. Other species recorded from the Forest are the **Dark Tussock *Dicallomera fascelina*** (40–53 mm, common), **Yellow-tail *Euproctis similis*** (35–45 mm, common), **White Satin Moth *Leucoma salicis*** (43–60 mm, local), **Black Arches *Lymantria monacha*** (44–54 mm, common) and **Gypsy Moth *Lymantria dispar*** (48–65 mm, rare).

1a	2a	3
1b	2b	4
5a	6a	7
5b	6b	8

Plates 1a & 1b
Buff-tip
b) larva [GP]

Plates 2a & 2b
Puss Moth
a) [RW]
b) larva defence [PG]

Plate 3
Sallow Kitten

Plate 4
Poplar Kitten [RC]

Plates 5a & 5b
Lobster Moth
a) [GP]
b) larva

Plates 6a & 6b
Pebble Prominent
a) [GP]
b) larva [DG]

Plate 7
Iron Prominent

Plate 8
Great Prominent [RC]

Prominents and allies continued on page 226

1	2
3	4
5	6
7	8
9	10

Plate 1
Lesser Swallow Prominent [RC]

Plate 2
Swallow Prominent [RC]

Plate 3
Coxcomb Prominent [RC]

Plate 4
Maple Prominent [RC]

Plate 5
Pale Prominent

Plate 6
Marbled Brown

Plate 7
Lunar Marbled Brown [RC]

Plate 8
Small Chocolate-tip [RC]

Plate 9
Chocolate-tip [RC]

Plate 10
Figure of Eight [RC]

1a	3a
1b	
2	3b
4a	4b
5a	6a
5b	6b

Plates 1a & 1b
Vapourer
a) male
b) larva

Plate 2
Dark Tussock [RC]

Plates 3a & 3b
Pale Tussock
b) larva

Plates 4a & 4b
Brown-tail
a) [RC]
b) larvae

Plates 5a & 5b
Yellow-tail
a) [RC]
b) larva

Plates 6a & 6b
Black Arches
a) male
b) larva [DG]

TIGERS, ERMINES, FOOTMEN – Family Arctiidae

UK: 32 species
New Forest: 28 species [88%]

One of Britain's most colourful moth families, well represented in the Forest. There are two subfamilies.

Subfamily Lithosiinae

Small to medium sized species with long forewings, known as footmen, with a number of mainly common species. The footmen are rather drab in comparison with representatives of the brightly colourful subfamily Arctiinae.

Dew Moth *Setina irrorella* (wingspan: 26–32 mm)
CURRENT STATUS IN THE NEW FOREST: Rare
IDENTIFICATION: Male with orange-yellow wings and three cross-rows of black spots; female smaller and paler.
HABITAT: Shingle beaches, cliffs and chalk or limestone hills. Found in the Forest on vegetation in the shingle at Hurst Castle. Recorded from Beaulieu and Brockenhurst in 1994 and just outside the Forest, found in parts of the Isle of Wight. Usually seen in June to July, the male flying in the day and night. Found in few widespread coastal areas in Britain, the larvae of this declining species overwinter and feed on lichens growing on the rocks.

There are several other species recorded in the Forest. One of the rarest, the **Dotted Footman *Pelosia muscerda*** (30–34 mm, very rare) was rediscovered in the Forest on 26 July 2008 at Ashurst and Ladycross, the first records since 1891 (107 years). The **Orange Footman *Eilema sororcula*** (27–30 mm, widespread), the **Hoary Footman *Eilema caniola*** (28–35 mm, local) less frequently recorded and the **Speckled Footman *Coscinia cribraria*** (33–40 mm) may be extinct in the Forest, last recorded in 1960. Other species are the **Round-winged Muslin *Thumatha senex*** (20–22 mm, widespread), **Rosy Footman *Miltochrista miniata*** (25–33 mm, common), **Muslin Footman *Nudaria mundana*** (19–23 mm, widespread), **Red-necked Footman *Atolmis rubricollis*** (28–36 mm, local), **Four-dotted Footman *Cybosia mesomella*** (29–34 mm, widespread), **Dingy Footman *Eilema griseola*** (32–40 mm, widespread), **Scarce Footman *Eilema complana*** (30–36 mm, widespread), **Buff Footman *Eilema depressa*** (28–36 mm, widespread), **Common Footman *Eilema lurideola*** (31–38 mm, widespread), **Four-spotted Footman *Lithosia quadra*** (35–55 mm, local) and the **Crimson Speckled *Utetheisa pulchella*** (29–42 mm, a very rare immigrant). Footmen larvae are seldom encountered in woodland but, depending on species, they feed on algae or lichens. The larvae overwinter, except for Orange and Red-necked, which overwinter as pupae.

1a	1b	2
3	4	5
6	7	8
9	10	11
12a	12b	13

Plates 1a & 1b
Dew Moth
b) larva [DG]

Plate 2
Rosy Footman

Plate 3
Red-necked Footman [RC

Plate 4
Four-dotted Footman [R

Plate 5
Dotted Footman [RC]

Plate 6
Orange Footman [RC]

Plate 7
Dingy Footman

Plate 8
Hoary Footman [RC]

Plate 9
Scarce Footman

Plate 10
Buff Footman [RC]

Plate 11
Common Footman

Plates 12a & 12b
Four-spotted Footman
a) female (bottom) and male [DG]
b) larva [DG]

Plate 13
Speckled Footman [DG]

Subfamily Arctiinae

These include the medium to large sized tiger moths; if disturbed, they flash open brightly coloured hindwings in a startle display to ward off possible predators. The hairy larvae are known as 'woolly bears'. Notes are given on selected species.

Garden Tiger *Arctia caja* (wingspan: 50–78 mm)

CURRENT STATUS IN THE NEW FOREST: Widespread
IDENTIFICATION: Large dark brown blotches on white forewings; hindwings red with large dark bluish spots.
HABITAT: Found in many habitats, likely to be noticed in gardens. Found in July to August, flying late at night. Widespread throughout Britain, including the Isle of Wight. The larvae feed on various wild and garden plants, including dandelion.

Cream-spot Tiger *Arctia villica britannica* (wingspan: 50–66 mm)

CURRENT STATUS IN THE NEW FOREST: Local
IDENTIFICATION: Black forewings with cream blotches; hindwings yellow with black spots and blotches. Abdomen red, yellowish near base.
HABITAT: Found in woodland, downland, coastal cliffs and sandhills between May to June. Common in the Hurst Castle area, when numerous males can be seen on low vegetation in the daytime, attracted to newly hatched females. Also found in the Forest surrounds mainly along the coast, Barton-on-Sea, Hordle and Hengistbury Head and the Isle of Wight. Locally common in southern England, extending towards Norfolk. In Wales, mainly in the south. The larvae overwinter and feed on a variety of plants.

Clouded Buff *Diacrisia sannio* (wingspan: 35–50 mm)

CURRENT STATUS IN THE NEW FOREST: Widespread
IDENTIFICATION: Yellow forewings with pink edges and central blotch; hindwings whitish with blackish clouding and again with pink edges.
HABITAT: Heathland, chalk downland and woodland clearings in June to July, the male flying in sunny weather. In the Forest, most likely to be found in heathland resting on heather or other vegetation, including Beaulieu Heath, Island Thorns and Setley. Widespread throughout much of Britain, including the Isle of Wight. The larvae overwinter and feed on low-growing plants, including heather.

Ruby Tiger *Phragmatobia fuliginosa* (wingspan: 28–38 mm)

CURRENT STATUS IN THE NEW FOREST: Widespread
IDENTIFICATION: Pinkish brown or deep pink forewings; hindwings bright pink, with sooty-grey areas.
HABITAT: Found in a variety of habitats in April to June and mid July to early September, the male sometimes flying fast in the day. Widespread throughout much of Britain, including the Isle of Wight. The larvae overwinter and feed on low-growing plants, including dandelion and dock.

Jersey Tiger *Euplagia quadripunctaria* (wingspan: 52–65 mm)

CURRENT STATUS IN THE NEW FOREST: Very rare, suspected immigrant
IDENTIFICATION: Black and creamy-white striped forewings; hindwings red or orange with black spots and blotches.
HABITAT: Found in mainly coastal habitats, likely to be noticed in gardens. Found in mid July to early September, flying in the day to visit flowers such as buddleja, but also attracted to light at night. In the Forest, rarely seen, but has been reported from Brockenhurst and the latest records from Normandy Marshes and Pennington in 2008 and 2009 indicate it might be becoming established in the Pennington / Lymington area. It has been established in the Isle of Wight since the 1990s. Found in mainly coastal parts of Devon and scattered elsewhere on the southern coast. The larvae feed on various plants.

1a		1b
2a		3
		4
2b	2c	5

Plates 1a & 1b
Garden Tiger
a) [RC]
b) larva

Plates 2a–2c
Cream-spot Tiger
a) [GP]
b) underside [GP]
c) larva

Plate 3
Clouded Buff male [RC]

Plate 4
Ruby Tiger

Plate 5
Jersey Tiger [RC]

Scarlet Tiger ***Callimorpha dominula*** (wingspan: 52–58 mm)
CURRENT STATUS IN THE NEW FOREST: Rare
IDENTIFICATION: Iridescent black with white and yellow spotted forewings; hindwings red with black spots and blotches.
HABITAT: Water meadows in June to July, flying in the day and often spotted at rest on vegetation. In the Forest, rarely seen, but has been reported from Beaulieu and Brockenhurst. Not recorded in the Isle of Wight. The species is common in the River Avon, Test and Itchen valleys, so it is not surprising they are recorded in the Forest surrounds at places like Totton, Ibsley Bridge and vicinity, also on the coast at Boscombe. A local species, found in parts of southern and western England, also southern and western Wales. The colourful larvae feed on various plants, including bramble, comfrey, hemp-agrimony and meadowsweet.

Cinnabar ***Tyria jacobaeae*** (wingspan: 35–45 mm)
CURRENT STATUS IN THE NEW FOREST: Widespread / common
IDENTIFICATION: Unmistakable, forewings black with red markings and spots, hindwings red with black margin.
HABITAT: Downland, dunes, fields and open woodland in mid May to early August, flying in the day in sunshine, or easily disturbed by walking by vegetation. Also flies at night. Widespread and usually common throughout Britain, except in Scotland where it is local and mainly coastal. The conspicuous larvae sport yellow and black warning colours and are a familiar sight on ragwort.

Other species recorded in the Forest are the **Wood Tiger *Parasemia plantaginis*** (34–42 mm, not recorded in the Forest in recent years) which is sometimes disturbed by day from heather, long grasses or other vegetation in heathland, downland and open woodland. In sunny weather during late May to July, males readily fly in search of females. Occasionally recorded at Martin Down, the larvae feed on various herbaceous plants, including dandelion and plantain, **White Ermine *Spilosoma lubricipeda*** (34–48 mm, common), **Buff Ermine *Spilosoma luteum*** (34–42 mm, common), **Water Ermine *Spilosoma urticae*** (38–46 mm, rare) and **Muslin Moth *Diaphora mendica*** (30–43 mm, widespread).

BLACK ARCHES – Family Nolidae

UK: 6 species
New Forest: 4 species [67%]

The Nolidae are a small group of whitish or grey moths, easily mistaken for micro moths. The **Small Black Arches *Meganola strigula*** (18–24 mm, widespread) and **Kent Black Arches *Meganola albula*** (18–24 mm, widespread) are the rarest British species, both reasonably widespread in the Forest. Other species recorded in the Forest are the **Short-cloaked Moth *Nola cucullatella*** (15–20 mm, widespread) and **Least Black Arches *Nola confusalis*** (16–24 mm, widespread).

1a		1b	1c
2a		2b	2c
3	4	5	
	6a	6b	
7	8	9	

Plates 1a–1c
Scarlet Tiger
a) startle display
b) at rest
c) larva

Plates 2a–2c
Cinnabar
a) startle display [GP]
b) at rest
c) larvae

Plate 3
Wood Tiger [SC]

Plate 4
White Ermine male [RC]

Plate 5
Muslin Moth [RC]

Plates 6a & 6b
Buff Ermine
a) male [RC]
b) female

Plate 7
Kent Black Arches [RC]

Plate 8
Short-cloaked Moth [RC]

Plate 9
Least Black Arches [RC]

NOCTUIDS – Family Noctuidae

UK: 406 species
New Forest: 272 species [67%]

Notes are given on the subfamilies which include species recorded from the Forest; only a small selection of species are mentioned.

Subfamily Noctuinae (Darts, yellow underwings and clays)

UK: 61 species
New Forest: 43 species [70%]

The Noctuinae hold their forewings flat over the body and strongly overlapping. Mainly various shades of brown, some with attractive markings, the **Large Yellow Underwing *Noctua pronuba*** (50–60 mm, common) is one of most recognised species, often seen in gardens. The **Archer's Dart *Agrotis vestigialis*** (30–40 mm, local) is frequent on the sand dunes of Hayling Island in July to September, but only occasional in other coastal areas and heathland in the Forest; the larvae feed on bedstraws and coastal vegetation. One of several similar looking moths, the **Heart and Dart *Agrotis exclamationis*** (35–44 mm, common) is likely to turn up in numbers at moth lights in May to August, along with the **Flame Shoulder *Ochropleura plecta*** (28–34 mm). The **True Lover's Knot *Lycophotia porphyrea*** (26–34 mm, common) is associated with heathland in June to August; later in the year (August to September), the **Heath Rustic *Xestia agathina*** (28–36 mm, local) also flies on heathland, larvae of both species feed on heathers. In June to July, the **Green Arches *Anaplectoides prasina*** (43–53 mm, local) is sometimes found in deciduous woodland.

Subfamily Hadeninae (Brocades, quakers and leaf-eating wainscots)

UK: 65 species
New Forest: 48 species [74%]

The **Beautiful Yellow Underwing *Anarta myrtilli*** (24–28 mm, common) is an attractive heathland species in the Forest, flying by day in April to August. The **Antler Moth *Cerapteryx graminis*** (27–39 mm, local) is an occasional day flier in grassy places, visiting flowers, although it also flies at night. See Plates overleaf on page 236.

Subfamily Cuculliinae (Sharks, pinions, shoulder-knots, chestnuts, sallows and allies)

UK: 66 species
New Forest: 42 species [64%]

The sharks are unmistakable, resting with wings tightly closed, a forward pointing thoracic crest reminiscent of a shark's fin. The colourful **Mullein *Shargacucullia verbasci*** (44–52 mm, widespread) larvae surprise gardeners and may appear soon after mullein is planted. A lichen mimic, the **Merveille du Jour *Dichonia aprilina*** (42–52 mm, common) is found in mature oak woodland in September to October. Another attractive species is the delicately marked **Sallow *Xanthia icteritia*** (32–40 mm, widespread). The **Southern Chestnut *Agrochola haematidea*** (32–38 mm, rare) was discovered in Britain in 1990 and at Linford in 1996. It is found in various parts of the Forest in late September to early November and has also been recorded in Dorset and Sussex, the larvae feeding on heather. See Plates overleaf on page 237.

1	2	3
4	5	6
7	8	9
10	11	12
13	14	15

Plate 1
Light Feathered Rustic
Agrotis cinerea
(33–40 mm) [RC]

Plate 2
Archer's Dart [SR]

Plate 3
Heart and Club
Agrotis clavis
(35–40 mm) [RC]

Plate 4
Heart and Dart [RC]

Plate 5
Shuttle-shaped Dart
***Agrotis puta* (30–32 mm** [RC]

Plate 6
Flame Shoulder [RC]

Plate 7
Large Yellow Underwing

Plate 8
Broad-bordered Yellow Underwing
Noctua fimbriata
(50–58 mm)

Plate 9
Lesser Broad-bordered Yellow Underwing
Noctua janthe
(34–44 mm)

Plate 10
Autumnal Rustic
Eugnorisma glareosa
(32–38 mm) [RC]

Plate 11
True Lover's Knot [DG]

Plate 12
Setaceous Hebrew Character
Xestia c-nigrum
(35–45 mm)

Plate 13
Double Square-spot
Xestia triangulum
(36–46 mm) [RC]

Plate 14
Heath Rustic [RC]

Plate 15
Green Arches RC]

1	2
3	4
5	6
7	8
9	10
11	12

Plate 1
Beautiful Yellow Underwing [GP]

Plate 2
Bordered Gothic
Heliophobus reticulata
(35–40 mm) [RC]

Plate 3
Dot Moth
Melanchra persicariae
(38–50 mm) [RC]

Plate 4
Dog's Tooth
Lacanobia suasa
(32–42 mm) [RC]

Plate 5
Broom Moth
Melanchra pisi
(33–42 mm) [RC]

Plate 6
Campion
Hadena rivularis
(30–36 mm) [RC]

Plate 7
Lychnis
Hadena bicruris
(30–40 mm) [RC]

Plate 8
Antler Moth [GP]

Plate 9
Blossom Underwing
Orthosia miniosa
(32–38 mm) [RC]

Plate 10
Common Quaker
Orthosia cerasi
(34–40 mm) [RC]

Plate 11
Smoky Wainscot
Mythimna impura
(31–38 mm) [RC]

Plate 12
Common Wainscot
Mythimna pallens
(32–40 mm) [RC]

1a	2	3
	4	
1b	5	6
7		8
9	10	11
12	13	14

Plates 1a & 1b
Mullein
a) [RW]
b) larva [GP]

Plate 2
Black Rustic
Aporophyla nigra
(40–46 mm) [RC]

Plate 3
Grey Shoulder-knot
Lithophane ornitopus
(34–42 mm) [RC]

Plate 4
Blair's Shoulder-knot
Lithophane leautieri
(39–44 mm) [RC]

Plate 5
Oak Rustic
Dryobota labecula
(27–31 mm) [RW]

Plate 6
Merveille du Jour

Plate 7
Brindled Green
Dryobotodes eremita
(32–39 mm) [RC]

Plate 8
Large Ranunculus
Polymixis flavicincta
(40–50 mm) [RC]

Plate 9
Feathered Ranunculus
Polymixis lichenea
(35–44 mm) [RC]

Plate 10
Chestnut *Conistra vaccinii*
(28–36 mm) [GP]

Plate 11
Southern Chestnut [KT]

Plate 12
Centre-barred Sallow
Atethmia centrago
(32–36 mm)

Plate 13
Pink-barred Sallow
Xanthia togata
(28–36 mm)

Plate 14
Sallow

Subfamily Acronictinae (Daggers)

UK: 14 species
New Forest: 11 species [79%]

The beautifully marked **Scarce Merveille du Jour *Moma alpium*** (32–40 mm, local) is another lichen mimic, now very local in parts of southern England, with the Forest one of its strongholds, the larvae feeding on oak. More typical 'dagger' markings are seen on the common **Grey Dagger *Acronicta psi*** (34–45 mm, widespread), only distinguishable with certainty from the **Dark Dagger *Acronicta tridens*** (35–43 mm, widespread) by checking genitalia. See Plates 1–9 opposite.

Subfamily Bryophilinae (Lichen feeders)

UK: 4 species
New Forest: 3 species [75%]

Small delicately patterned species, including the rather variable **Marbled Beauty *Cryphia domestica*** (22–30 mm, widespread); there are no shortage of lichens in the Forest for these species. See Plates 10–12 opposite.

Subfamily Amphipyrinae (Arches, brindles, minors, rustics and allies)

UK: 104 species
New Forest: 70 species [67%]

Shine a torch on large oaks in the Forest with sap runs, and there may be numerous **Copper Underwing *Amphipyra pyramidea*** (47–54 mm, common) on the bark, along with the closely related **Svensson's Copper Underwing *Amphipyra berbera*** (47–56 mm, widespread), which are also commonly seen at sugar rather than light. A larger moth occasionally recorded in the Forest is the **Old Lady *Mormo maura*** (64–74 mm, widespread), which sometimes frequents old garden sheds and outbuildings. Members of the public are likely to see one of the commonest species at rest in the day, the **Angle Shades *Phlogophora meticulosa*** (45–52 mm, common), a possible sighting any time of the year but mainly in May to June and August to October. The **Reddish Buff *Acosmetia caliginosa*** (25–30 mm, extinct) breeds on the Ise of Wight and a reintroduction attempt is being made in the Forest. See Plates overleaf on pages 240 and 241.

A moth trapping evening in Ivy Wood; a notebook to record finds, identification guides and containers are essential items

1a	1b	2
3a	3b	4
5	6	7a	7b
8a	8b	9
10	11	12

Plates 1a & b
Scarce Merveille du Jour
a) [RC]
b) larva [DG]

Plate 2
Poplar Grey
Acronicta megacephala
(40–44 mm) [RC]

Plates 3a & 3b
Sycamore *Acronicta aceri*
(40–45 mm)
a) [RC]
b) larva [GP]

Plate 4
Miller *Acronicta leporina*
(38–43 mm) [RC]

Plate 5
Alder Moth *Acronicta alni*
(37–43 mm) [RC]

Plate 6
Dark Dagger [RC]

Plates 7a & 7b
Grey Dagger
a) [GP]
b) larva [DG]

Plates 8a & 8b
Knot Grass *Acronicta rumicis*
(34–44 mm)
a) [RC]
b) larva

Plate 9
Coronet
Craniophora ligustri
form *coronula*
(35–43 mm) [RC]

Plate 10
Tree-lichen Beauty
Cryphia algae
(24–30 mm) [RC]

Plate 11
Marbled Beauty [RC]

Plate 12
Marbled Green
Cryphia muralis
(27–34 mm) [RC]

1	2
3	4
5	6
7	8
9	10

Plate 1
Copper Underwing feeding

Plate 2
Svensson's Copper Underwing [RC]

Plate 3
Mouse Moth
Amphipyra tragopoginis
(32–40 mm) [RC]

Plate 4
Old Lady [RC]

Plate 5
Bird's Wing
Dypterygia scabriuscula
(34–42 mm) [CT]

Plate 6
Straw Underwing
Thalpophila matura
(38–46 mm) [RC]

Plate 7
Small Angle Shades
Euplexia lucipara
(30–35 mm) [RC]

Plate 8
Angle Shades

Plate 9
White-spotted Pinion
Cosmia diffinis
(29–36 mm) [RC]

Plate 10
Lunar-spotted Pinion
Cosmia pyralina
(29–34 mm) [RC]

1	2
3	4
5	6
7	8
9 10	11

Plate 1
Dark Arches
Apamea monoglypha
(46–54 mm) [RC]

Plate 2
Clouded-bordered Brindle
Apamea crenata
(36–44 mm) [RC]

Plate 3
Middle-barred Minor
Oligia fasciuncula
(22–26 mm) [RC]

Plate 4
Rosy Minor
Mesoligia literosa
(25–30 mm) [RC]

Plate 5
Small Dotted Buff
Photedes minima
(25–30 mm) [RC]

Plate 6
Dusky Sallow
Eremobia ochroleuca
(34–37 mm)

Plate 7
Rosy Rustic
Hydraecia micacea
(34–50 mm) [RC]

Plate 8
Frosted Orange
Gortyna flavago
(32–44 mm) [RC]

Plate 9
Treble Lines
Charanyca trigrammica
(33–40 mm) [RC]

Plate 10
Mottled Rustic
Caradrina morpheus
(32–38 mm) [RC]

Plate 11
Reddish Buff [IP]

Subfamily Stiriinae

UK: 1 species
New Forest: 1 species [100%]

The **Small Yellow Underwing *Panemeria tenebrata*** (19–22 mm, local) is only occasional in the Forest, more widespread in meadows and downs in the Forest surrounds and Isle of Wight. This day flying species is found in May to early June.

Subfamily Heliothinae

UK: 8 species
New Forest: 5 species [63%]

The **Marbled Clover *Heliothis viriplaca*** (30–36 mm, rare) and similar-looking **Shoulder-striped Clover *Heliothis maritima*** (30–36 mm, rare) are day flying rarities worth looking for on clover and heather flowers. The Marbled Clover is a suspected immigrant, whilst in Hampshire, the Shoulder-striped Clover is a resident, mainly found in the Forest (places like Brockenhurst, Denny, Matley Bog, Ocknell Plain, but few recent records) on damp heathland in June to July. See Plates 2–6 opposite.

Subfamily Eustrotiinae

UK: 7 species
New Forest: 4 species [57%]

Several attractive small species, like the **Marbled White Spot *Protodeltote pygarga*** (21–30 mm, widespread), found in late May to July. There have been few recent records of the **Silver Hook *Deltote uncula*** (22–26 mm, rare) from Holmsley and Pig Bush in 2006, although it was recorded from Beaulieu, Brockenhurst and Godshill in the 1980s. It is also recorded in the Forest surrounds and worth looking for in boggy heathland.

Subfamily Acontiinae

UK: 2 species
New Forest: 1 species [50%]

The **Pale Shoulder *Acontia lucida*** (26–30 mm, very rare migrant) was recorded at Linford in 1986, a new record for Hampshire.

Subfamily Eariadinae

UK: 3 species
New Forest: 2 species [67%]

The **Cream-bordered Green Pea *Earias clorana*** (20–24 mm, local) is occasionally recorded in the Forest and immediate surrounds.

Subfamily Chloephorinae

UK: 5 species
New Forest: 4 species [80%]

This subfamily includes the attractive **Scarce Silver-lines *Bena bicolorana*** (40–48 mm, widespread) and **Green Silver-lines *Pseudoips prasinana*** (32–40 mm, widespread), both found in oak woodlands, although larvae of the latter commoner species also feeds on aspen, beech, birch, hazel and others.

1	2	3
4	5a 5b	6
7 / 8	11	
9 / 10	12	

Plate 1
Small Yellow Underwing
[KT]

Plate 2
Bordered Sallow
Pyrrhia umbra
(32–38 mm) [RC]

Plate 3
Scarce Bordered Straw
Helicoverpa armigera
(38–42 mm) [RC]

Plate 4
Marbled Clover

Plates 5a & 5b
Shoulder-striped Clover
a) [RC]
b) larva [DG]

Plate 6
Bordered Straw
Heliothis peltigera
(34–42 mm) [RC]

Plate 7
Marbled White Spot [RC]

Plate 8
Silver Hook [RC]

Plate 9
Pale Shoulder [RC]

Plate 10
Cream-bordered Green Pea [RC]

Plate 11
Scarce Silver-lines [RC]

Plate 12
Green Silver-lines

Subfamily Pantheinae

UK: 1 species
New Forest: 1 species [100%]

The **Nut-tree Tussock *Colocasia coryli*** (30–38 mm, common) is found in deciduous woodland from April to mid June and late July to early September. The larvae feed on a range of trees and shrubs including beech, birch, hazel and hornbeam.

Subfamily Plusiinae (Silver and golden Ys, gems, brasses and allies)

UK: 23 species
New Forest: 14 species [61%]

Most species hold the forewings at a steep angle, these have metallic marks. In addition, there are tufts on the body. The **Silver Y *Autographa gamma*** (32–52 mm, common) is often our commonest day flying moth, flying in sunny weather, otherwise easily disturbed; they also fly at night and are found all year, but usually between May to September. The resident population is reinforced by immigrants and the larvae feed on numerous low growing plants. A selection of mainly common Forest species is shown, except for **Deswick's Plusia *Macdunnoughia confusa*** (32–38 mm), which is a rare immigrant, recorded in Ashurst in October 2007.

Subfamily Catocalinae (Red underwings and allies)

UK: 13 species
New Forest: 7 species [54%]

These are the most sought after of all the noctuids. The striking day flying **Mother Shipton *Callistege mi*** (30–34 mm, local) and **Burnet Companion *Euclidia glyphica*** (28–34 mm, local) and a welcome sight in meadows and woodland clearings in May through to July, but neither are common in the Forest, although they are more widespread in the surrounds, including the Isle of Wight. More detailed notes on given on the blue and red underwings found in the Forest, see overleaf, pages 246 and 247. The **Lunar Double-stripe *Minucia lunaris*** (50–60 mm) is a rare immigrant..

Walking along coastal paths on the Isle of Wight usually produce a few day-flying moths, including Burnet Companion and Mother Shipton

1	2	3
4	5	6a
7	8	6b
9	10	11
12	13	14

Plate 1
Nut-tree Tussock [RC]

Plate 2
Burnished Brass
***Diachrysia chrysitis* above**
Cryptic Burnished Brass
Diachrysia stenochrysitis
(34–44 mm) below [DG]

Plate 3
Dewick's Plusia
Macdunnoughia confusa
(32–38 mm) [KG]

Plate 4
Gold Spot *Plusia festucae*
(34–46 mm) [RC]

Plate 5
Lempke's Gold Spot
Plusia putnami
(32–42 mm) [RC]

Plates 6a & 6b
Silver Y

Plate 7
Beautiful Golden Y
Autographa pulchrina
(36–44 mm) [RC]

Plate 8
Plain Golden Y
Autographa jota
(38–46 mm) [RC]

Plate 9
Gold Spangle
Autographa bractea
(40–50 mm) [RC]

Plate 10
Dark Spectacle
Abrostola triplasia
(34–40 mm) [RC]

Plate 11
Spectacle
Abrostola tripartita
(32–38 mm) [RC]

Plate 12
Lunar Double-stripe [RC]

Plate 13
Mother Shipton

Plate 14
Burnet Companion

Clifden Nonpareil *Catocala fraxini* (wingspan: 90–106 mm)
CURRENT STATUS IN THE NEW FOREST: Rare
IDENTIFICATION: Grey forewings, black hindwings with violet-blue central band.
HABITAT: Aspen woods. May be attracted to sugar or lights in September, also occasionally noticed flying around the top of oak trees in sunshine. Recorded in south Brockenhurst, also the Forest surrounds. Regarded as an immigrant and transitory resident, but in some areas, including Brockenhurst, they are being attracted to light in consecutive years. An irregular scarce species in southern and eastern England, occasionally further north.

Red Underwing *Catocala nupta* (wingspan: 70–90 mm)
CURRENT STATUS IN THE NEW FOREST: Widespread
IDENTIFICATION: Grey forewings with jagged crosslines and markings, red hindwings with black bands.
HABITAT: Woodlands and parks. May be attracted to sap runs, sugar or lights in August and October. The commonest of the red underwings, a widespread species in southern England ranging northwards to Yorkshire, but scarce in southwest England and west Wales. The larva feeds on aspen, poplar and willow.

Light Crimson Underwing *Catocala promissa* (wingspan: 50–60 mm)
CURRENT STATUS IN THE NEW FOREST: Rare, but still reliable in some areas
IDENTIFICATION: Greyish brown forewings with irregular crosslines and bands, some whitish markings; crimson hindwings with black bands, the central band gently wavy.
HABITAT: Mature oak woodlands and parks where they may be attracted to sugar or lights in mid July to early September. In the Forest, possibly active flying around the oak canopy in the afternoon and also be seen on sap, for instance at Ladycross. A rare species formerly in various parts of southern England, now mainly restricted to the New Forest, but also recorded in Dorset and other parts of Hampshire. In 2008 there were 21 records of this species attracted to moth lights; 29 in 2007; all in the Forest. The larvae feed on oak.

Dark Crimson Underwing *Catocala sponsa* (wingspan: 58–74 mm)
CURRENT STATUS IN THE NEW FOREST: Rare
IDENTIFICATION: Greyish brown forewings with irregular crosslines and bands, possibly darker and less variegated than the similar, but often slightly smaller Light Crimson Underwing; crimson hindwings with black bands, the central band a 'w' shape.
HABITAT: Mature oak woodlands where they may be attracted to sugar or lights in late July to early September. In the Forest, possibly active flying around the oak canopy in late afternoon and also be seen on sap, for instance at Ladycross where they are sometimes with Light Crimson Underwings. A rare species, the Forest is the stronghold. The few records in the vicinity of the Forest or Isle of Wight indicate that the species may disperse, or the records might relate to migrants. The larvae feed on oak.

1		2
3a		3b
4a		4b
		4c

Plate 1
Clifden Nonpareil [RW]

Plate 2
Red Underwing [RC]

Plates 3a & 3b
Light Crimson Underwi
a) [GP]
b) larva [DG]

Plates 4a–4c
Dark Crimson Underwin
a) [GP]
b) larva [DG]
c) at rest

Subfamily Ophiderinae

UK: 7 species
New Forest: 4 species [57%]

The **Herald *Scoliopteryx libatrix*** (44–48 mm, common) is an attractive species which overwinters as an adult and may be seen in woodlands, commons and gardens from late July to November and after hibernation from March to June. The larvae feed on poplar, sallow and willow, amongst others. The **Four-spotted *Tyta luctuosa*** (25–29 mm, extinct) has not been recorded in the Forest since c.1930, but there was a possible sighting from Martin Down in 1982 and one was recorded from Totland, Isle of Wight in 2004. See Plates 2–4 opposite for species widespread in the Forest.

Subfamily Rivulinae

UK: 4 species
New Forest: 3 species [75%]

Includes the **Beautiful Hook-tip *Laspeyria flexula*** (28–36 mm, widespread) whose larvae feed on lichens and algae in woodlands. The **Waved Black *Parascotia fuliginaria*** (24–30 mm, local), which is found in June to July and in the Forest has been recorded in several areas, including Beaulieu and Brockenhurst. The larvae feed on fungi, for example growing on tree trunks.

Subfamily Hypeninae (Snouts)

UK: 5 species
New Forest: 3 species [60%]

Characterised by their long snouts, the **Snout *Hypena proboscidalis*** (36–42 mm, common) is associated with nettle. The rarer **Buttoned Snout *Hypena rostralis*** (27–32 mm, rare) is a much slimmer species, the larva feeding on hop. It has been recorded from Brockenhurst. The much smaller **Pinion-streaked Snout *Schrankia costaestrigalis*** (16–22 mm, widespread), is associated with damp woods and boggy heathland.

Subfamily Strepsimaninae

UK: 3 species
New Forest: 3 species [100%]

Rather small species, including the **Marsh Oblique-barred *Hypenodes humidalis*** (14–15 mm, local), which is found in some Forest bogs.

Subfamily Herminiinae (Fan-foots)

UK: 10 species
New Forest: 4 species [40%]

The **Fan Foot *Zanclognatha tarsipennalis*** [2489, common] (30–35 mm) is readily distinguished from the **Small Fan Foot *Herminia grisealis*** (24–28 mm, common); both species in deciduous woodland.

1	2	3
4	5	
6	7	8
9	10	
11	12	13

Plate 1
Four-spotted [RC]

Plate 2
Blackneck
Lygephila pastinum
(41–48 mm) [RC]

Plate 3
Herald [GP]

Plate 4
Small Purple-barred
Phytometra viridaria
(19–20 mm) [RC]

Plate 5
Beautiful Hook-tip

Plate 6
Straw Dot
Rivula sericealis
(19–25 mm)

Plate 7
Waved Black [RC]

Plate 8
Snout [RC]

Plate 9
Buttoned Snout [RC]

Plate 10
Pinion-streaked Snout [RC]

Plate 11
Marsh Oblique Barred [RC]

Plate 12
Fan-foot [RC]

Plate 13
Small Fan-foot [RC]

MICRO MOTHS – various Families

UK: c.1,600 micro moths (in Hampshire c.1,250)
New Forest: 810 [51%], including extinctions. It is estimated that at least 80% of the Hampshire micros should be found in the New Forest, which would increase the number of micros to c.1,000 [63%]

Details of families are given in the photographic sections below. These small insects (although some are larger than some macro moths) include some surprisingly colourful species and the group warrant more attention, particularly from recorders and photographers. The absence of a single detailed field guide and difficulty in identifying some similar species are contributing factors, although since about 2000 there have been some useful websites available to recorders.

A few notes are given on the micro moths, but the Plates on pages 251–253 should enable at least provisional identification of some species (the Micropterigidae are small c.8 mm wingspan, many c.15–20 mm, the Pyralidae, in particular, sometimes considerably larger). Many species are associated with woodlands and are attracted to light, but there are also heathland specialities: a) drier areas: ***Crambus hamella*** (24–27 mm, local), ***Scythris empetrella*** (8–10 mm, local) found in the Lyndhurst area and Dorset on sandy heathland and ***Pachythelia villosella*** (22–28 mm, local), a bagworm whose case is sometimes spotted on a tree trunk; although not common, they are recorded in areas like Beaulieu Road Station and only found in Dorset and Hampshire, and ***Apomyelois bistriatella*** (18–25 mm, local), associated with a fungus on recently burnt gorse and birch; b) boggy areas: the Forest is the stronghold for another crambid, ***Crambus silvella*** (22–26 mm, local) and ***Crambus uliginosellus*** (18–23 mm, local) is another sought after species. The tortricid ***Sparganothis pilleriana*** (15–22 mm, widespread) and the attractive **Brown China Mark *Elophila nymphaeata*** (25–33 mm, widespread) with aquatic larvae, are likely to be observed. Larvae of the plume moth ***Buckleria paludum*** (11–13 mm, widespread) even feed on the insect-attracting round-leaved sundew.

Damage caused by Horse Chestnut Leaf-miner *Cameraria ohridella* (not to be confused with a fungus), first found in Britain in 2002 and already common in parts of England, including the New Forest, and Wales

<table>
<tr><td>1</td><td>2a</td><td>2b</td><td>2c</td></tr>
<tr><td>3</td><td>4</td><td>5a</td><td>5b</td></tr>
<tr><td>6a</td><td>6b</td><td>6c</td></tr>
<tr><td>7a</td><td>7b</td><td>7c</td></tr>
<tr><td>7d</td><td>7e</td><td>7f</td></tr>
<tr><td>8</td><td>9a</td><td>9b</td></tr>
</table>

Plate 1
Family Micropterigidae
Micropterix calthella

Plates 2a–2c
Family Incurvariidae
a) *Lampronia oehlmanniella* [RC]
b) *Nemophora degeerell* [RC]
c) *Adela cuprella* female

Plate 3
Family Psychidae
Pachythelia villosella
larval case

Plate 4
Family Tineidae
Euplocamus anthracinali [RC]

Plates 5a & 5b
Family Gracillariidae
a) *Caloptilia robustella* [
b) *Phyllonorycter hilarell* [RC]

Plates 6a–6c
Family Yponomeutidae
a) *Argyresthia brockeell* [RC]
b) Spindle Ermine *Yponomeuta cagnagel* [RC]
c) Hawthorn Moth *Scythropia crataegell* [RC]

Plates 7a–7f
Family Oecophoridae
a) *Batia lunaris* [RC]
b) *Esperia sulphurella*
c) *Carcina quercana* [RC]
d) *Agonopterix alstroemeriana* [RC]
e) *Ethmia dodecea* [DG]
f) *Metzneria aprilella* [RC

Plate 8
Family Cosmopterigidae
Cosmopterix scribaiella [

Plates 9a & 9b
Family Cochylidae
a) *Agapeta hamana* [RC]
b) *Aethes rubigana* [RC]

1a	1b	1c
1d	1e	1f
1g	1h	1i
1j	1k	1l
1m	1n	1o
1p	1q	2

Plates 1a–1q
Family Tortricidae
a) Barred Fruit-tree Tortrix *Pandemis cerasana* [RC]
b) Large Fruit-tree Tortrix *Archips podana* [RC]
c) Varigated Golden Tortrix *Archips xylosteana* [RC]
d) *Syndemis musculana* [RC]
e) *Lozotaeniodes formosanus* [RC]
f) *Lozotaeniodes forsterana* [RC]
g) *Pseudargyrotoza conwagana* [RC]
h) Green Oak Tortrix *Tortrix viridana* [RC]
i) *Acleris laterana* [RC]
j) *Acleris notana* [RC]
k) Garden Rose Tortrix *Acleris variegana* [RC
l) *Acleris cristana* [RC]
m) *Acleris literana* [RC]
n) *Apotomis betuletana* [RC]
o) Bramble Shoot Moth *Epiblema uddmanniana* [RC]
p) *Rhyacionia pinicolan* [RC]
q) *Pammene regiana* [RC]

Plate 2
Family Alucitidae
Many Plumed Moth
Alucita hexadactyla

1a	1b	1c
1d	1e	1f
1g	1h	1i
1j	1k	
1l	1m	1n
2a	2b	

Plates 1a–1n
Family Pyralidae
a) *Crambus silvella* [RC]
b) *Crambus hamella* [RC]
c) *Agriphila latistria* [RC]
d) *Scoparia ambigualis*
e) Brown China Mark *Elophila nymphaeata* [SF]
f) *Evergestis limbata* [RC]
g) *Pyrausta aurata* [PC]
h) *Pyrausta purpuralis*
i) *Pyrausta nigrata* [RC]
j) Small Magpie *Eurrhypara hortulata*
k) *Eurrhypara coronata* [RC]
l) Meal Moth *Pyralis farinalis* [RC]
m) *Conobathra repandana* [RC]
n) *Phycitodes binaevella* [RC]

Plates 2a & 2b
Family Pterophoridae
a) *Amblyptilia acanthadactyla* [RC]
b) White-plume Moth *Pterophorus pentadactyla* [RC]

FLIES – Order DIPTERA

UK: 7,000 species
New Forest: estimated 4,550 species [65%]; some families are poorly recorded

Flies are the second largest order in Britain, behind the Hymenoptera; there are probably in the region of 150,000 species worldwide. In Britain there are tiny midges less than 1 mm long to 60 mm craneflies. Whilst flies may have a bad reputation, being associated with rotting flesh and disease, as well as being a nuisance for 'biting' people on hot, sunny days, some have amazing colours and are an attractive part of our insect fauna, with many beneficial as pollinators, or by eating aphids. Diptera means 'two-winged' which applies to most species, although they do have a pair of tiny pin-shaped hindwings, known as halteres. A small number of flies completely lack wings. In all cases the life history is one of complete metamorphosis, so adults lay eggs which hatch into larvae, legless maggots, some with biting jaws, others without, as they may just suck up liquids. The larva forms a pupa, before the adult emerges. Some larvae are beneficial, including maggots which are still used in some hospitals to clean wounds, eating the dead tissue. More typically, the maggots of many species break down organic material, for example feeding in rotting wood, fungi, decaying flesh, flower and seed heads and dung. Some live in the soil or water; others are leaf miners, or are parasites of larvae or predators. Adults lack jaws; mouthparts are designed to suck moisture or nectar, although this is adapted in some species for piercing surfaces to suck blood. The relatively few specialists studying flies means that most families are not well researched in the New Forest, except for popular insects such as hoverflies. Flies can be particularly conspicuous visiting flowers along woodland rides. The coverage in this book is a small selection of the ordinary, spectacular and rare species found in the Forest, hence not all families are included.

1	2
	3
	4
5	

Plate 1 ***Tipula flavolineata*** **(a cranefly)**

Plate 2 ***Xylota segnis*** **(a hoverfly) in flight**

Plate 3 **Square-spot Deerfly (a horsefly) female**

Plate 4 ***Sicus ferrugineus*** **(a thick-headed fly) feeding**

Plate 5 **Hornet Robberfly female egglaying**

Buckland Rings near Lymington, a good site for Hornet Robberfly and other dung-loving flies

Suborder Nematocera

CRANEFLIES and ALLIES – 4 Families and 2 additional non-related Families, but similar-looking long-legged insects

UK: c.350 species
New Forest: estimated 180 species [51%]

Many people know the small to large craneflies as 'Daddy Long Legs', the legs can easily break off if grabbed by a possible predator, but at least the insect may survive. Adults have reduced mouthparts but some feed on flowers; larvae of the large craneflies are sometimes known as 'leather jackets' and live in soil; a few attack roots but most feed on decaying leaf-litter or sometimes in moss or decaying wood and many are aquatic. Craneflies live in many types of habitat, fly by day or at night and are sometimes attracted to lights. Six families of flies count as craneflies. The big ones are mostly Long-palped (Tipulidae) whilst the largest group comprises the Short-palped Craneflies (mainly Limoniidae), Hairy-eyed craneflies (Pediciidae) and Damsel Craneflies (Cylindrotomidae, only four species). Two further small families are included for present purposes, the Winter Gnats (Trichoceridae) and the Fold-winged Craneflies (Ptychopteridae); the latter look like craneflies but are only distantly related. In size they range from the **Giant Cranefly *Tipula maxima*** (body length c.38 mm, wingspan c.60 mm, leg span c.100 mm, Britain's largest fly, well represented in the Forest between May to July, in damp areas, including heathland; at the other extreme with a wingspan of about 5 mm. The New Forest is a fantastic place for craneflies since there are fine examples of ideal habitat. The ancient woodlands are the only place in Britain where two species have been recorded, ***T. sarajevensis*** and ***T. siebkei***, whilst ***T. mutila*** has only been recorded at one other place; these are small elusive species (wing length 9–13 mm) and have not been seen for many years, a challenge being to rediscover them. However, the woods are also famous for rare craneflies associated with veteran trees, especially beech; the most spectacular are the wasp mimicking craneflies, the Combe-horns. The Forest is the last stronghold for ***Ctenophora ornata*** (body length 15–25 mm, rare) which should be searched for in June to July, with recent records from Anses, Brinken, Denny and Roydon Woods, Ladycross and Parkhill Inclosure, amongst others. ***Ctenophora flaveolata*** (18–22 mm, rare) is another species associated with ancient beech woods in April to May, also ***Ctenophora pectinicornis*** (18–27 mm, local) found in Denny Wood and elsewhere. ***Tanyptera atrata*** (12–20 mm) has only been recorded in the Forest surrounds, which is surprising, as it prefers old forest areas and heathland. Walking through various forest bogs may disturb the beautifully marked ***Pedicia rivosa*** (c.25 mm, widespread). A selection of other widespread Forest species is shown.

<table>
<tr><td rowspan="2">1</td><td>2a</td><td rowspan="2">3</td></tr>
<tr><td>2b</td></tr>
<tr><td>4</td><td>5</td><td>6</td></tr>
<tr><td>7</td><td>8a</td><td>8b</td></tr>
<tr><td>9</td><td>10</td><td>11</td></tr>
</table>

Plate 1
Giant Cranefly female

Plates 2a & 2b
Tipula paludosa
a) male
b) female

Plate 3
Tipula vernalis
mating pair

Plate 4
Ctenophora flaveolata
female [SC]

Plate 5
Ctenophora ornata
male [DG]

Plate 6
Ctenophora pectinicornis
male

Plate 7
Tanyptera atrata
female

Plates 8a & 8b
Pedicia rivosa
a) male
b) female

Plate 9
Dictenidia bimaculata
male

Plate 10
Ptychoptera contaminata
male

Plate 11
Ptychoptera albimana
male [SF]

ST MARK'S FLIES – Family Bibionidae

UK: 20 species
New Forest: estimated 13 species [65%]

The **St Mark's Fly *Bibio marci*** (10–15 mm, common) is often seen flying low over vegetation in April to June in grasslands, hedgerows, woodland margins and coastal habitats, where the larvae live in the soil in rotting vegetation.

MOTHFLIES – Family Psychodidae

UK: 95 species
New Forest: estimated 62 species [65%]

Small moth-like flies frequently seen on vegetation, often alongside or near water. These include various, similar ***Pericoma*** species (2–3 mm, widespread).

MOSQUITOES and GNATS – Family Culicidae

UK: 34 species
New Forest: estimated 22 species [65%]

Mostly small to medium sized flies, of which females have piercing mouthparts. Mainly tropical mosquitoes have a bad reputation for being vectors of serious diseases, including malaria. The larvae do well in the Forest, as they feed on detritus, bacteria and algae in shallow stagnant water, including the many temporary pools. A few species are predators. Adult hosts include vertebrates and large numbers can be a nuisance biting livestock and humans, although it is only the females which feed on blood. Most likely to be seen in the Forest is the mosquito ***Culex pipiens*** (c.6 mm, widespread). ***Chironomus luridus*** (c.10 mm, common) belongs to the related family Chironomidae (Non-biting Midges); the red aquatic larvae of the latter species are known as bloodworms.

Suborder Brachycera

SNIPEFLIES – Family Rhagionidae

UK: 15 species
New Forest: estimated 10 species [65%]

Conspicuous looking small to large flies with long abdomen, legs and wings. The Forest's fauna includes the rather variable **Marsh Snipefly *Rhagio tringarius*** (8–12.5 mm, common), found in marshes and wet meadows, watersides or woodland margins; often seen sitting on vegetation in May to September. The **Little Snipefly *Chrysopilus asiliformis*** (4.5–6 mm, common) and **Black Snipefly *Chrysopilus cristatus*** (6–8 mm, common) are found in marshes and wet meadows, whilst the **Downlooker Snipefly *Rhagio scolopaceus*** (8–16 mm, widespread) is often seen on tree trunks.

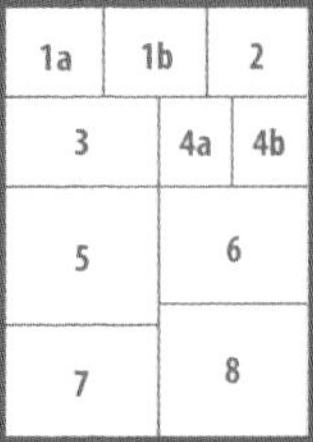

1a	1b	2
3	4a	4b
5	6	
7	8	

Plates 1a & 1b
St Mark's Fly
a) male
b) female

Plate 2
***Pericoma* species**

Plate 3
Culex pipiens
female

Plates 4a & 4b
Chironomus luridus
a) male
b) female

Plate 5
Marsh Snipefly [SF]

Plate 6
Little Snipefly [SF]

Plate 7
Black Snipefly [SF]

Plate 8
Downlooker Snipefly [SF]

HORSEFLIES – Family Tabanidae

UK: 30 species
New Forest: at least 23 species [77%]

Stout looking, medium to large flies with large eyes. Females have a piercing proboscis and feed on blood of mammals including humans, so it is not surprising they are well represented in the Forest, with all its grazing livestock. People usually see them on livestock. The larvae are aquatic, semi-aquatic or live in soil and litter. Unpopular with many, all four of the colourful deerfly ***Chrysops*** species are found in the Forest and have eyes of stunning colours: the **Splayed Deerfly *C. caecutiens*** (9–10 mm, common), **Twin-lobed Deerfly *C. relictus*** (8–8.5 mm, widespread), **Black Deerfly *C. sepulcralis*** (7–8.5 mm, very rare) and **Square-spot Deerfly *C. viduatus*** (8.5–10 mm, widespread). Both sexes differ and they favour lush marshy areas, including watery places by heathland and woodland. They are found from mid May to about September, but the Black Deerfly usually makes a later appearance from July. Although beautiful flies which sometimes feed on nectar and pollen, females feed on the blood of mammals including humans; they are attracted to cars. Most horseflies are usually drabber in colour than deerflies; the **Golden Horsefly *Atylotus fulvus*** (13–15 mm, local) is found in valley mires of the Forest in mid June to mid August, the **Saltmarsh Horsefly *Atylotus latistriatus*** (13–14 mm, rare) favours coastal sites such as Keyhaven. The ***Tabanus*** species include the **Dark Giant Horsefly *T. sudeticus*** (21–24 mm, widespread), Britain's largest horsefly, also smaller species such as the **Large Marsh Horsefly *T. autumnalis*** (16–22 mm, widespread), the **Band-eyed Brown Horsefly *T. bromius*** (13.5–15 mm, widespread) and **Plain-eyed Brown Horsefly *T. miki*** (15 mm, very rare). Clegs ***Haematopota*** species have attractive, mottled wings, the **Notch-horned Cleg *H. pluvialis*** (8–11.5 mm, widespread) is a voracious biter of humans, and particularly in coastal areas; in a book by members of the Bournemouth Natural History Society book (1914), it is described as a 'troublesome persecutor'. The **Long-horned Cleg *H. grandis*** (9–13 mm, rare) is restricted to the coast. ***Hybomitra*** species have hairy eyes, several species are present in the Forest, including the **Scarce Forest Horsefly *H. solstitialis*** (10–13 mm, very rare), **Hairy-legged Horsefly *H. bimaculata*** (13–16.5 mm, widespread) and **Bright Horsefly *H. distinguenda*** (15–18 mm, widespread).

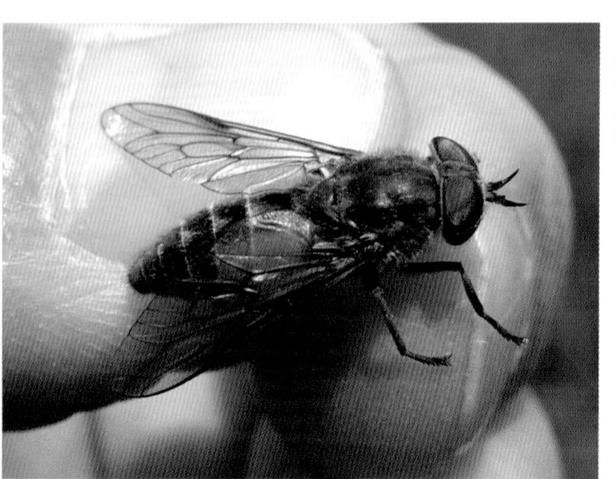

Rarer species require close examination: *Hybomitra solstitialis* [SF]

1a	1b	2
3	4a	4b
5	6	7
8	9	10
11	12a	12b

Plates 1a & 1b
Splayed Deerfly
a) male
b) female

Plate 2
Twin-lobed Deerfly
female

Plate 3
Black Deerfly

Plates 4a & 4b
Square-spot Deerfly
a) male [SF]
b) female

Plate 5
Golden Horsefly

Plate 6
Saltmarsh Horsefly [SF]

Plate 7
Dark Giant Horsefly

Plate 8
Large Marsh Horsefly

Plate 9
Band-eyed Brown Horsefly

Plate 10
Notch-horned Cleg

Plate 11
Long-horned Cleg [SF]

Plates 12a & 12b
Bright Horsefly
b) showing eye pattern

SOLDIERFLIES – Family Stratiomyidae

UK: 48 species
New Forest: estimated 29 species [60%]

Small to large flies, usually with striking coloration (hence the name soldierflies after brightly coloured uniforms of some soldiers); antennae with 7–10 segments. May be found in various habitats from woodland to waterside or coast, on flowers or vegetation. The larvae are aquatic or terrestrial, feeding on algae or decaying vegetable matter. The striking yellow and black **Banded General *Stratiomys potamida*** (12.5 mm, probably very rare in the Forest, rare in surrounds) is usually seen resting on hogweed or hemlock water-dropwort in late May to early September. The larvae are aquatic. Whilst sightings in England and south Wales generally have been more frequent from the late 1970s, this is not reflected by recent records in the Forest, although in the surrounds it has been recorded from Lower Test Marshes near Totton in 2000, Barton-on-Sea in 2010 and appears widespread on the Isle of Wight; one to look out for in the Forest. The often larger **Flecked General *Stratiomys singularior*** (12.5–15 mm, local) is mainly found in brackish coastal marshes along ditches, including Keyhaven Marshes and the Forest surrounds. Adults visit hogweed flowers in late May to early September. A small black and white bodied species, the **Flecked Snout *Nemotelus notatus*** (5–5.5 mm, local) is mainly found in saltmarshes, such as Keyhaven Marshes in May to August, also on the coast near the Forest. The **Twin-spot Centurion *Sargus bipunctatus*** (12–13 mm, common) has an attractive green thorax and is likely to be sunning itself on vegetation in areas with cow dung mainly in August to September. A selection of other widespread Forest species is shown.

BEE-FLIES – Family Bombyliidae

UK: 9 species
New Forest: at least 5 species [56%]

Bee-flies are small to large (3–12.5 mm body length) with some species recognised by a large proboscis. They are parasites of solitary bees and wasps and sometimes other insects. In spring from about mid March many gardeners in the Forest will see the commonest species, the furry brown **Dark-edged Bee-fly *Bombylius major*** (6–12.5 mm, common), which hovers around primroses and many other flowers with its oversized proboscis until about late June; also in woodlands and coastal areas. The **Dotted Bee-fly *Bombylius discolor*** (8–12 mm, rare) also flies in spring; it is more likely to be encountered in the Forest surrounds on coastal cliffs, for example on the Isle of Wight, whilst the **Heath Bee-fly *Bombylius minor*** (7–8.5 mm, rare) prefers heathland, flying in July and August. It has been recorded from the western fringe of the Forest, the Isle of Wight, Dorset and Isle of Man, also in Wales (Barmouth). The **Mottled Bee-fly *Thyridanthrax fenestratus*** (9–12.5 mm, rare) is a rather different-looking species with a short proboscis, confined to heathlands in parts of Dorset, Hampshire, Surrey and West Sussex. It occurs at scattered locations within the Forest in sandy areas with strong populations of its host, the sand wasp *Ammophila pubescens*. Adults can be seen sunbathing on bare ground, or hovering close to the ground in late May to early September.

<table>
<tr><td>1</td><td>2</td><td>3</td></tr>
<tr><td>4</td><td>5</td><td>6</td></tr>
<tr><td>7</td><td>8</td><td>9</td></tr>
<tr><td rowspan="2">10</td><td>11a</td><td>11b</td></tr>
<tr><td>12</td><td>13</td></tr>
</table>

Plate 1
Banded General [SF]

Plate 2
Flecked General

Plate 3
Flecked Snout [SF]

Plate 4
Twin-spot Centurion

Plate 5
Broad Centurion
Chloromyia formosa
(8–9 mm)

Plate 6
Barred Snout
Nemotelus uliginosus
(4.5–5.5 mm) [SF]

Plate 7
Orange-horned Green Colonel
Odontomyia angulata
(7.5–9.5 mm) [SF]

Plate 8
Common Green Colonel
Oplodontha viridula
(6–8 mm) [SF]

Plate 9
Pygmy Soldier
Oxycera pygmaea
(3–4 mm) [SF]

Plate 10
Dotted Bee-fly

Plates 11a & 11b
Dark-edged Bee-fly
a) at rest
b) feeding, with proboscis fully in primrose flower

Plate 12
Heath Bee-fly

Plate 13
Mottled Bee-fly

STILETTO-FLIES – Family Therevidae

UK: 14 species
New Forest: at least 4 species [29%]

Medium sized flies where the conical abdomen has been likened to a stiletto; the larvae are predators in soil. There are several species in the Forest, including the **Common Stiletto *Thereva nobilitata*** (10–13 mm, common). The **Coastal Silver-stiletto *Acrosathe annulata*** (8–11 mm, rare) is found on coastal dunes and more rarely, sandpits.

ROBBERFLIES – Family Asilidae

UK: 29 species
New Forest: at least 15 species [52%]

The robberflies are mainly medium to large, with sharp piercing mouthparts to kill other insects and are often seen in the Forest paired up, or eating prey. Sun lovers, they rest on fences, posts, logs or stones and are therefore likely to be noticed. When they pounce, it is rapid. The largest and most stunning member of the family is alas, one of the rarest and appears to be declining. The **Hornet Robberfly *Asilus crabroniformis*** (18–28 mm, rare) is a hornet mimic, with a yellow tip to its abdomen, hidden by the wings at rest, when the insect is practically brown and almost vanishes. Heathlands, meadows and downs are suitable habitat and they are fairly common in some parts of Hampshire, like Stockbridge Down in mid June to October. Scattered in the Forest, although formerly widespread; recorded from the Lymington surrounds and Shirley Holms in 2010. An adult uses a hunting perch, such as a stick or dung, taking 10–30 minutes to suck its prey dry. Eggs are laid in or under the dry crust of old cattle dung, sometimes horses and rabbits, or in nearby soil. The larvae are also predators of dung beetles and other organisms, burying in the soil before pupating. Various smaller robberflies are frequently seen in the Forest, the **Brown Heath Robberfly *Machimus cingulatus*** (10–13 mm, common) and **Fan-bristled Robberfly *Dysmachus trigonus*** (12–17 mm, common) are particularly abundant on the open heathland in the Forest. A selection of other Forest species is shown.

LONG-LEGGED FLIES – Family Dolichopodidae

UK: 287 species
New Forest: estimated 187 species [65%]

Tiny to medium sized flies, usually metallic green. These include some of the most abundant flies of mires and coastal wetland, including saltmarsh. ***Dolichopus atratus*** (5–6 mm, common) is typically found in bogs, ***Machaerium maritimae*** (c.5 mm, local) in saltmarsh, ***Argyra diaphana*** (7–8 mm, widespread) in damp woods. Males of ***Poecilobothrus nobilitatus*** (c.7 mm, widespread) have black and white wings, which they wave in a courtship display.

DANCE FLIES – Families Empididae and Hybotidae

UK: 384 species
New Forest: estimated 250 species [65%].

Tiny to large flies, often abundant in wetlands and woodlands. Adults are predatory and have rigid biting mouthparts. ***Empis tessellata*** (9–13 mm, common) can be particularly conspicuous on flowers or vegetation in late spring. Two other common Forest species are shown opposite.

1	2	3
4a		4b
5	6 / 7	8
9, 10	11	12
13	14	15

Plate 1
Coastal Silver-stiletto

Plate 2
Common Stiletto [SF]

Plate 3
Fan-bristled Robberfly

Plates 4a & 4b
Hornet Robberfly
a) male
b) female

Plate 5
Brown Heath Robberfly [SF]

Plate 6
Kite-tailed Robberfly
Machimus atricapillus
(12–15 mm) [SF]

Plate 7
Common Awl Robberfly
Neoitamus cyanurus
(12–19 mm)

Plate 8
Dune Robberfly
Philonicus albiceps
(13–18 mm)

Plate 9
Dolichopus atratus [SF]

Plate 10
Machaerium maritimae [SF]

Plate 11
Argyra diaphana [SF]

Plate 12
Poecilobothrus nobilitatus [SF]

Plate 13
Empis tessellata

Plate 14
Empis stercorea
(c.9 mm)

Plate 15
Bicellaria vana
(c.5 mm) [SF]

HOVERFLIES – Family Syrphidae

UK: 274 species (223 species in Hampshire)
New Forest: at least 212 species [77%]

Hoverflies are a group of small to large sun loving flies, often black with white or yellow markings on the abdomen. Well represented in the Forest, walk through woodland rides in summer and hoverflies will be nectaring on available flowers or just hovering in the area, defending territories. The larvae of many species are popular with gardeners in that they often feed on aphids, but some are plant eaters or scavengers. Good places to look for adults are ancient woodlands such as Denny Wood, also Inclosures with plenty of nectar flowers, including New Copse and Wootton Coppice, also meadows, streamsides, heathlands and gardens. Many species are wasp mimics, including ***Chrysotoxum festivum*** (wing length 8–12 mm, local); others are bee mimics, notably ***Volucella bombylans*** (wing length 8–14 mm, widespread) and ***Arctophila superbiens*** (wing length 10–13.5 mm, local). The large hoverflies of the genus ***Volucella*** develop in the nests of social wasps or bumblebees and are found from May to September or later, the distinctive black and white ***V. pellucens*** (wing length 10–15.5 mm, common) the commonest, but the other species ***V. inanis*** (wing length 12.25–14.25 mm, local), ***V. inflata*** (wing length 11–12.75 mm, rare) and the largest British species ***V. zonaria*** (wing length 15.5–19.5 mm, local) are all likely to be seen in the Forest from time to time. *V. zonaria* only became established in Britain in 1940 and often visits flowers in gardens; as they sometimes enter houses, they can cause alarm to those who do not realise they are harmless hoverflies. Whilst many species can be observed in the Forest, the **Drone Fly *Eristalis tenax*** (wing length 9.75–13 mm, common) and ***Sericomyia silentis*** (wing length 9.5–14 mm, common) are particularly conspicuous. ***Xanthogramma pedissequum*** (wing length 6.5–10.25 mm, local) is a striking black and yellow species. Some are the rarer Forest species are associated with old trees and decaying wood in spring and early summer, for example the uncommon ***Criorhina*** species (8–14 mm), which are found in Denny Wood and some other locations on flowers or around old beech logs or stumps along with rarities like the bee mimics ***Pocota personata*** (wing length 11–13 mm, rare) and ***Brachypalpus laphriformis*** (wing length 8.5–10.75 mm, local); also the red-belted ***Brachypalpoides lentus*** (wing length 10–12 mm, local) and part orange winged ***Caliprobola speciosa*** (wing length 11–12.5 mm, rare). A number of other mainly common species found in the Forest are illustrated on pages 268–271 overleaf.

Volucella **species larva, in wasps nest** [CT]

1	2	3
4	5	6
7	8	9
10	11	12
13	14	15

Plate 1 ***Chrysotoxum festivum*** [SF]

Plate 2 ***Arctophila superbiens***

Plate 3 ***Volucella bombylans***

Plate 4 ***Volucella pellucens***

Plate 5 ***Volucella inanis*** [GP]

Plate 6 ***Volucella inflata***

Plate 7 ***Volucella zonaria***

Plate 8 **Drone Fly** [GP]

Plate 9 ***Sericomyia silentis***

Plate10 ***Xanthogramma pedissequum*** [GP]

Plate 11 ***Criorhina asilica*** **(9.5–11 mm)** [SF]

Plate 12 ***Pocota personata*** [SF]

Plate 13 ***Brachypalpus laphriformis***

Plate 14 ***Brachypalpoides lentus***

Plate 15 ***Caliprobola speciosa***

1	2	3
4	5	6
7		8
9	10	11
12		13

Plate 1
Anasimyia contracta
(5–7 mm) [SF]

Plate 2
Anasimyia lineata
(6–8 mm) [SF]

Plate 3
Brachyopa bicolor
(6.5–9 mm, rare)

Plate 4
Chalcosyrphus nemorum
(6.5–8 mm)

Plate 5
Cheilosia illustrata
(8.5–10 mm)

Plate 6
Cheilosia scutellata
(6–9 mm) [SF]

Plate 7
Chrysogaster solstitialis
(6–7 mm) [SF]

Plate 8
Chrysotoxum bicinctum
(7–10 mm)

Plate 9
Criorhina berberina
(8–12 mm)

Plate 10
Criorhina floccosa
(10–13 mm)

Plate 11
Epistrophe eligans
(6–9.5 mm) [SF]

Plate 12
Epistrophe grossulariae
(9–12 mm) [SF]

Plate 13
Episyrphus balteatus
(6–10 mm)

1	2	3
4	5	6
7		8
9	10	11
12		13

Plate 1
Eristalinus aeneus
(6–9.5 mm) [SF]

Plate 2
Eristalis abusivus
(8–9.5 mm) [SF]

Plate 3
Eristalis horticola
(8–11.5 mm)

Plate 4
Eristalis intricarius
(8–12 mm)

Plate 5
Ferdinandea cuprea
(7.5–11 mm)

Plate 6
Helophilus pendulus
(8.5–11 mm)

Plate 7
Leucozona glaucia
(8–11 mm)

Plate 8
Mallota cimbiciformis
(11–12.5 mm, rare) [SF]

Plate 9
Melangyna quadrimaculata
(7–9 mm) [SF]

Plate 10
Melanogaster aerosa
(5.5–7 mm) [SF]

Plate 11
Melanostoma mellinum
(5–7 mm) [SF]

Plate 12
Meliscaeva auricollis
(6–9.5 mm) [SF]

Plate 13
Meliscaeva cinctella
(7–10 mm) [SF]

1		2
3	4	5
6	7	8
9	10	11
12		13

Plate 1
Narcissus Fly
Merodon equestris
(8.5–10 mm)

Plate 2
Microdon analis
(7–8 mm, local)

Plate 3
Myathropea florae
(7–12 mm)

Plate 4
Neoascia obliqua
(3.5–5.5 mm) [SF]

Plate 5
Paragus haemorrhous
(3.5–4 mm) [SF]

Plate 6
Parhelophilus frutetorum
(7–9 mm) [SF]

Plate 7
Pipiza noctiluca
(6.5–8 mm) [SF]

Plate 8
Platycheirus clypeatus
(5–7.5 mm) [SF]

Plate 9
Platycheirus immarginatus
(5.5–7 mm) [SF]

Plate 10
Platycheirus occultus
(5.5–6.5 mm) [SF]

Plate 11
Platycheirus peltatus
(7–9 mm) [SF]

Plate 12
Portevinia maculata
(6–8 mm) [SF]

Plate 13
Psilota anthracina
(6–7.5 mm, rare)

1	2	3
4		5
6	7	8
9	10	11
12		13

Plate 1
Rhingia campestris
(6–9.5 mm) [SF]

Plate 2
Riponnensia splendens
(5.5–7 mm)

Plate 3
Scaeva pyrastri
(9–12.5 mm)

Plate 4
Sericomyia lappona
(9–11 mm)

Plate 5
Sphaerophoria rueppellii
(4–6.5 mm) [SF]

Plate 6
Sphaerophoria scripta
(5–7 mm)

Plate 7
Sphegina elegans
(5–7 mm) [SF]

Plate 8
Syrphus vitripennis
(7–10 mm) [SF]

Plate 9
Syritta pipiens **(4–7 mm)**
[SF]

Plate 10
Trichopsomyia flavitarsis
(4–6 mm) [SF]

Plate 11
Tropidia scita
(5.5–8 mm) [SF]

Plate 12
Xylota abiens **(6–8 mm)**
[SF]

Plate 13
Xylota sylvarum
(7–12 mm)

CALYPTERATES

KEDS and BIRDLICE-FLIES – Family Hippoboscidae

UK: 14 species
New Forest: estimated 8 species [60%]

A small group of almost flattened, but powerful looking parasitic flies. All are ectoparasites of birds or mammals, feeding on blood, some have reduced wings. The **Forest Fly *Hippobosca equina*** (6–8 mm, local) is fully winged and prefer horses, cattle and deer, but sometimes humans attract them; this is how they are likely to be spotted near wooded areas in the Forest, flying close by or landing on people. The Forest is the stronghold for this notorious species and a 1914 report by Bournemouth Natural History Society implies that during military manoeuvres in the Forest, 'animals were maddened by its persistent attacks'. Several other bird parasites plus one deer parasite are also present in the Forest.

DUNGFLIES – Family Scathophagidae

UK: 54 species
New Forest: estimated 35 species [65%]

Small to large, usually slender, with bristles. The **Yellow Dungfly *Scathophaga stercoraria*** (8–10 mm, common) is attracted to cow dung in numbers, where they prey on mainly small insects on the dung. A selection of other Forest species is shown in Plates 2–7 opposite.

ANTHOMYIID FLIES – Family Anthomyiidae

UK: 238 species
New Forest: estimated 155 species [65%]

Small to large, slender flies, with various habitats. ***Fucellia*** species (c.6 mm, local) occurs in coastal areas on rotting organic matter washed up by the sea.

HOUSEFLIES and ALLIES – Family Muscidae

UK: 281 species
New Forest: estimated 183 species [65%]

A large group of small to large flies usually grey to black, but some metallic green or blue. They include some of the most abundant flies in the Forest, particularly those associated with dung. Adults of many species visit flowers for nectar, but some are predators or feed on blood. The larvae can be carnivores, feed on decaying matter such as plant material or dung and in some cases are at least part aquatic. The **Face Fly *Musca autumnalis*** (7–8 mm, common) is a pest of horses and cattle in the Forest, transmitting diseases. Large numbers can occur indoors, seeking somewhere to hibernate for the winter. Several other species common in the Forest are shown in Plates 9–14 opposite.

1a	1b	2
3	4	5
6	7	8
9	10	11
12	13	14

Plates 1a & 1b
Forest Fly

Plate 2
Yellow Dungfly

Plate 3
Scathophaga scybalaria [SF]

Plate 4
Scathophaga suilla [SF]

Plate 5
Ceratinostoma ostiorum [SF]

Plate 6
Cleigastra apicalis [SF]

Plate 7
***Pogonota* species** [SF]

Plate 8
***Fucellia* species** [SF]

Plate 9
Face Fly [SF]

Plate 10
Graphomya maculata [SF]

Plate 11
Mesembrina meridiana [SF]

Plate 12
Neomyia viridescens

Plate 13
Polietes domitor [SF]

Plate 14
Stomoxys calcitrans [SF]

BLUEBOTTLES, GREENBOTTLES and BLOWFLIES – Family Calliphoridae

UK: 38 species
New Forest: 25 species [65%]

Mostly rather stout, small to large flies; some species are metallic, notably bluebottles ***Calliphora*** species and greenbottles ***Lucilia*** species. Adults soak up fluids and again some are unpopular in homes. Many species develop in carrion, but clusterflies *Pollenia* species are earthworm predators and ***Protocaliphora*** species are ectoparasites of nesting birds. The **Bluebottles *Calliphora vicina*** and ***vomitoria*** (10–14 mm, common) and **Greenbottle *Lucilia caear*** (8–10 mm, common) are amongst Britain's best known flies, often basking on walls and fences and entering the house when doors and windows are left open; they will lay eggs on any scraps of meat and fish which may result in an infestation of maggots in the house. Cluster Flies, for example ***Pollenia rudis*** (c.10 mm, common) are usually easily identified by their chequered abdomen and golden furred thorax; in autumn they congregate before finding shelter for the winter, which may include the interior of houses. ***Cynomya mortuorum*** (c.10 mm, local) is easily recognised by its yellowish jowls and is usually found on carrion or dung.

FLESH FLIES – Family Sarcophagidae

UK: 60 species
New Forest: 39 species [65%]

Small to large species, usually stout and bristly, often with a chequered abdomen and never metallic. The red-eyed **Flesh Fly *Sarcophaga carnaria*** (10–15 mm, common) is one of several similar species; females deposit small larvae rather than eggs. Related species develop in snails and carrion. Another group of species including ***Metopia*** and ***Miltogramma*** develop in the nests of solitary bees and wasps,

PARASITIC FLIES – Family Tachinidae

UK: 270 species
New Forest: 176 species [65%]

Tachinids are small to large, often bristly, flies; the larvae are parasitoids of other insects, predominantly the caterpillars of butterflies and moths. Eggs are normally laid on or near the host, which the larvae penetrate. The largest species is ***Tachina grossa*** (14–20 mm, widespread), a parasite of moth larvae which is black with a yellow face and can be seen on flowers mainly during July and August in meadows, heathlands and woodland margins; along with ***Tachina fera*** (8–12 mm, common). By contrast, the spectacular ***Phasia hemiptera*** (7–14 mm, local) is a parasite of bugs, particularly the Green and Red-legged Shieldbug and can be seen in wooded areas from May to August. Only males have coloured wings. ***Linnaemya vulpina*** (9–11 mm) is a parasite of True Lover's Knot caterpillars on heathers. Several tachinids are parasitoids of chafer beetle grubs in sandy soil, for example ***Dexia rustica*** (8–10 mm, common). ***Eurithia anthophila*** (8–12 mm, common) and some similar species can be abundant on angelica and hogweed flowers in late summer. A selection of other Forest species is shown in Plates 9–17 opposite, also ***Gymnosoma rotundatum*** (6–8 mm, not yet recorded in Forest, rare in surrounds).

1	2	3	4
5	6	7	8
9	10	11	
12	13	14	
15	16	17	

Plate 1
Calliphora vicina

Plate 2
Calliphora vomitoria [SF]

Plate 3
Lucilia caesar [SF]

Plate 4
Pollenia rudis [SF]

Plate 5
Cynomya mortuorum

Plate 6
Protocalliphora azurea [SF]

Plate 7
Flesh Fly *Sarcophaga* species

Plate 8
Metopia argyrocephala [SF]

Plate 9
Tachina grossa

Plate 10
Tachina fera

Plate 11
***Phasia hemiptera* male**

Plate 12
Linnaemyia vulpina [SF]

Plate 13
Dexia rustica [SF]

Plate 14
Eurithia anthophila [SF]

Plate 15
Dexiosoma caninum [SF]

Plate 16
Nowickia ferox

Plate 17
Gymnosoma rotundatum [GR]

ACALYPTERATES

THICK-HEADED FLIES – Family Conopidae

UK: 24 species
New Forest: at least 12 species [50%]

Small to large slender to stout flies often wasp-like, black and yellow. Conopids are parasitoids of adult bees and wasps, the female depositing an egg in the host's abdomen whilst in flight. The larva develops and pupates when the host dies. Adults look for sunny, warm spots with plenty of nectar sources, such as heather or ragwort. ***Conops quadrifasciatus***, ***Conops flavipes*** and ***Sicus ferrugineus*** (all 8–13 mm, widespread) are parasitoids of bumblebees and can be seen from May to September. ***Conops vesicularis*** (c.13 mm, local) is a larger hornet mimic occasionally seen in the Forest during May and June. ***Myopa*** species (5–11 mm) occur locally in the Forest during spring and attack mining bees. ***Physcocephala rufipes*** (10–18 mm, widespread) is another species likely to be noticed on composites and umbellifers, or just sitting around on nearby vegetation.

RUST FLIES – Family Psilidae

UK: 26 species
New Forest: estimated 17 species [65%]

Small to medium sized flies, including agricultural pests living in roots as larvae. ***Loxocera aristata*** (8–13 mm, widespread) occurs in wetlands where it is associated with rushes.

LANCE FLIES – Family Lonchaeidae

UK: 44 species
New Forest: estimated 29 species [65%]

Usually stout and metallic, small to medium sized flies; females have an ovipositor. Most ***Lonchaea*** larvae feed on bark beetles beneath bark on dead or dying timber, with adults found nearby, sometimes in numbers.

PICTURE-WINGED FLIES – Families Tephritidae, Ulidiidae, Pallopteridae and Platystomatidae

UK: 75 species
New Forest: estimated 49 species [65%]

The small to medium sized picture-winged flies often sport mottled or patterned wings. The wings are sometimes waving, the males keen to impress females or challenge another male's territory. Tephritid females have a rigid ovipositor to deposit eggs in living plant tissue, the larvae live in the plant and some species induce galls. In the Forest there are plenty of species to look for, one of the most beautiful being ***Urophora quadrifasciata*** (2–3 mm). Species characteristic of saltmarsh in the Keyhaven area include ***Campiglossa plantaginis*** (c.5 mm, common), attacking sea aster, the scarcer ***Myopites eximius*** (3–4 mm, local), attacking golden samphire and ***Melieria picta*** (4–5.5 mm, local) probably developing in decaying vegetation. ***Palloptera scutellata*** (c.5 mm, local) associated with rushes in wetlands. A selection of other Forest species is shown.

1	2	3	
4	5	6	
7	8	9	
10	11	12	13
14	15	16	17
18	19	20	21

Plate 1
Conops quadrifasciatus [SF]

Plate 2
Conops flavipes [SF]

Plate 3
Conops vesicularis

Plate 4
Myopa buccata

Plate 5
Myopa testacea [SF]

Plate 6
Sicus ferrugineus

Plate 7
Physocephala rufipes

Plate 8
Loxocera aristata [SF]

Plate 9
Lonchaea species [SF]

Plate 10
Urophora cardui

Plate 11
Urophora quadrifasciata [SF]

Plate 12
Campiglossa plantaginis [SF]

Plate 13
Myopites eximia [SF]

Plate 14
Melieria picta [SF]

Plate 15
Palloptera scutellata

Plate 16
Cerajocera tussilaginis [SF]

Plate 17
Ceroxys urticae [SF]

Plate 18
Euleia heraclei

Plate 19
Rivellia syngenesiae [SF]

Plate 20
Sphenella marginata [SF]

Plate 21
Xyphosia miliaria

SNAIL-KILLING FLIES – Family Sciomyzidae

UK: 68 species
New Forest: estimated 44 species [65%]

Small to medium flies with variable body colour and often distinctive wing markings. The larvae of nearly all species feed on snails, usually aquatic, occasionally terrestrial. They feed for some time before consuming the snail's vital organs. The richest assemblages occur in fen and marsh, ***Dictya umbrarum*** (c.6 mm, local) is present in most of the larger bogs. ***Sepedon sphegea*** (7–8 mm, local) is usually associated with pools and ***Renocera pallida*** (5–6 mm, local) prefers wet alder woodland. A selection of other Forest species is shown in Plates 1–9 opposite.

BLACK SCAVENGER or ENSIGN FLIES – Family Sepsidae

UK: 28 species
New Forest: estimated 18 species [65%]

Small flies associated with animal dung which are common in the open Forest, including ***Nemopoda nitidula*** (4–5.5 mm, common).

FRIT or GRASS FLIES – Family Chloropidae

UK: 177 species
New Forest: estimated 115 species [65%]

Tiny to medium-sized flies, several species associated with reed beds, including ***Lipara lucens*** (c.7 mm, local), which creates distinctive cigar cells on common reed. These galls support a variety of other insects. ***Platycephala planifrons*** (c.7 mm, local) develops in reed stems, but does not make a gall. There are several scarce species associated with saltmarsh.

SHORE FLIES – Family Ephydridae

UK: 148 species
New Forest: estimated 96 species [65%]

Tiny (1 mm) to medium sized flies which may occur in good numbers in mire and wet coastal habitats. The larvae of some develop in wet mud and feed on micro-organisms such as algae. The **Mantis Fly *Ochthera mantis*** (c.5 mm) has distinctive swollen forelegs used for catching other insects and can be found in Forest bogs, often in the vicinity of sundews; both having to cope with a protein-poor environment. Several ***Notiphila*** species can be found in coastal and inland swamp, including ***Notiphila riparia*** (c.4 mm, widespread).

FLEAS – Order SIPHONAPTERA

UK: 57 species
New Forest: estimated 34 species [60%]

A small group of wingless, shiny, hairy insects (1–8 mm) with a small, tough, laterally flattened body. Adults have blood sucking mouthparts. Hind legs are evolved so they are able to jump. There is a complete life cycle: egg, larva, pupa and adult, living as ectoparasites (on the outside) of birds and mammals – only the adults are parasitic and they can survive months without a blood meal. The legless, eyeless larvae feed on organic matter near the host. Fleas are difficult to identify, but are well known for their ability to transit diseases such as plague and typhus; a few also come into contact with people and domestic pets. The **Hedgehog Flea *Archaeopsylla erinacei*** (c.3 mm) can be prolific on hedgehogs and is known to rarely bite humans.

1	2	3
4	5	6
7	8	9
10	11a 11b	12
13	14	15

Plate 1
Dictya umbrarum [SF]

Plate 2
Sepedon sphegea [SF]

Plate 3
Renocera pallida [SF]

Plate 4
Hydromya dorsalis [SF]

Plate 5
Ilione albiseta [SF]

Plate 6
Psacadina verbekei [SF]

Plate 7
Sciomyza simplex [SF]

Plate 8
Tetanocera fuscinervis [SF]

Plate 9
Coremacera marginata [PCr]

Plate 10
Nemopoda nitidula [SF]

Plates 11a & 11b
Lipara lucens
a) [SF]
b) gall [SF]

Plate 12
Platycephala planifrons [SF]

Plate 13
Ochthera mantis [SF]

Plate 14
Notiphila riparia [SF]

Plate 15
Hedgehog Flea [RK]

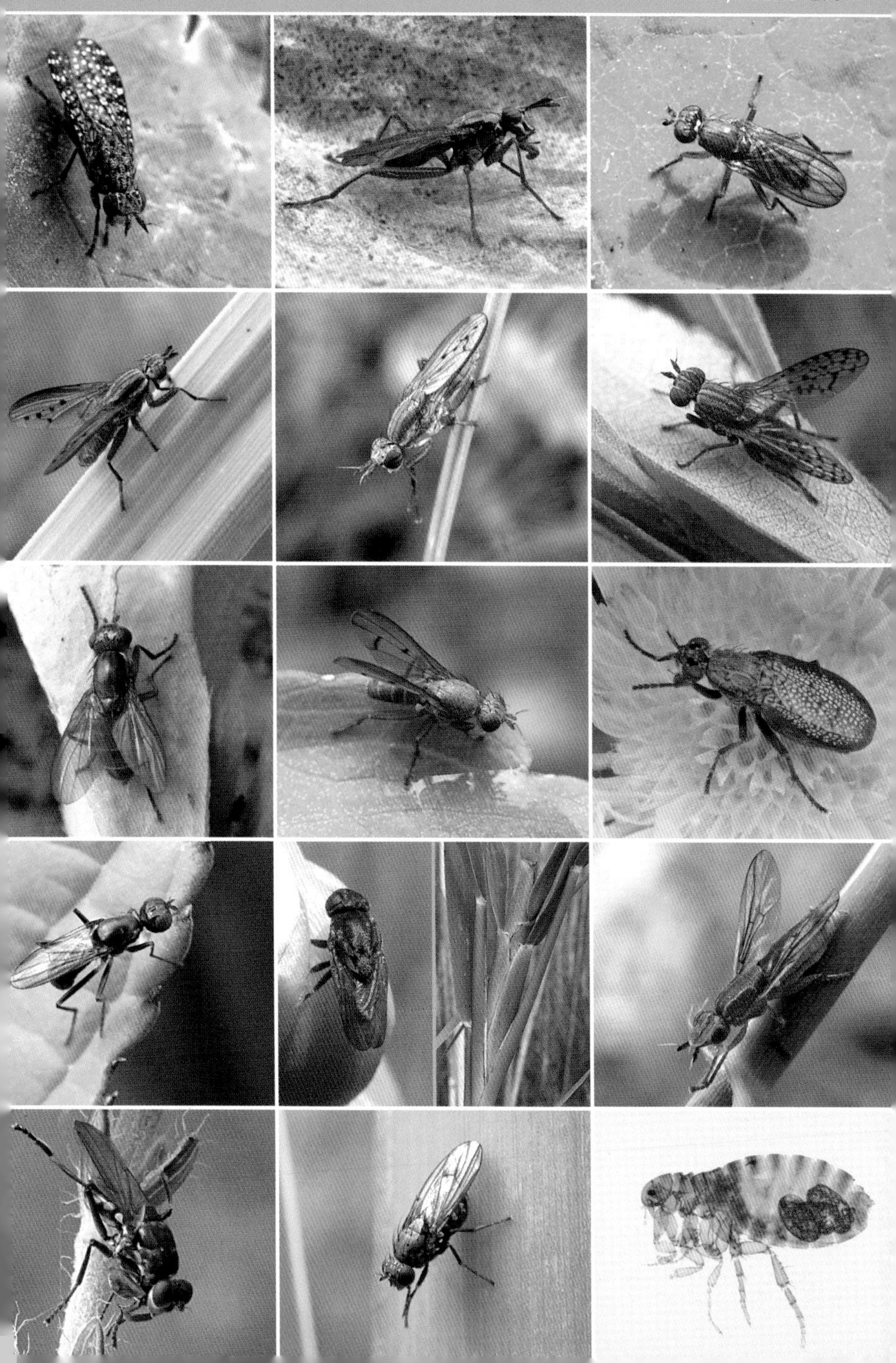

ANTS, WASPS, BEES and RELATED INSECTS – Order HYMENOPTERA

UK: 7,500 species
New Forest: estimated 4,500 species [60%] based on samples of Families, may be conservative

This is the largest order in Britain, ahead of Diptera and Coleoptera, ranging from tiny parasitic wasps to a giant ichneumon, up to 100 mm long including the ovipositor; otherwise about half that length. Most people have heard of bees, wasps and ants (combined, they are known as Aculeates) and some are fearful of the reputation they have, in stinging people. However, these are a minority of species. The numbers in this order escalate when one includes 'Parasitica', the ichneumons and parasitic wasps all belonging to the suborder Apocrita. The sawflies belong to a separate suborder Symphyta. The Hymenoptera typically have two pairs of membranous wings, the forewings larger; they have mouthparts for biting and chewing, feeding on plants, pollen and nectar and wood, seeds; some are cleptoparasites (steal food) or parasitoids (parasites that kill their host) of other invertebrates. The life-cycle is one of complete metamorphosis (development): egg, larva, pupa and adult; larvae are legless except for sawflies which have small fore, mid and hind legs, resembling butterfly and moth caterpillars. The most useful species is the honeybee, valued for its honey, beeswax and royal jelly. Many species fly to flowers to collect pollen and nectar, including wasps which also seek prey in the form of other insects. The fast flying bees are particularly efficient pollinators of crops and play a significant role in feeding the world's human population, a huge contribution to the world's economy. The sophisticated behaviour of social insects in a bee-hive or ants nest is remarkable. Then there are some small wasps with a jewel-like beauty. Certain Hymenoptera are rather under-recorded in the New Forest, as in other parts of Britain, except perhaps for bees and some wasps. The photographs in this book show a representative selection of species in the Forest; identification of species can be a challenge and often voucher specimens are necessary due to close resemblance to other species.

Southern Wood Ant nest

1	2
3	4
5	6

Plate 1
Southern Wood Ants attacking click beetle

Plate 2
Pompilid wasp hunting for spider

Plate 3
Hornet nest, guarded by several workers

Plate 4
Ammophila sabulosa **(a digger wasp) and prey**

Plate 5
Ivy Bee male interaction [GP]

Plate 6
Honeybee

SAWFLIES and WOOD WASPS – Suborder Symphyta

UK: c.500 species
New Forest: estimated 300 species [60%]

Sawflies are often bright, weak-flying insects mainly in the day, often in wet habitats. Adults sometimes nectar on flowers, but often eat other insects. Most larvae appear caterpillar-like on vegetation with fleshy false legs (prolegs), although a few induce gall-formulation. The largest species is one of the most spectacular, the **Wood Wasp or Horntail *Urocerus gigas*** (25–40 mm, local) which resembles a wasp. The ovipositor is used by females like a drill to lays eggs in unhealthy pines. This species is best looked for during the daytime in and around coniferous woodland, for example around decaying standing pines or stacks of recently cut pine logs in Inclosures such as New Copse in May to October. Not all species possess a saw-like ovipositor though and certainly not as long. An effective wasp mimic is the vivid ***Tenthredo scrophulariae*** (12–15 mm, common) in June to August; the larvae feed on mullein and figwort. The **Turnip Sawfly *Athalia rosae*** (7–8 mm, local) is a strangely shaped, but attractive insect, which sometimes swarms and mates in vast numbers in September, hence are often considered a pest by turnip and cabbage family growers. ***Rhogogaster viridis*** (c.10 mm, widespread) catches insects on flowers. Other widespread Forest species include ***Tenthreda temula*** [= ***T. celtica***] (c.12 mm), one of several attractive and, in some cases, similar-looking *Tenthreda* species; ***Arge cyanocrocea*** (7–8 mm) and **Alder Sawfly *Eriocampa ovata*** (6–7 mm) found in May to August. Sawflies are under-studied, but sometimes rather colourful insects.

1		
2	3	4a / 4b
5	6	7

Plate 1
Wood Wasp

Plate 2
Tenthredo temula

Plate 3
Tenthredo scrophulariae

Plates 4a & 4b
Turnip Sawfly
b) emergence

Plate 5
Rhogogaster viridis

Plate 6
Arge cyanocrocea

Plate 7
Alder Sawfly

Turnip Sawfly swarming on flowers and in the air, Barton-on-Sea

Suborder Apocrita

Aculeates – ANTS, WASPS AND BEES

VELVET ANTS – Family Mutillidae

UK: 3 species
New Forest: 3 species [100%]

Males of these medium to large solitary wasps are winged, females wingless; they are known for their painful sting. The **Large Velvet Ant *Mutilla europaea*** (7.5–15 mm, local) is a parasitoid of bumblebee larvae. In the Forest and surrounds they are found in grasslands and heathlands and most likely to be seen in spring after hibernation and when new adults are produced between July and September. They can walk very quickly and can sting painfully in defence. The often smaller **Black-headed Velvet Ant *Myrmosa atra*** (4–11 mm, local) is a more widely distributed species, which attacks ground-nesting solitary bees or wasps. The **Small Velvet Ant *Smicromyrme rufipes*** (4.5–5.5 mm, rare) is a parasitoid on several subterranean nesting bees and wasps; it has been recorded in the Forest and surrounds, particularly near the coast.

ANTS – Family Formicidae

UK: 50 species
New Forest: at least 28 species [56%]

The remarkable social behaviour of these insects has always fascinated people. The life-cycle often lasts more than one year, with nests in dead wood, soil, under a stone or raised above ground in a mound of earth or plant debris. Whilst some species of ants eat seeds, many feed on the honey dew secreted by aphids, which they then protect. Some species sting or bite in defence. Males and queens are winged, workers and queens of some species wingless (body length 2.5–11 mm). Apart from common ants in gardens, if one had to name a single ant walkers in the Forest would be likely to see, it would certainly be the large **Southern Wood Ant *Formica rufa*** (c.10 mm, common). The huge mounds in mainly coniferous woodlands are unmistakable, look closely and there might be thousands of ants busy working, the workers sporting a red thorax. When hunting, there is often a huge trail of many thousands of ants, tearing apart insects found en route and taking them back to the nest. The ants make good use of pine needles on the ground when constructing the nest. In defence, this species bites and sprays formic acid. Mutual relationships with other insects are little known in some cases, including a link with the Rose Chafer beetle, whose larvae presumably help keep the nest clean, affording them protection from potential predators. The **Black Bog Ant *Formica picea*** (4–9 mm, local), is a black, shiny medium-sized species found in the Forest, Dorset and a locality in south Wales. An old record from the Isle of Wight might be in error. It may be found in tussocks of purple moor grass where wet heath meets bog. The large red and black **Slavemaker Ant *Formica sanguinea*** (4.5–8 mm, local) often takes over another *Formica* ants nest by killing the queen, and using the workers to bring up her offspring. The **Large Black Ant *Formica fusca*** (c.6 mm, common) is a frequently seen black species. A selection of other Forest species is shown; several species can be difficult to identify from photographs and may require examining under a microscope.

1a	1b	2
3a		3c
3b		3d
4	5	6	7
8		9

Plates 1a & 1b
Large Velvet Ant
a) male
b) female

Plate 2
Small Velvet Ant [TB]

Plates 3a–3d
Southern Wood Ant
a) nest activity
b) with caterpillar prey
c) queen
d) queen without wings

Plate 4
Black Bog Ant

Plate 5
Large Black Ant with New Forest Shieldbugs

Plate 6
Slavemaker Ant

Plate 7
Black Ant *Lasius niger* queen

Plate 8
***Lasius platythorax* nest**

Plate 9
***Myrmica* species nest**

SPIDER-HUNTING WASPS – Family Pompilidae

UK: 41 species
New Forest: at least 27 species [66%]

Very active solitary wasps (4–18 mm), often seen investigating sandy slopes or taking short flights. Many species have a slender black or black and red abdomen, with long legs. Most spider-hunting wasps nest in the ground and provision each nest cell with one paralysed spider. It is fascinating to observe the spider being dragged at rapid pace and somehow squeezed into the burrow. ***Anoplius viaticus*** (7–15 mm, common) is found on heathland in the Forest. One of the best sites to observe pompilids is the disused railway cutting at Brownloaf. Here, one may find at least three rare species, our largest pompilid ***Cryptocheilus notatus*** (up to 18 mm), also ***Aporus unicolor*** (c.10 mm) which attacks the Purse-web Spider and the colourful ***Ceropales variegata*** (c.10 mm).

SOCIAL, MASON and POTTER WASPS – Family Vespidae

UK: 32 species
New Forest: 22 species [69%]

Social wasps (subfamily Vespinae) live in large colonies within nests constructed of wood pulp. A single queen is served by several hundred smaller workers who bring in food in the form of caterpillars, other insects and nectar. New queens and drones (males) are produced from mid summer onwards. They are well known as certain species regularly live in and around houses, keeping pest control businesses occupied. Although the abdomen is often variable in pattern, the various species can often be identified by looking at the head and thoracic patterns. Workers can give a nasty sting, but despite their bad reputation, they can be useful in the garden by killing pests such as caterpillars, which are fed to the larvae. Queens hibernate over winter in outhouses, log piles and crevices and re-emerge from March. In autumn certain species feed on fallen fruit, including the largest species in the Forest, the **Hornet *Vespa crabro*** (18–35 mm, widespread), which is frequently seen in Forest rides speeding from flower to flower in the hope of preying on other insects, or flying into crevices in rotting wood. The fragments of wood are brought back to the nest as building material. Aerial nests are found in hollow trees in mature woodlands and parks, usually from May to October. They are attracted to lights and are sometimes a nuisance in moth traps. New queens and males (the latter with longer antennae) emerge from the nest in September to October, mate and disperse. The males die, but the queens hibernate to form a nest in spring. Other species likely to be seen in the Forest include the **Common Wasp *Vespula vulgaris*** (10–18 mm, common) which nests in the ground as well as roof spaces, and the **Tree Wasp *Dolichovespula sylvestris*** (12–18 mm, common) which either nests in the ground or in bushes and trees. The similar-sized **Median or French Wasp *Dolichovespula media*** (common) and **Saxon Wasp *Dolichovespula saxonica*** (widespread) are both recent colonists in Britain, now well established in the Forest and surrounds. The 'potter wasp' hunts larvae of moths and beetles for its offspring and build a mud-constructed nest, that of ***Eumenes coarctatus*** (10–15 mm, local) a clay pot attached to heather or gorse; this is the only potter wasp in southern England. A selection of other Forest species is shown.

1a		2	
1b	1c		
3a		3b	3c
4	5	6a	6b
7a	7b	8	9
10a	10b	11	

Plates 1a–1c
Anoplius viaticus
b) paralysing spider
c) transferring spider to burrow

Plate 2
Aporus unicolor **(left),** ***Cryptocheilus notatus*** **(centre) and** ***Ceropales variegata*** **(right)** [SF]

Plates 3a–3c
Hornet
a) worker
b) male, note long antennae
c) peering out of crevice

Plate 4
Common Wasp

Plate 5
Tree Wasp worker [GP]

Plates 6a & 6b
Saxon Wasp

Plates 7a & 7b
Median Wasp

Plate 8
Red Wasp ***Vespula rufa*** **(11–18 mm)** [SF]

Plate 9
German Wasp
Vespula germanica
(13–20 mm) [SF]

Plates 10a & 10b
Eumenes coarctatus
a) [GH]
b) at clay pot nest [JW]

Plate 11
Odynerus spinipes
(8–12.5 mm) [SF]

DIGGER WASPS – Family Sphecidae

UK: 4 species
New Forest: 2 species [50%], but 100% in Forest surrounds

Sphecids are solitary caterpillar-hunting wasps of butterflies, moths and sawflies. The red and black ***Ammophila*** species, ***A. sabulosa*** (15–25 mm, widespread) and ***A. pubescens*** (12–20 mm, widespread) are sometimes seen carrying caterpillars to be buried in an underground tunnel. An egg is then laid on the paralysed larva. ***Podalonia*** species are local along the coast in the Forest surrounds: the **Hairy Sand Wasp *Podalonia hirsuta*** (13–24 mm) lives in subterranean nests in open sandy soil and is sometimes observed in the Bournemouth area, as is the rarer, rather similar, less hairy ***Podalonia affinis*** (16–20 mm).

DIGGER WASPS – Family Crabronidae

UK: c.118 species
New Forest: at least 77 species [65%]

Crabronids are solitary wasps, which visit flowers for nectar and prey on various arthropods. They nest variously in the ground, dead wood and hollow stems. Many species have attractive yellow and black-striped abdomens, including several large, widespread ***Cerceris*** species. ***Crabro peltarius*** (10–14 mm, local) preys on flies in heathland sandpits. Smaller digger wasps such as ***Pemphredon*** and ***Trypoxylon*** are entirely black, but some ***Crossocerus*** species are yellow-marked. The **Bee Wolf *Philanthus triangulum*** (8–18 mm, local) occurs in sandy areas on the coast and within heathland. The females catch honeybees and carry them home upside down to their underground nests. Formerly rare, this species is now found at various places in the Forest and surrounds, including Barton-on-Sea, Boscombe, Hengistbury Head, the Isle of Wight and others. A selection of other Forest species is shown.

Bee Wolf social interaction [GP]

1		2	
3a		3b	
4a	4b	5	6
7	8		9
10	11	12	13

Plate 1
Ammophila sabulosa and prey [GP]

Plate 2
Ammophila pubescens [SF]

Plates 3a & 3b
Hairy Sand Wasp
b) at burrow

Plates 4a & 4b
Cerceris arenaria
b) with weevil prey

Plate 5
Cerceris ruficornis [SF]

Plate 6
Cerceris rybyensis

Plate 7
Slender-bodied Digger Wasp
Crabro cribrarius

Plate 8
Bee Wolf carrying honeybee prey

Plate 9
Astata boops

Plate 10
Argogorytes mystaceus

Plate 11
Field Digger Wasp
Mellinus arvensis

Plate 12
Common Spiny Digger Wasp
Oxybelus uniglumis

Plate 13
Ectemnius continuus [SF]

BEES – Family Apidae

UK: c.270 species
New Forest: 187 species [69%]
[see breakdown below for group of bees]

A familiar sight feeding on flowers, bees are popular with many people, although some are wary of them stinging. However, females only use their stings in defence and, with the exception of the honeybee, do not die afterwards. Bees range in size from 4 mm to 25 mm in body length and most British species are solitary i.e. each nest is the work of a single female, working alone to excavate and provision her nest burrow. Whilst some bees may be seen nesting in large numbers they are not necessarily exhibiting social behaviour, only the bumblebees, honeybees and some halictine bees are truly social insects. In certain sites in the New Forest, bee-keepers are permitted by the Forestry Commission to place beehives, for a fee. Bees are probably best known for their role in pollinating flowers, their hairy legs and bodies adapted to help gather pollen, which is taken back to their nests by females, via pollen baskets, or specialised clusters of hairs on part of the tibia on the hind legs. The larvae feed on the pollen and nectar. There are estimates that one third of the human food supply depends on insect pollination, much of it accomplished by bees, often the particularly efficient Honeybee *Apis mellifera*. There has, however, been a general decline of many bee species in Europe and it is thought there may be several factors, particularly fewer wildflowers, combined with intensive farming techniques and the varroa mite (honeybee only), which carries a virus.

In Britain the social bees, namely bumblebees and honeybees are well known. Bumblebees include look-alike cuckoo bumblebees, which lay eggs in the nest of another bumblebee and therefore do not need to collect pollen. The usually much smaller solitary bees are the largest but least well studied of the group; they in turn have some cuckoo bees, which benefit from the work of others.

Ideal places to look for bees in the New Forest are churchyards, gardens, heathlands, hedgerows, meadows, parks, sandpits and woodland rides, wherever there is a plentiful supply of flowers. Denny Wood, Keyhaven and surrounds; New Copse Inclosure, Setley and Wootton Coppice Inclosure are good general sites. Outside the Forest, Barton Common and cliffs, and Hengistbury Head, are also productive.

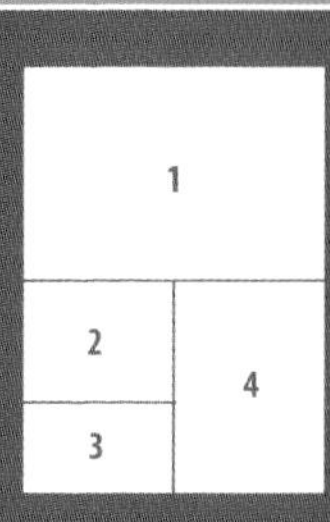

Plate 1
Andrena ferox **nesting area**

Plate 2
Ivy Bee mating cluster

Plate 3
Bee hives

Plate 4
Red-tailed Bumblebee
[PCr]

Barton-on-Sea, home to the Ivy Bee

Solitary bees and associated cuckoo bees

UK: c.244 species
New Forest: 166 species [68%]

Solitary bees nest in a variety of places above ground, such as in walls, wood and the ground. The female builds the nest herself and lays eggs, then abandons it. Solitary bees are considered to be very efficient pollinators and include Carder Bees, Carpenter Bees, Leaf-cutter Bees, Mason Bees, Mining Bees, White-faced bees and others. They are found in various habitats; a good place to start watching is a garden or on the coast. The **Ivy Bee *Colletes hederae*** (c.13 mm, local), is a mining bee only added to the British insect list in 2001. It is spreading rapidly along the coast of southern England and inland and can be seen from mid-September to November in nesting sites of hundreds or thousands on undercliffs at Barton-on-Sea, Hordle and Bournemouth area, particularly suitable sandy spots near flowering ivy, where they obtain pollen. They are also abundant in gardens in Lymington, and less often inland in the Forest, for example Brockenhurst and Parc Pale. The close relative ***Colletes halophilus*** (c.10 mm, rare) is found from August to October on salt marshes, heavily relying on sea aster pollen. There are a few records on the coast in the Forest, such as Hurst Spit, also in the surrounds, including the Isle of Wight. The more widespread ***Colletes succinctus*** (c.10 mm, widespread) found in heathland, is similar. ***Andrena argentata*** (8 mm, rare) and ***Nomada baccata*** (7 mm, rare) are heath specialists, host and cleptoparasite. *Andrena argentata* is sometimes seen in a mating frenzy, where clusters may be observed. *Nomada baccata* stay near the nesting sites in usually small numbers (but sometimes in hundreds) ready to move in, as they rely on the food stored by the host species for its offspring. One of Britain's most endangered mining bees is ***Andrena ferox*** (8–13 mm, rare), which nests gregariously in open, sunny situations in Denny and Hollands Woods; many females often use a communal nest entrance, but each has its own nest within the soil. This is a spring species, obtaining pollen from oak flowers from late April to early June and subsequent generations use the same nest entrance each year. ***Dasypoda hirtipes*** (c.12 mm, rare, local on coast near Forest) is mainly found on heathland and coastal dunes in southern England. ***Macropis europaea*** (10 mm, rare) is likely to be found in wetlands, collecting pollen only from yellow loosestrife and floral oil. Some of the commonest bees are the ground-nesting ***Lasioglossum*** species (c.8–10 mm). ***Megachile versicolor*** (10–13 mm, widespread) is a leaf-cutter bee, which neatly cuts pieces of leaves or petals, hence its common name. ***Coelioxys conoidea*** (11–15 mm, local) is a parasite of ***Megachile maritima*** (11–16 mm, local), which is mainly a coastal species, but also found in other sandy habitats. A selection of other Forest species is shown.

1	2	3
4	5a	5b

6	7	8	9
10	11	12	13
14	15	16	17

18	19	20

Plate 1
Ivy Bee female collecting pollen

Plate 2
Colletes halophilus [SF]

Plate 3
Colletes succinctus [SF]

Plate 4
Andrena argentata [SF]

Plates 5a & 5b
Andrena ferox
a) male
b) female

Plate 6
Andrena flavipes [SF]

Plate 7
Tawny Mining Bee
***Andrena fulva* female**

Plate 8
Nomada baccata

Plate 9
Nomada fucata

Plate 10
Dasypoda hirtipes [SF]

Plate 11
Macropis europaea [SF]

Plate 12
Lasioglossum calceatum

Plate 13
Lasioglossum malachurum [SF]

Plate 14
Megachile versicolor [SF]

Plate 15
Megachile maritima

Plate 16
Coelioxys conoidea

Plate 17
Wool Carder Bee
Anthidium manicatum

Plate 18
Melecta albifrons

Plate 19
Red Mason Bee
***Osmia rufa* male**

Plate 20
Sphecodes pellucidus [SF]

Social bees: i) Bumblebees

UK: 25 species, including 2 extinct
New Forest: 20 species, including extinct [80%], with other species reported close to the boundary

Each colony has an amazing working and communication structure. The queen is the egg-layer, workers (sterile females) care for the larvae, whilst older workers fly to find nectar and pollen. The queen emerges in spring following hibernation and collects pollen from available flowers. The pollen is stored in the nest, which, depending on species, may be underground, such as in abandoned rodent nests and compost heaps, or above ground in grass tussocks, old birds nests and in birds nest-boxes. Eggs are laid on the pollen, and a small supply of nectar stored up in the nest for feeding. When workers emerge, they care for the larvae, whilst older individuals provide nectar and pollen, leaving the queen to remain in the nest to continue egg-laying. In late summer or autumn, some of these eggs have developed into queens and males, leaving the old queens, workers and males to die. Only the new queens hibernate, to start the cycle again. Each colony has up to around 200 insects depending on species.

The British bumblebees range in size from 12–22 mm, with the queens always the largest individuals. In the UK, there are only six common, widespread species, which are also well represented in the Forest: **Garden Bumblebee *Bombus hortorum***, **Red-tailed Bumblebee *Bombus lapidarius***, **White-tailed Bumblebee *Bombus lucorum***, **Common Carder Bumblebee *Bombus pascuorum***, **Early Bumblebee *Bombus pratorum*** and the **Buff-tailed Bumblebee *Bombus terrestris***. There are six UK species of cuckoos in the nests of other bumblebees and are usually almost as widespread as the host, but less abundant. **Barbut's Cuckoo Bumblebee *Bombus barbutellus***, **Forest Cuckoo Bumblebee *Bombus sylvestris***, **Vestal Cuckoo Bumblebee *Bombus vestalis***, **Hill Cuckoo Bumblebee *Bombus rupestris*** [the least abundant species, found in southern England, which takes over nests of *Bombus lapidarius*] and **Field Cuckoo Bumblebee *Bombus campestris*** have all been recorded in the Forest, whilst the **Gypsy Cuckoo Bumblebee *Bombus bohemicus*** has been recorded in Hampshire and may occur in the Forest. Other bumblebees occasionally seen include the **Tree Bumblebee *Bombus hypnorum*** (local) first recorded in Britain in 2001, but extending its range in southern England and with isolated records as far north as Cumbria and Northumbria. Look for it in gardens and woodland margins on brambles, for example around Lyndhurst and Setley. The **Heath Bumblebee *Bombus jonellus*** (local) is worth searching for on heathland and there is a possibility of some of the rarer bumblebees in the Forest, but realistically only about 12 species are likely to be encountered in the Forest at present. Although there are old records of the **Brown-banded Carder Bumblebee *Bombus humilis***, this species prefers flower rich grassland and heathland and is more likely to be found near the coast, particularly in the Forest surrounds at Hengistbury Head and Stanpit. A selection of other Forest species is shown.

1	2	3	
4	5	6	
7	8	9	10
11		12	13
14a	14b	15	16

Plate 1
Garden Bumblebee [SF]

Plate 2
Red-tailed Bumblebee

Plate 3
White-tailed Bumblebee queen [SF]

Plate 4
Common Carder Bumblebee [GP]

Plate 5
Early Bumblebee

Plate 6
Buff-tailed Bumblebee

Plate 7
Barbut's Cuckoo Bumblebee [SF]

Plate 8
Forest Cuckoo Bumblebee [SF]

Plate 9
Vestal Cuckoo Bumblebee

Plate 10
Hill Cuckoo Bumblebee

Plate 11
Field Cuckoo Bumblebee [SF]

Plate 12
Tree Bumblebee

Plate 13
Heath Bumblebee [SF]

Plates 14a & 14b
Brown-banded Carder Bumblebee
a) worker [SF]
b) sunbleached queen

Plate 15
Red-shanked Carder Bumblebee
Bombus ruderarius
queen [SF]

Plate 16
Large Garden Bumblebee
Bombus ruderatus [SF]

Social bees: ii) Honeybees

UK: 1 species
New Forest: 1 species [100%]

The **Honeybee *Apis mellifera*** (12–16 mm, common) has a more complex colony than bumblebees. The queen is responsible for egg-laying and does not collect pollen. Huge colonies of up to around 100,000 workers produce a large amount of honey, allowing the colony to overwinter. The bees produce honey and store it in wax combs and use the same hive from one year to the next. Males produced in spring and later are killed by the workers towards the end of the season, after mating with new queens. In the Forest, the honeybee is a frequent sight, particularly in gardens and on heathlands.

CUCKOO WASPS – Family Chrysidae

UK: 31 species
New Forest: 17 species [55%]

Because of their brilliant metallic colours, the small and medium-size chrysidids are also known as jewel or ruby-tailed wasps. Adults fly in sunny weather from April to October (depending on species), investigating holes and crevices for nests of hosts of other Hymenoptera for their larvae. Adults feed on nectar. One of the commonest is the ***Chrysis ignita*** species group (5–15 mm), with several similar species. A selection of other Forest species is shown.

Parasitica – PARASITIC WASPS

ICHNEUMONIDS – Families Ichneumonidae and Braconidae

UK: c.3,300 species
New Forest: estimated 1,980 species [60%]

Antennae long, with at least 16 segments, these parasitoids are a rather under-studied family. They nearly always kill the host, which ranges from an aphid, egg, to butterfly and moth larvae. Those living inside the host (either one or many thousands in the same host) are endoparasitoids, or outside the host ectoparasitoids. The really exciting species in the Forest are the giants which may be seen if patient by patrolling fresh felled logs during sunny weather. The **Sabre Wasp *Rhyssa persuasoria*** (20–50 mm, 100 mm including the ovipositor, local) is the largest and is found in June to September in pine woods, looking for wood wasp larvae. The author was so carried away watching and photographing variably sized females ovipositing in pine logs at Ivy Wood, that a pesky little specimen was almost ignored. This turned out to be the male! Drilling can take as little as five minutes and has even been observed taking place at midnight. Another giant with long egg-laying equipment is ***Ephilates manifestator*** (c.20 mm, large specimens up to 70 mm including the ovipositor, local), often seen investigating logs for signs of beetle larvae. ***Gasteruption jaculator*** (10–18 mm, widespread) with a white tip on the end of its ovipositor, is a parasitoid of stem-nesting aculeates of the genus *Hylaeus*. A selection of other Forest species is shown.

Various other families of wasps are also included in the 'Parasitica' including small Gall Wasps (Cynipidae) (up to 5 mm), responsible for galls often seen on plants. The **Knopper Gall *Andricus quercuscalicis*** develops on acorns in autumn. The wasp shown investigating the area is a chalcid wasp ***Ormyrus*** species, probably a parasite of *Andricus*.

1a	5	
1b	6	
2	7	8
3	9	10
4	11	12

Plates 1a & 1b
Honeybee
a) nest [CT]
b) male

Plate 2
***Chrysis ignita* group**
(9 mm)

Plate 3
Hedychridium roseum

Plate 4
Trichrysis cyanea

Plate 5
Rhyssa persuasoria
female egglaying

Plate 6
Ephialtes manifestator

Plate 7
Gasteruption jaculator

Plate 8
Enicospilus ramidulus
(c. 13 mm)

Plate 9
Coelichneumon deliratorius
(10–16 mm)

Plate 10
Amblyteles armatorius
(12–16 mm)

Plate 11
Chalcid wasp *Ormyrus* species

Plate 12
Knopper Gall

1	2
3	
4	

Plate 1
Silverfish [SF]

Plate 2
Sea Bristletail [CT]

Plate 3
Bristletail species

Plate 4
Tomoceros longicornis
[a springtail]

PRIMITIVE INSECT ORDERS

Whilst the classification is subject to different opinions, there are usually considered to be two orders of primitive wingless insects, with immature stages resembling small adults. These are the rather similar Silverfish [Order Thysanura] with 2 UK species and the Bristletails [Order Archaeognantha], with 7 UK species. Both orders are represented in the Forest and surrounds, with the **Silverfish *Lepisma saccharina*** (c.15 mm, widespread) likely to be encountered in cool, damp parts of houses, particularly where there is food available, such as cereals. The largest species of bristletail in the UK is the fast-running **Sea Bristletail *Petrobius maritimus*** (up to 18 mm, local), which lives on the seashore and is often seen on rocks. The other species figured (c.10 mm, local) is occasionally found under debris in heathland.

NON-INSECTS

Formerly regarded as insects, but now generally listed as non-insect Hexapods, are the Proturans [Protura], Springtails [Collembola] and Two-tailed Bristletails [Diplura]. A common Forest species is shown, ***Tomocerus longicornis*** (c.4 mm), often seen in woodlands and recognised by its fairly large size and abdominal hairs. Other arthropods (animals without a backbone), but with more than six legs present in insects are the Myriapods, which include Millepedes [Diplopoda] and Centipedes [Chilopoda]. The Arachnids include Ticks and Mites [Acari] and Spiders [Araneae], the Crustacea include Woodlice [Isopoda].

APPENDIX 1 – References

HISTORY OF ENTOMOLOGY IN THE NEW FOREST

Goss, E. (Ed.) (1900) *in The Victoria History of the Counties of England: a history of Hampshire and the Isle of Wight*. Part 1. London: Archibald Constable and Co., Ltd. [insects section, pp. 109–162].

LePard D.A. (2000) The brotherhood of the net. Nova Foresta Magazine 6(3): 18–20.

Oates, M. (1996) The demise of butterflies in the New Forest. British Wildlife 7: 205–216.

Salmon, M.A. (2000) *The Aurelian legacy*. Colchester, Harley Books.

Salmon, M.A. & Edwards P.J. (2005) *The Aurelian's fireside companion*. Lymington, Paphia Publishing Ltd.

HABITATS

Chatters, C. (2009) *Flowers of the Forest. Plants and people in the New Forest National Park*. Old Basing: WILD*Guides* Ltd [includes many references to habitats].

Goriup, P. (Ed.) (1999) *The New Forest woodlands*. Newbury: Pisces Publications.

Newton, A.C. (Ed.) (2010) *Biodiversity in the New Forest*. Newbury: Pisces Publications [includes chapters on dragonflies and damselflies, saproxylic beetles, butterflies and moths, the New Forest Cicada and other invertebrates].

Sterry, P. (1995) *Regional Wildlife. New Forest*. Shepperton: Dial House [includes a brief section on habitats and 11 pages on insects, covering c. 30 species].

Tubbs, C.R (1986) *The New Forest*. New Naturalist No. 73. London: Collins. *Reprinted and revised as*:

Tubbs, C.R (2001) *The New Forest: History, Ecology and Conservation*. Lyndhurst: Ninth Centenary Trust.

The following is a selected bibliography and list of websites to deal with identification and / or assist with species of the major orders found in the New Forest. As mentioned elsewhere, care is needed as mainly smaller species in some orders are difficult to identify, often having several similar species. This particularly includes micro-moths, some Coleoptera, Diptera and Hymenoptera:

INSECTS, general guides

Alexander, K.N.A. (2002) The invertebrates of living and decaying timber in Britain & Ireland. A provisional annotated checklist. English Nature Research report No. 467. Peterborough, English Nature.

Barnard, P.C. (1999) *Identifying British insects and arachnids: an annotated bibliography of key works*. Cambridge: Cambridge University Press [useful for numerous references on all orders].

Chinery, M. (2005) *Collins Complete Guide to British insects*. London: HarperCollins Publishers Ltd.

Shirt, D.B. (ed.) (1987) *British Red Data Books: 2. Insects*. Peterborough: Nature Conservancy Council [whilst out of date, the data sheets for endangered species remain useful].

Various Field Studies Council charts on insect groups http://www.field-studies-council.org/publications/identificationguides.aspx

NBN Gateway http://data.nbn.org.uk/ [for indicative distribution maps of British insects].

Pinchen, B.J. (1999) Scarce and threatened invertebrates of the New Forest. A summary of their status and habitat requirements. New Forest LIFE Project. [Unpublished]

Peachey, C. (1984) Invertebrate Site Register Report 52, Part II – Review of the Invertebrate Sites in England, Provisional Review of the New Forest, Hants. London: Nature Conservancy Council. [Unpublished]

Wright, R.N. & Westerhoff, D.V. (2001) New Forest SAC management plan. Lyndhurst: English Nature [updated listings of significant invertebrates, with a summary of main orders]. [Unpublished]

ODONATA [Dragonflies & Damselflies]

There are various useful websites on Odonata of Hampshire and the New Forest run by individuals.

Dijkstra, K.B. & Lewington, R. (2006) *Field Guide to the dragonflies of Britain and Europe*. Gillingham: British Wildlife Publishing.

Smallshire, D. & Swash, A. (2010) *Britain's dragonflies. A field guide to the damselflies and dragonflies of Britain and Ireland*. 2nd Edition. Old Basing: WILD*Guides* Ltd [identification of adults and nymphs].

Taverner, J., Cham, S., Hold, A. *et al* (2004) *The dragonflies of Hampshire*. Newbury: Pisces Publications.

Welstead, N. & T. (1984) *The dragonflies of the New Forest*. Southampton: Hampshire and Isle of Wight Naturalists' Trust.

British Dragonfly Society http://www.dragonflysoc.org.uk/home.html

ORTHOPTERA [Bush-crickets, Crickets, Grasshoppers & allies]

Evans, M. & Edmondson, R. (2007) *A photographic guide to the grasshoppers & crickets of Britain & Ireland*. King's Lynn: WGUK [useful when examining colour forms of species].

Haes, E.C.M. & Harding, P.T. (1997) *Atlas of grasshoppers, crickets and allied insects in Britain and Ireland*. ITE research publication no. 11. London: The Stationery Office.

Marshall, J.A. & Haes, E.C.M. (1988) *Grasshoppers and allied insects of Great Britain and Ireland*. Colchester: Harley Books.

Welstead, A.R. (1988) Orthoptera of the New Forest and its environs 1980 to 1988. Hythe [brief notes on species and distribution maps]. [Unpublished]

HEMIPTERA [Bugs]

Kirby, P. (1992) *A review of the scarce and threatened Hemiptera of Great Britain*. UK Nature Conservation 2. Peterborough: Joint Nature Conservation Committee.

Pinchen, B.J. & Ward, L.K. (2002) The history, ecology and conservation of the New Forest cicada in Britain. British Wildlife 13: 258–266.

Southwood, T.R.E & Leston, D. (1959) *Land and water bugs of the British Isles*. London: F. Warne & Co.

Anon (2007) *Shieldbugs of Southampton*. Southampton Natural History Society.

British Bugs http://www.britishbugs.org.uk/

COLEOPTERA [Beetles]

Cooter, J. & Barclay, M.V.L. (2006) *A Coleopterist's Handbook*. 4th Edition. The Amateur Entomologist Vol. 11. Orpington: The Amateur Entomologists' Society.

Duff, A.G. (2008) *Checklist of beetles of the British Isles*. Wells. Downloadable from http://www.coleopterist.org.uk/

Hubble, D. (2010) *Keys to the adults of Seed and Leaf Beetles of the British Isles (Coleoptera: Bruchidae, Orsodacnidae, Megalopodidae & Chrysomelidae)*. Test Version. AIDGAP, FSC Publications.
Luff, M.L. (2007) *The Carabidae (ground beetles) of Britain & Ireland*. 2nd Edition. Handbooks for the Identification of British Insects Vol. 4, Part 2. St. Albans: Royal Entomological Society.
The Coleopterist http://www.coleopterist.org.uk/ and other specialist websites.

LEPIDOPTERA [Butterflies & Moths]

Barker, A. & Budd, P. (2005) *Butterflies of Southampton and surrounding area*. Butterfly Conservation (Hampshire & Isle of Wight Branch).
Goater, B. (1974) *The butterflies & moths of Hampshire and the Isle of Wight*. Faringdon: Classey.
Goater, B. & Norriss, T. (2001) *Moths of Hampshire and the Isle of Wight*. Newbury: Pisces Publications.
Harmer, A.S. (1999) *Variation in British butterflies*. Lymington: Paphia Publishing Ltd.
Manley, C. (2008) *British moths and butterflies. A photographic guide*. London: A & C Black.
Oates, M.R. (1996) The demise of butterflies in the New Forest. British Wildlife 7(4): 205–216.
Oates, M., Taverner, J., Green, D., *et al.* (2000) *The butterflies of Hampshire*. Newbury: Pisces Publications.
Skinner, B. (1984) *Colour identification guide to moths of the British Isles*. Harmondsworth: Viking [2nd Edition 1998, 3rd Edition 2009, Apollo Books].
Thomas, J. & Lewington, R. (2010) *The butterflies of Britain & Ireland*. Gillingham: British Wildlife Publishing Ltd.
Townsend, M. & Waring, P. (2007) *Concise guide to the moths of Great Britain and Ireland*. Gillingham: British Wildlife Publishing.
Alan Thornbury's Hampshire butterflies http://www.purple-emperor.co.uk/ [including useful notes on butterfly sites]
Butterfly Conservation, Hampshire and Isle of Wight Branch http://www.hantsiow-butterflies.org.uk [the main site is: http://www.butterfly-conservation.org]
Eggs, larvae, pupae and adult Butterflies and Moths http://www.ukleps.org/
Hants moths – the Moths of Hampshire and Isle of Wight http://www.hantsmoths.org.uk/
UK Butterflies http://www.ukbutterflies.co.uk/
UK Moths http://ukmoths.org.uk/

DIPTERA [Flies]

Chandler, P.J. (ed.) (2010) *A Dipterist's Handbook*. 2nd Edition. The Amateur Entomologist Vol. 15. Orpington: The Amateur Entomologists' Society.
Stubbs, A.E. & Drake, M. (2001) *British soldierflies and their allies*. Reading: British Entomological and Natural History Society.
Stubbs, A.E. & Falk, S. (2002) *British hoverflies*. 2nd Edition. Reading: British Entomological and Natural History Society.
Dipterists Forum. The Society for the study of flies (Diptera). http://www.dipteristsforum.org.uk/
Falk, S. (2010) The flies, bees and wasps of the East Dorset – West Hampshire Coast: Hengistbury Head to Hythe Spartina Marsh. [Unpublished]
Falk, S. (draft seen 2010) The summer fly fauna of the New Forest valley mires [from extensive fieldwork, with detailed species listings]. [Unpublished]

HYMENOPTERA [Bees, Wasps, Ants & related insects]

Baldock, D.W. (2010) *Wasps of Surrey*. Woking: Surrey Wildlife Trust [the Trust have also published books on ants, bees and on several other entomological subjects].
Edwards, M. & Jenner, M. (2009) *Field Guide to the Bumblebees of Great Britain & Ireland*. Revised Edition, Ocelli.
Bees, Wasps & Ants Recording Society http://www.bwars.com/

INSECT RECORDING SCHEMES / HAMPSHIRE SPECIALIST RECORDING GROUPS

Refer to the latest HBIC Newsletter, pdf obtainable via http://www3.hants.gov.uk/biodiversity/hbic/hbic-news_events/hbic-news-newsletter.htm which provides current details of recording schemes and Hampshire specialist recording groups, notably the New Forest Study Group and Southampton Natural History Society.

INSECT SOCIETIES (not already referred to, some are publishers of useful identification guides)

Amateur Entomologists' Society http://www.amentsoc.org/
British Entomological and Natural History Society http://www.benhs.org.uk/
Buglife – The Invertebrate Conservation Trust http://www.buglife.org.uk/
Royal Entomological Society http://www.royensoc.co.uk/ Code for Insect Collecting – download from http://www.royensoc.co.uk/InvLink/Index.html

OTHER ORGANISATIONS INVOLVED WITH CONSERVATION

Hampshire & Isle of Wight Wildlife Trust http://www.hwt.org.uk/
People's Trust for endangered species http://www.ptes.org/ [for example, Noble Chafer]

GOVERNMENT BODIES AND CHARITIES MANAGING LAND

Forestry Commission http://www.forestry.gov.uk/newforest [manage the crown lands]
Hampshire County Council http://www3.hants.gov.uk/countryside [manages Buckland Rings, Calshot Marshes, Hyde and Gorley Commons, Keyhaven Marshes [part] and Lepe Country Park]
National Trust http://www.nationaltrust.org.uk [manages Bramshaw Commons, Foxbury Plantation, Hale Purlieu, Hightown and Ibsley Commons]
Natural England http://www.naturalengland.org.uk [manages National Nature Reserves: Kingston Great Common, Langley Wood and North Solent]
Hampshire & Isle of Wight Wildlife Trust http://www.hwt.org.uk/ [manages Copythorne Common, Fletchwood Meadows, Holmsley Gravel Pit, Keyhaven and Pennington Marshes, Linwood, Lymington Reedbeds and Roydon Woods]
See also New Forest National Park Authority www.newforestnpa.gov.uk who arranged a New Forest National Park Bioblitz in 2010 and 2011. This is a mix of public engagement and scientific recording, with the general public, other naturalists and recorders involved in a 24 hour recording blitz.

APPENDIX 2 – National status categories

Red List = Red Data Book species, known from less than 15 10-km squares, in the subcategories, RDB1 endangered (5 or fewer squares, in danger of extinction), RDB2 vulnerable (6–10 squares) or RDB3 rare (11–15 squares). RDBk = Insufficiently known. Revisions to the categories mean butterflies, dragonflies and certain other groups are now assessed under varied criteria as Red list EX = Extinct, EW = Extinct in the Wild, CR = Critically Endangered, EN = Endangered, VU = Vulnerable, NT = Near Threatened, amongst others. LC = Least Concern is of limited value, as many common species are assigned the least concern category [only provided where the population status has been evaluated]. It is difficult to link older and more recent categories as new IUCN based ones place more of an emphasis on rate of decline, rather than simply rarity, which works better only for well recorded groups.

Nationally Notable = Scarce, known from less than 100 10-km squares since 1980, noted as A (16–30 squares) or B (31–100 squares) [often abbreviated as Na or Nb respectively, but not differentiated in some species, which are abbreviated as N].

A summary of the Red list and Nationally Scarce insect species recorded in the Forest since 1970 is listed below, based on corrected information in the New Forest SAC Management Plan (2001), other literature (some unpublished) and later records, hence figures below are significantly higher. In a few cases, species may now be extinct in the Forest, for example Common Club-tail, High Brown Fritillary and Marsh Fritillary. The categories are subject to change from time to time when re-evaluated. There are a number of downgradings one could make at the time of writing, for example the Box Leatherbug (RDB1) is now spreading, the Bee Killer (RDB2) commoner, also recent arrivals such as the Saxon Wasp (RDBk) and Median Wasp N, are more widespread than when assessed; whilst other species without a conservation status are in need of one. However, these listings put in perspective how rich in rarities the Forest insect fauna is.

	RDB1	RDB2	RDB3	RBBk	New Red list	Nationally Scarce	Total
Odonata	–	–	–	–	5	–	5
Orthoptera	1	1	1	–	–	7	10
Blattodea	–	–	–	–	–	3	3
Hemiptera	2	–	4	1	–	15	22
Coleoptera	19	13	33	19	–	251	335
Lepidoptera							
Butterflies	–	–	–	–	16	–	16
Moths	7	5	19	–	–	148	179
Diptera	11	19	15	2	8	108	163
Hymenoptera	6	4	22	2	–	60	94

The above figures exclude insects only found pre-1970, some of which are likely to be extinct in the Forest. The data includes the following species illustrated and / or mentioned in this book:

Odonata pp 24–45: Southern Damselfly (EN), Variable Damselfly, Scarce Blue-tailed Damselfly, Scarce Chaser, Common Club-tail (all NT).

Orthoptera pp 48–67: Mole Cricket (RDB1), Large Marsh Grasshopper (RDB2), Heath Grasshopper (RDB3) and the Nationally Scarce: Long-winged Cone-head, Wood Cricket, Cepero's Ground-hopper, Grey Bush-cricket, Bog Bush-cricket, Roesel's Bush-cricket and Woodland Grasshopper. The list excludes: Field Cricket (RDB1) (attempted reintroduction), Wart-biter (RDB1) and Rufous Grasshopper (Nb), the latter two species not found since 1970.

Blattodea pp 70–71: Nationally Scarce: Dusky Cockroach, Tawny Cockroach, Lesser Cockroach.

Hemiptera pp 74–103: New Forest Cicada, Box Leatherbug (both RDB1), New Forest Shieldbug, *Pachybrachius luridus* (both RDB3) [Red list species not illustrated in this book: *Rhopalus rufus*, *Lygus pratensis* (both RDB3), *Limotettix atricapillus* (RDBk)]. Nationally Scarce species include: Cow-wheat Shieldbug, Scarce Tortoise Shieldbug, *Rhyparochromus pini*, *Megalonotus dilatatus*, *Rhopalus maculatus*, *Pentastiridius leporinus* and *Aquarius paludum*. Excluded from the figures are: Vernal Shieldbug (RDB3) and the Nationally Scarce: Bordered Shieldbug, Dalman's Leatherbug and *Dicranocephalus medius*, which occur in the Forest surrounds.

Coleoptera pp 108–155: *Pterostichus aterrimus*, Kugelann's Ground Beetle *Poecilus kugelanni*, Hornet Rove Beetle *Velleius dilatatus*, Beaulieu Dung Beetle *Aphodius niger*, *Sitaris muralis*, *Melandrya barbata*, *Bagous brevis*, *Bagous czwalinai* (all RDB1), Brown Diving Beetle *Agabus brunneus*, Noble Chafer *Gnorimus nobilis*, *Diaperis boleti*, *Lymexylon navale* (all RDB2), *Ampedus cinnabarinus*, Scarlet Malachite *Malachius aeneus*, Burnt-tip Grammoptera *Grammoptera ustulata*, Tawny Longhorn Beetle *Paracorymbia fulva*, Six-spotted Longhorn Beetle *Anoplodera sexguttata*, White-clouded Longhorn Beetle *Mesosa nebulosa*, *Bagous frit* (all RDB3), *Staphylinus caesareus* (RDBk), *Planeustomus flavicollis* (RDB indeterminable) [Red list species not mentioned in this book: *Acylophorus glaberrimus*, *Eucnemis capucina*, *Gyrinus natator*, *Heptaulacus testudinarius*, *Longitarsus nigerrimus*, *Tachys obtusiusculus*, *Elaphropus walkerianus*, *Megapenthes lugens*, *Silvanoprus fagi*, *Ampedus nigerrimus* and *Eutheia linearis* (all RDB1) and various other lower ranked Red list species]. Nationally Scarce species include: Heath Tiger Beetle *Cicindela sylvatica*, *Carabus nitens*, *Calosoma inquisitor*, *Helophorus griseus*, *Dendroxena quadrimaculata*, Stag Beetle *Lucanus cervus*, *Trypocopris pyrenaeus*, *Trypocopris vernalis*, *Ampedus pomonae*, *Ampedus quercicola*, *Ampedus sanguinolentus*, *Calambus bipustulatus*, *Platycis minutus*, *Thymalus limbatus*, *Tillus elongatus*, Scarce 7-spot Ladybird *Coccinella magnifica*, *Prionychus ater*, *Pseudocistela ceramboides*, *Opatrum sabulosum*, Black-headed Cardinal *Pyrochroa coccinea*, *Melandrya caraboides*, *Phloiotrya vaudoueri*, Tanner Beetle *Prionus coriarius*, Golden-haired Longhorn Beetle *Leptura aurulenta*, Large Black Longhorn Beetle *Stictoleptura scutellata*, Musk Beetle *Aromia moschata*, Rufous-shouldered Longhorn Beetle *Anaglyptus mysticus*, *Donacia crassipes*, *Chrysolina oricalcia*, *Cassida nobilis*, *Platypus cylindrus*, *Tomoxia bucephala*. There are many other Nationally Scarce species not illustrated in this book. Rarer species from the Forest surrounds include *Drypta dentata* (RDB1), the Nationally Scarce *Chrysolina violacea*, *Liparus coronatus* and Cramp-ball Fungus Weevil *Platyrhinus resinosus*.

Lepidoptera (1) butterflies pp 158–193: High Brown Fritillary (CR), White-letter Hairstreak, Duke of Burgundy, Pearl-bordered Fritillary, Glanville Fritillary (all EN), Dingy Skipper, Grizzled Skipper,

Silver-studded Blue, White Admiral, Marsh Fritillary, Grayling (all VU), Small Blue, Purple Emperor, Small Pearl-bordered Fritillary, Wall, Small Heath (all NT). Excluded: Heath Fritillary (re-introduction attempt), Large Tortoiseshell (classified as extinct) and other species with pre-1970 records.

Lepidoptera (2) moths pp 194–253: Scarce Chocolate-tip, Reddish Buff (both RDB1), *Pachythelia villosella*, Speckled Footman, Southern Chestnut, Dark Crimson Underwing (all RDB2), Triangle, *Crambus silvella*, Dingy Mocha, Portland Ribbon Wave, Dotted Footman, Scarce Merveille du Jour, Marbled Clover, Shoulder-striped Clover, Light Crimson Underwing (all RDB3) [Red list species not mentioned / illustrated in this book: *Acanthopsyche atra*, *Acrolepiosis marcidella*, *Aplota palpella*, *Scythris empetrella*, *Archips oporana* (all RDB1), *Stenoptilia pneumonanthes* RDB2, *Stigmella samiatella*, *Lampronia fuscatella*, *Catoptilia falconipenella*, Leek Moth *Acrolepiopsis assectella*, *Biselachista trapeziella*, *Grapholita tenebrosana*, *Platytes alpinella*, *Buckleria paludum*, Pauper Pug *Eupithecia egenaria* and Silver Barred *Deltote bankiana* (all RDB3)]. Nationally Scarce species include: Goat Moth, Festoon, Currant Clearwing, Yellow-legged Clearwing, Sallow Clearwing, Orange-tailed Clearwing, Red-belted Clearwing, Red-tipped Clearwing, Six-belted Clearwing, *Crambus hamella*, Light Orange Underwing, Small Grass Emerald, Mocha, Rosy Wave, Purple-bordered Gold, Dotted Border, Marbled Pug, Dentated Pug, Little Thorn, Horse Chestnut, Bordered Grey, Ringed Carpet, Great Oak Beauty, Narrow-bordered Bee Hawkmoth, Broad-bordered Bee Hawkmoth, Small Chocolate-tip, Dew Moth, Red-necked Footman, Orange Footman, Hoary Footman, Jersey Tiger, Small Black Arches, Kent Black Arches, Marbled Green, Cream-bordered Green Pea, Waved Black, Buttoned Snout, Marsh Oblique-barred, also various other micro moths. Some Nationally Scarce macro and micro moths are not illustrated and the list excludes certain species, including: White-barred Clearwing (last Forest record 1949) and Argent & Sable (last Forest record 1966). Barker and Green in 'Butterflies and moths', Biodiversity in the New Forest (2010) list 72 Red list and 192 Nationally Scarce Lepidoptera in the Forest since records began and provide a long list of 'lost' species.

Diptera pp 254-279: *Ctenophora ornata*, Black Deerfly *Chrysops sepulcralis*, Saltmarsh Horsefly *Atylotus latistriatus*, *Caliprobola speciosa* (all RDB1), *Ctenophora flaveolata*, Heath Bee-fly *Bombylius minor*, *Pocota personata* (all RDB2), *Psilota antracina*, *Brachyopa bicolor*, Mottled Bee-fly *Thyridanthrax fenestratus*, Long-horned Cleg *Haematopota grandis* (all RDB3), Plain-eyed Brown Horsefly *Tabanus miki*, Forest Fly *Hippobosca equina* (both RDBk), Scarce Forest Horsefly *Hybomitra solstitialis* pRDB (critical) [various other Red list species are not illustrated in this book, including the Giant Wood-gnat *Neoempheria lineola* (RDB2, a rare fungus gnat (Mycetophilidae))]. Nationally Scarce species include: *Ctenophora pectinicornis*, Hornet Robberfly *Asilus crabroniformis*, Pygmy Soldier *Oxycera pygmaea*, Golden Horsefly *Atylotus fulvus*, *Volucella zonaria*, *Volucella inflata*, *Criorhina asilica*, *Criorhina ranunculi*, *Brachypalpus laphriformis*, *Mallota cimbiciformis*, *Melanogaster aerosa*, *Microdon analis*, *Neoascia obliqua*, *Platycheirus immarginatus*, *Xylota abiens*, *Xylota jakutorum* and *Conops vesicularis*. Rarer species from the Forest surrounds include the Nationally Scarce Dotted Bee-fly *Bombylius discolor*.

Hymenoptera pp 280–297: Black Bog Ant *Formica picea*, *Ceropales variegata*, *Andrena ferox* (all RDB1), Bee Wolf *Philanthus triangulum*, *Cryptocheilus notatus* (both RDB2), Saxon Wasp *Dolichovespula saxonica* (RDBk) [Red list species not illustrated in this book: *Homonotus sanguinolentus*, *Crossocerus vagabundus*, *Nomada ferruginara* (all RDB1), *Nomada signata*, *Mimesa bicolor* (both RDB2) and several RDB3 species; with other possible additions, where it is not clear whether they occur in the Forest or the immediate surrounds]. Nationally Scarce species include: Large Velvet Ant *Mutilla europaea*, Small Velvet Ant *Smicromyrme rufipes*, Median Wasp *Dolichovespula media*, *Aporus unicolor*, *Eumenes coarctatus*, *Colletes halophilus*, *Andrena argentata*, *Nomada baccata*, *Nomada fucata*, *Dasypoda hirtipes*, *Macropis europaea* and Slavemaker Ant *Formica sanguinea*. Rarer species from the Forest surrounds include *Podalonia affinis* (RDB3), the Nationally Scarce *Podalonia hirsuta* and *Bombus humilis*. A revised Red list for the British aculeates is in preparation.

For further details on conservation designations on UK taxa, review http://www.jncc.gov.uk/page-3408 where a spreadsheet can be downloaded.

Criorhina ranunculi **(11–14 mm)**

Xylota jakutorum **(7.5–8 mm)**

APPENDIX 3 – Gazetteer of place names

(a) in the Forest or immediate border

Acres Down SU2608
Anses Wood SU2212
Ashurst SU3300
Ashurst Wood SU3309
Ashley Hole SU2114
Badminston SU4601
Balmer Lawn SU3003
Bank SU2807
Beaulieu SU3802
Beaulieu Road Station SU3406
Beaulieu Heath SU3500
Bishop's Dyke SU3405
Bolderwood SU2408
Bolton's Bench SU3008
Bramshaw Wood SU2515
Brinken Wood SU2705
Broad Bottom SU1904
Brockenhurst SU3002
Brockishill Inclosure SU3011
Brook SU2614
Broomy Pond SU2110
Brownloaf SU1902
Buckland Rings SZ3196
Buckler's Hard SU4000
Burbush Hill SU2001
Burley SU2103
Burley Old Inclosure SU2404
Buskett's Lawn Inclosure SU3110
Butt's Lawn SU2902
Cadnam Common SU2815
Calshot SU4701
Castle Hill SU1616
Church Moor SU2406
Churchplace Inclosure SU3309
Clay Hill Heath SU2201
Clumber Inclosure SU2603
Costicles Inclosure SU3210
Cranes Moor SU1902
Crock Hill SU2114
Crockford Bridge SZ3599
Crockford Stream SZ3698
Culverley SU3604
Deerleep Inclosure SU3409
Denny Wood SU3305
Dibden Bottom SU3806
Duckhole Bog SU2502
Efford SZ3093
Exbury SU4200
Eyeworth Pond SU2214
Fritham SU2314
Exbury Gardens SU4200
Eyeworth Pond SU2214
Fawley SU4503
Ferny Crofts SU3605
Fritham SU2314
Furzey Lawn Inclosure SU2910
Furzey Pond SU3806
Gibbet Wood SU2514
Goatspen Plain SU2201
Godshill Wood SU1616
Gritnam Wood SU2806
Half Moon Common SU2916
Hatchet Pond SU3601
Hawkhill Inclosure SU3502
Hengistbury Head SZ1691
Hinchelsea Bog SU2700
Highland Water SU2409
Hollands Wood SU3004
Holmhill Inclosure SU2508
Holmsley Bog SZ2201
Hurst Castle SZ3190
Hurst Spit SZ3090
Island Thorns Inclosure SU2115
Ivy Wood SU3202
Keyhaven Marshes SZ3191
King's Garn Gutter Inclosure SU2513
King's Hat Inclosure SU3805
Knightwood Inclosure SU2606
Knightwood Oak SU2606
Ladycross SU3302
Latchmore Brook SU1812
Lepe Country Park SZ4598
Linwood SU1810
Linford Bottom SU1807
Linwood, Coppice of SU2514
Little Wootton Inclosure SU2298
Lodgehill Inclosure SU3109
Longdown SU3508
Long Pond South SU1901
Lyndhurst SU2908
Mallard Wood SU3209
Mark Ash SU2407
Markway Inclosure SU2402
Marlborough Deep SZ2298
Matley Bog SU3307
Matley Wood SU3307
Millyford Bridge SU2607
Mockbeggar SU1609
Needs Ore SZ4297
New Copse Inclosure SU3202
Normandy Marshes SZ3394
Ober Water SU2702
Ocknell Plain SU2211
Ogden's Purlieu SU1811
Park Ground Inclosure SU3006
Parc Pale SU3107
Parkhill Inclosure SU3104
Pennington Marshes SZ3191
Perrywood Haseley Inclosure SU3203
Peaked Hill SU3699
Perrywood Ivy Inclosure SU3202
Pig Bush SU3604
Pignal Inclosure SU3104
Pinnick Wood SU1807
Pondhead Inclosure SU3007
Poundhill Inclosure SU2704
Puck Pitt's Inclosure SU2509
Puttles Bridge SU2702
Queen's Bower SU2804
Rakes Brakes Bottom SU2112
Red Hill Bog SU2601
Rhinefield SU2604
Roe Wood Inclosure SU2008
Roydon Woods SU3100
Rush Bush SU3806
Rushbush Pond SU3806
Setley SU3000
Shatterford Bottom SU3406
Shirley Holms SZ2998
Sloden Inclosure SU2113
Slufters Inclosure SU2210
South Gorley SU1610
Sowley Pond SZ3796
Stoney Cross SU2611
Stubbs Wood SU3603
Sway SZ2898
Tantany Wood SU3604
Vales Moor SU1804
Vinney Ridge Inclosure SU2605
Warwick Slade SU2706
White Moor SU3108
Whitley Wood SU2905
Whitten Pond SU2001
Widden Bottom SZ2899
Wilverley SU2500
Woodfidley SU3404
Wootton Bridge SZ2499
Wootton Coppice Inclosure SZ2499

(b) in the surrounding area

Arreton Down, IOW SZ5387
Avon Heath Country Park SU1203
Barton-on-Sea SZ2492
Bentley Wood SU2529
Blashford Lakes SU1407
Boscombe SZ1291
Bournemouth SZ0891
Bransgore SZ1897
Canford Heath SU0295
Chewton Bunny SZ2193
Christchurch, Nea Meadows SZ2093
Christchurch, Town Common SZ1495
Corfe Castle SU9682
Corfe Common SU9581
Eling SU3612
Emer Bog SU3921
Fletchwood Meadows SU3311
Fordingbridge SU1513
Godwinscroft SU1996
Hayling Island SZ3294
Hengistbury Head SZ1691
Holdenhurst SZ1295
Hordle undercliffs SZ2692
Hythe SU4207
Ibsley SU1509
Lord's Wood, Southampton SU3917
Lower Test Marshes SU3614
Lymington SZ3295
Magdalen Hill Down SU5029
Martin Down SU0320
Milford-on-Sea SZ2991
Milton Abbas SU8001
Mudeford Woods SZ1892
New Milton SZ2496
Noar Hill SU7431
Old Burlesdon Nature Haven SU4809
Pokesdown SY1292
Poole SY9992
Purewell Meadows SZ1693
Ringwood Forest SU1005
Rowlands Castle SU7414
Shipton Bellinger SU2245
Slepe Heath SY9585
Sopley Common SZ1297
Southampton Common SU4113
Southampton, Peartree Green SU4311
Southbourne SZ1291
St Boniface Down, IOW SZ5678
Stanpit Marsh SZ1792
Stanswood Valley SU4600
Stoborough SZ9787
Stockbridge Down SU3734
Testwood Lakes SU3415
Throop SZ1195
Totton SU3613
Tricketts Cross SU0901
Wareham SY9287
West Wood, Netley SU4509
Woodhouse Copse, IOW SZ5393

INDEX OF ENGLISH AND SCIENTIFIC NAMES (Photograph page numbers in bold)